Upgrade A-Level PHYSICS

Jim Breithaupt MSc, C.Phys, M.Inst.P,
Head of Science and Maths,
Wigan Campus, Wigan and Leigh College

Stanley Thornes (Publishers) Ltd

First published in 1996 by:
Stanley Thornes (Publishers) Ltd
Ellenborough House
Wellington Street
CHELTENHAM GL50 1YW
England

96 97 98 99 00 / 10 9 8 7 6 5 4 3 2 1

A catalogue record for this book is available from the British Library.

ISBN 0–7487–2385–4

Typeset by Tech-Set, Gateshead, Tyne & Wear.
Printed and bound in Great Britain at Scotprint Ltd, Musselburgh

CONTENTS LIST

PREFACE

To the student

This book is intended to offer you further understanding and practice in core A level physics topics to help you secure good grades at A level. The emphasis in this book is on the compulsory core topics which constitute half of every A level physics syllabus. No matter which A level physics syllabus you are studying or whether the syllabus is modular or linear, every A level physics student must study the compulsory core topics. In addition, these topics underpin the wide range of optional topics beyond the compulsory core. Hence, by achieving a deeper grasp of these compulsory topics, you should benefit by scoring higher marks not only on compulsory topics but also on optional topics underpinned by these compulsory topics.

Upgrade Physics is neither a textbook nor a revision guide. It is recommended for use as an in-course study book after a topic has been covered in class using a textbook, preferably *Understanding Physics for Advanced Level* by the same author, which is now in full colour in its latest edition, and is written to take you up to grade A standard on your A level physics course; you can then use *Upgrade Physics* to consolidate your position. Special attention has been paid in *Upgrade Physics* to points which are frequently questioned at A level and topics are analysed in depth to S level standard to give extra confidence to enable you to perform really well at A level. Worked examples with comments are included in most chapters and applications of physics analysed at A level standard are included to demonstrate the relevance of A level physics.

Each chapter concludes with a set of recent A level and S level questions. These are graded to include shorter A level questions, longer A level questions and some Special paper questions. Numerical answers are provided at the end of the book. Mastery of the mathematical techniques in the book is not essential to answer most of the questions well although there is little doubt that a sound grasp of these techniques will further boost your confidence, particularly if you intend to study physics or engineering beyond A level. One final point worth noting is that A level physics candidates unable to explain their knowledge of the subject rarely achieve the top grades. Those who struggle in an examination to find appropriate phrases or words or who present their answers carelessly usually lack in-depth knowledge and understanding of the subject. *Upgrade Physics* is intended to enable you to approach examinations with confidence so you can do justice to your ability in the subject.

To the teacher

The in-depth topics in this book provide an extended treatment of **core** topics in *Understanding Physics for Advanced Level* to enable your students to consolidate their grasp of these topics developed through using *Understanding Physics for Advanced Level*. Optional topics in applied physics, astronomy, communications, electronics, materials, relativity, particle physics, and 'Turning points in physics' are not covered in this book as they are covered in detail in *Understanding Physics for Advanced Level*.

This book could be used in 'supported self study' mode, particularly by those students in a class who assimilate core topics more quickly than others and who would benefit from extra encouragement in physics in preparation for module tests or end-of-course examinations.

Acknowledgements

I am indebted to former A level students whose searching questions provided the impetus for this book. Their motivation and desire to delve deeper into the subject has been a source of continued refreshment to me throughout. I would also like to acknowledge the support of my family throughout the preparation of this book, particularly my wife for secretarial support and continued encouragement. I am also grateful to the publishing team at Stanley Thornes Ltd, in particular to Margaret O'Gorman, Lorna Godson and Adrian Wheaton who respectively initiated, edited and oversaw the project.

I am grateful to the following examination Boards for giving permission to use questions from recent past papers in the book:

Associated Examining Board; University of Cambridge Local Examinations Syndicate; University of London Examinations and Assessment Council; Northern Examinations and Assessment Board; Northern Ireland Council for the Curriculum, Examinations and Assessment; University of Oxford Delegacy of Local Examinations; Oxford and Cambridge Schools Examination Board; Welsh Joint Education Committee.

Jim Breithaupt

1 STATICS AND SAFETY

What you need to know now

- ❑ For a point object in equilibrium, the resultant force on the object is zero.
- ❑ For a body in equilibrium, the resultant force on the object is zero and the principle of moments about any fixed point applies.
- ❑ A couple is a pair of equal and opposite forces not in the same line. The moment of a couple is the same about any point and is equal to the force × the perpendicular distance between the two lines of action.

What you need to know next

Free-body diagrams

Any object in equilibrium is acted upon by forces due to other objects. A free-body diagram shows only the forces acting on a body; it does not show the forces exerted by the body.

Consider the horizontal beam resting unequally on two pillars as in Fig 1.1(a). The beam experiences a force due to the Earth's gravity and a support force due to each pillar. Because the beam is in equilibrium, the weight is equal and opposite to the sum of the two support forces. Hence the resultant force on the beam is zero.

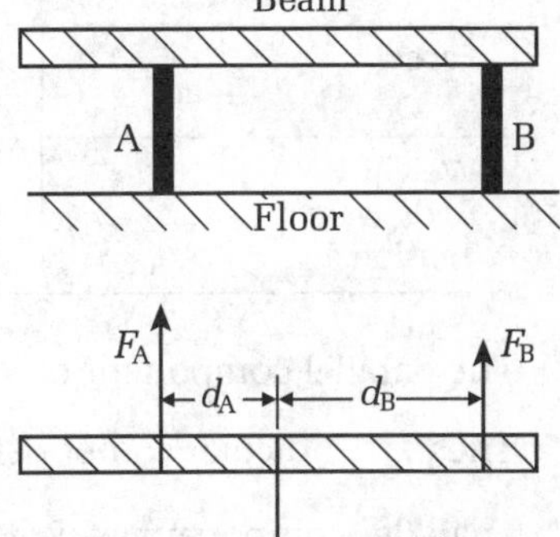

Fig 1.1 Forces on a beam

Fig 1.1(b) shows a free-body diagram of the beam. This diagram shows only the forces acting on the beam and does not show the pillars or the forces acting on the pillars due to the beam. To determine the magnitude of the support forces F_A and F_B, apply the Principle of Moments about the centre of gravity to give

$$F_A d_A = F_B d_B$$

where d_A and d_B are the respective distances from A and B to the centre of gravity.

Hence $\dfrac{F_A}{F_B} = \dfrac{d_B}{d_A}$.

Since $F_A + F_B = W$ where W is the total weight of the beam, F_A and F_B can be calculated separately. Note that pillar A exerts an upward force F_A on the beam which exerts an equal and opposite force on the pillar. Likewise, pillar B exerts an upward force F_B on the beam which exerts an equal and opposite force on pillar B.

Case study The physics of lifting

Lifting is a process that can damage the spine if it is not done correctly.

- Fig 1.2(a) shows an object of weight W being lifted incorrectly. The spine pivots about the hip joints and the muscles between the spine and the hip pull on the spine to prevent the spine being pulled over by the object's weight W and the weight W_0 of the upper part of the body itself.

- Fig 1.2(b) also shows the free-body diagram of the spine where the spine is at angle α to the vertical. The moment of the object's weight W about the pivot is $Wd \sin \alpha$ where d is the distance from the pivot to the point on the spine where W acts. The moment of W_0 is $W_0 d_0 \sin \alpha$ where d_0 is the distance from the pivot to the centre of gravity of the upper part of the body.

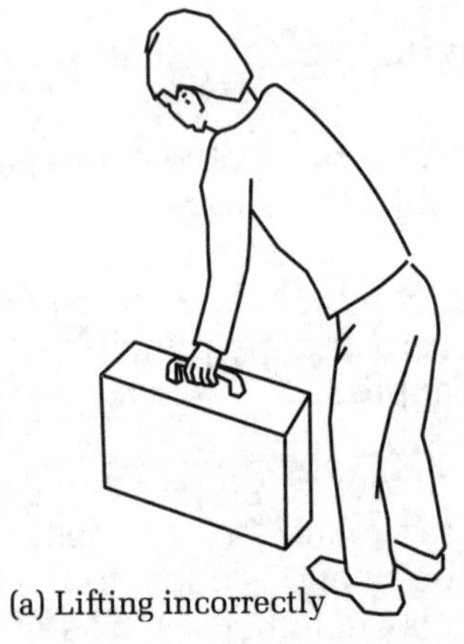

(a) Lifting incorrectly

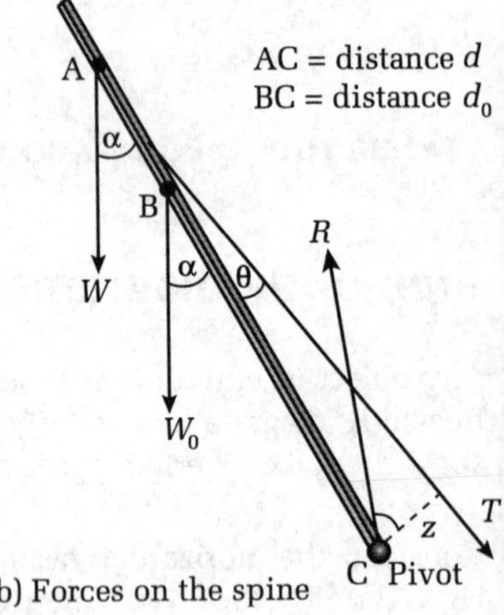

(b) Forces on the spine

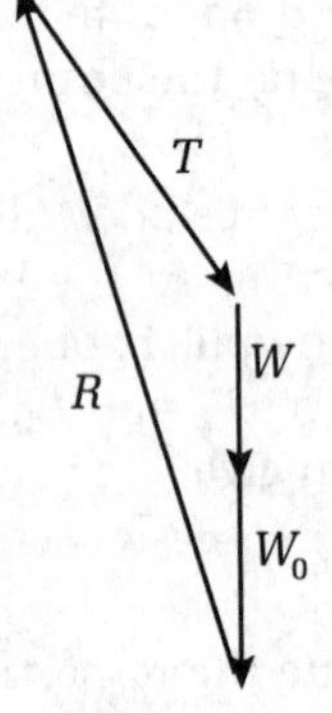

(c) Vector polygon

Fig 1.2

The tension T in the back muscles provides an opposing moment Tz where z is the perpendicular distance from the line of action of T and the pivot. For steady lifting to occur, $Tz = Wd \sin \alpha + W_0 d_0 \sin \alpha$; hence the tension must equal $(Wd + W_0 d_0) \sin \alpha / z$. The extra tension due to the weight being lifted is therefore $Wd \sin \alpha / z$. Since z is much smaller than d, the extra tension is much greater than the weight being lifted. For example, if $d = 0.8$ m, $z = 0.05$ m and $\alpha = 30°$, then the extra tension is $8 \times$ the weight being lifted.

The spine is subjected to forces W, W_0 and T which are opposed by the reaction R of the pelvis on the spine. To determine R, **either**

1. construct a vector diagram using W, W_0 and T as three sides of a four-sided polygon as in Fig 1.2(c). The fourth side represents the reaction R, **or**

2. resolve W, W_0 and T parallel and perpendicular to the spine to give the parallel and perpendicular components of R.

Force	Parallel component	Perpendicular component
Weight W	$W \sin \alpha$	$W \sin \alpha$
Body weight W_0	$W_0 \cos \alpha$	$W_0 \sin \alpha$
Tension T	$T \cos \theta$	$T \sin \theta$

The parallel component of R is $W \cos \alpha + W_0 \cos \alpha + T \cos \theta$.

The perpendicular component of R is $W \sin \alpha + W_0 \sin \alpha + T \sin \theta$.

The parallel component of R, $R_\parallel$, acts up the spine and the other parallel components combine to act down the spine. Hence the spinal vertebrae and the discs between the vertebrae are squashed.

$$R_\parallel = W_0 \cos \alpha + W \cos \alpha + T \cos \theta$$

$$= W_0 \cos \alpha + W \cos \alpha + (Wd + W_0 d_0) \sin \alpha \cos \theta / z,$$

since $T = (Wd + W_0 d_0) \sin \alpha / z$.

Typically, $d_0/z \approx 10$, $d/z \approx 15$ and $\theta \leqslant 10°$;

hence $R_\parallel = (W_0 \cos \alpha + 10 W_0 \sin \alpha) + (W \cos \alpha + 15 W \sin \alpha)$.

Thus the compressive force on the spine varies according to the weight W and the angle α.

1. When $\alpha = 0$, $R_{\parallel} = W_0 + W$.

2. When $\alpha = 90°$, $R_{\parallel} = 10W_0 + 15W$.

Clearly, the compressive force in the spine when lifting an object is least if the spine is vertical. Fig 1.3 shows an object being lifted correctly. The spine is upright here and the object is lifted by straightening at the knees. The 'extra' force in the spine is equal and opposite to the weight of the object; hence the force on the spine is much smaller in this posture than in Fig 1.2(a).

Fig 1.3 Correct lifting

Worked example

Fig 1.4(a) shows the foot of a basketball player of mass 70 kg as the player stands on tiptoe on that foot. The bone structure of the foot is shown in the diagram. A simple mechanical model is shown in Fig 1.4(b).

(a) What is the magnitude and direction of the reaction R of the ground on the foot? — 2 marks

(b) (i) State whether the tendon is in tension or compression.
(ii) Calculate the force of the tendon on the heel of the foot. — 3 marks

(c) (i) State whether the tibia is in tension or compression.
(ii) Calculate the force of the tibia on the foot. — 3 marks

(d) Compare the force of the tibia on the foot in this situation with the situation when the basketball player stands normally on both feet. — 2 marks

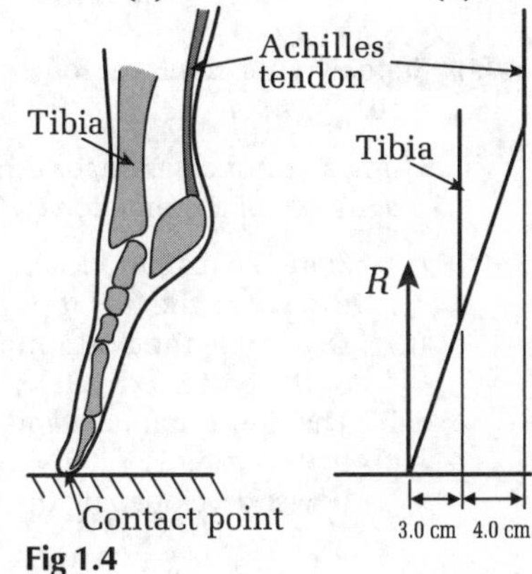

Fig 1.4

Solution

(a) The reaction is the only support force on the player and therefore is equal and opposite to the weight. Hence the reaction equals 686 N ✓ ($= 70 \times 9.8$ N) and acts vertically upwards. ✓

(b) (i) The tendon pulls on the heel and so is in tension. ✓
(ii) Taking moments about the point where the tibia is in contact with the foot gives

$$T \times 0.040 = 686 \times 0.03 \quad ✓$$

Hence $T = 686 \times 0.03/0.04 = 514.5$ N. ✓

(c) (i) The tibia pushes on the foot hence is in compression. ✓
(ii) The force in the tibia $= R + T$ ✓ $= 686 + 514.5 = 1200.5$ N. ✓

(d) Normally, the total weight is shared equally on each foot. Each foot therefore experiences a force of 343 N ($= 0.5 \times 686$ N) from the tibia. ✓ Hence, the force of the tibia on the foot when on tiptoe on one foot is approximately 3.5 ($= 1200/343$) times the normal force. ✓

Questions

1. In the leisure pursuit called parascending a person attached to a parachute is towed over the sea by a tow-rope attached to a motor boat, as shown in Fig 1.5(a).

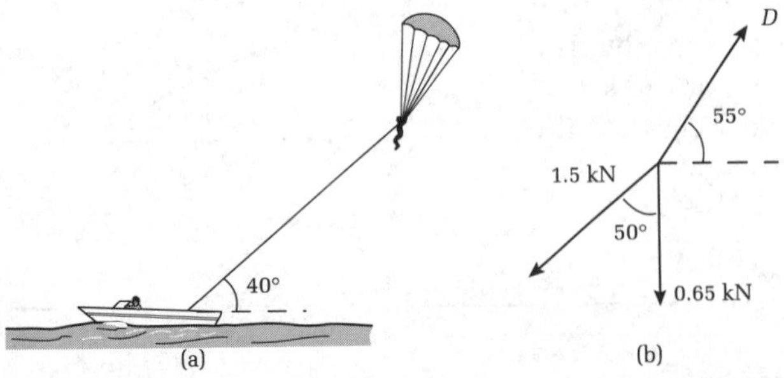

Fig 1.5

Fig 1.5(b) shows the directions of the forces acting on a person of weight 0.65 kN when being towed horizontally at a constant speed of $8.5\,\mathrm{m\,s^{-1}}$. The 1.5 kN force is the tension in the tow-rope and the force labelled *D* is the drag force.

(a) State why the resultant force on the person must be zero.

(b) Using a vector diagram, or otherwise, determine the magnitude of the drag force.

(c) (i) State the magnitude and direction of the force exerted *by* the tow-rope *on* the boat.
(ii) Determine the horizontal resistance to motion of the boat produced by the tow-rope.
(iii) The horizontal resistance to motion produced by the water is 1200 N. Determine the useful power developed by the boat's motor.

(AEB Summer '94)

2. A muscle exerciser consists of two steel ropes attached to the ends of a strong spring contained in a telescopic tube. When the ropes are pulled sideways in opposite directions, as shown in the simplified diagram, the spring is compressed.

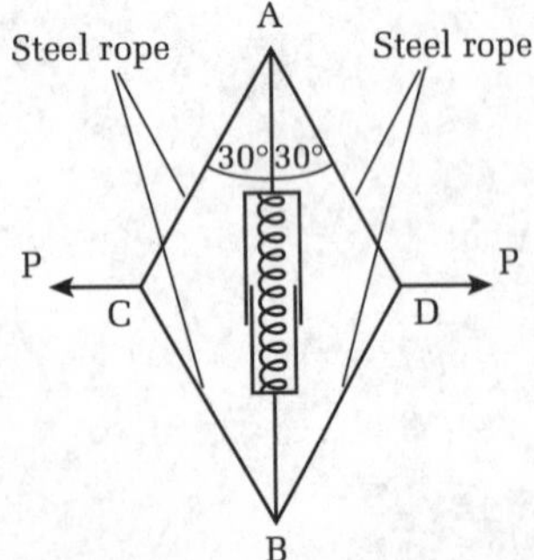

Fig 1.6

The spring has an uncompressed length of 0.80 m. The force *F* (in N) required to compress the spring to a length *x* (in m) is calculated from the equation

$$F = 500\,(0.80 - x)$$

The ropes are pulled with equal and opposite forces, *P*, so that the spring is compressed to a length of 0.60 m and the ropes make an angle of 30° with the length of the spring.

(a) Calculate
(i) the force, *F*,
(ii) the work done in compressing the spring.

(b) By considering the forces at A or B, calculate the tension in each rope.

(c) By considering the forces at C or D, calculate the force, *P*.

(NEAB June '91)

3. Fig 1.7 illustrates a side view of a piano whose weight, 2500 N acts along a vertical line 30 cm from the front of the piano.

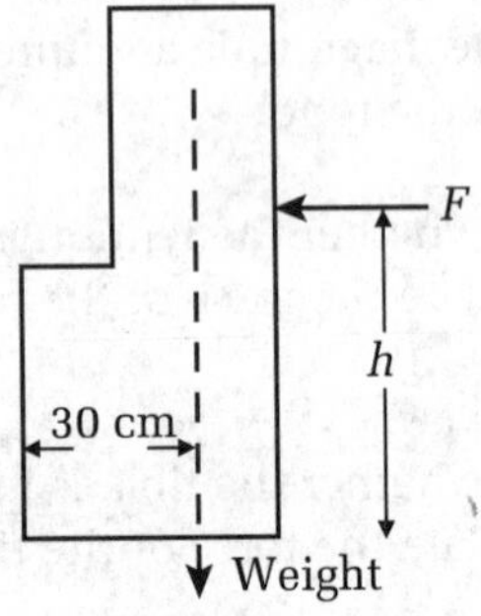

Fig 1.7

Two men try to push the piano across the floor by applying a horizontal force *F* to the back of the piano at a distance *h* above the ground. When *h* is less than 95 cm the piano slides across the floor. When *h* is greater than 95 cm the piano begins to tip.
Draw a free-body force diagram of the piano as it begins to tip.
Calculate the magnitude of the force *F* for $h = 95$ cm.

(ULEAC June '93)

4. (a) (i) State Newton's third law of motion.
A book rests on a horizontal table, as shown in Fig 1.8.

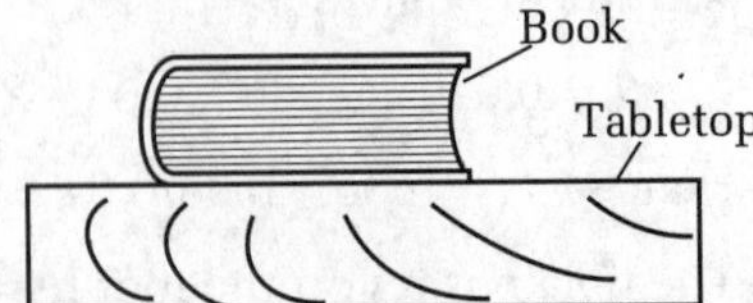

Fig 1.8

(ii) What forces act on the book?
(iii) What is the resultant of these forces?
(iv) Explain how Newton's third law applies to the system of book and table.

(b) (i) State the principle of moments, applied to a body in equilibrium under the action of a set of coplanar forces.
Fig 1.9 shows schematically the arrangement of some of the bones and muscles in a human arm. The forearm is freely jointed to the upper arm at the elbow. The biceps muscle is used to change the angle θ between forearm and upper arm.

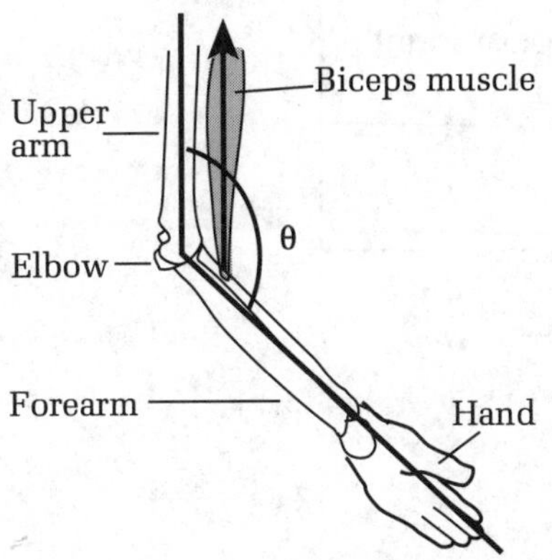

Fig 1.9

A certain athlete's forearm is 350 mm long between the elbow joint and the palm of her hand. The mass of her forearm and hand is 2.0 kg, and its weight may be assumed to act at a point 160 mm from the elbow. The biceps muscle may be considered to be attached to the forearm at a point 40 mm from the elbow. The athlete holds a shot, of mass 4.0 kg, in the palm of her hand. Initially (Fig 1.10) her forearm is horizontal, and the upper arm and the biceps muscle are vertical.

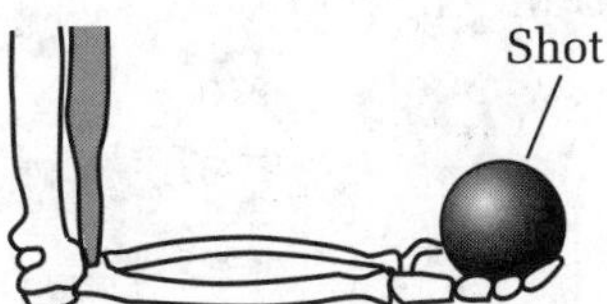

Fig 1.10

(ii) What force must the biceps muscle exert to hold the forearm horizontal?
Still holding the shot, the athlete pivots her forearm so that it moves from the horizontal position to one making an angle of 60° with the upper arm. The upper arm and the biceps muscles remain vertical (Fig 1.11).

(iii) What force does the biceps muscle exert when the forearm has reached the 60° position?

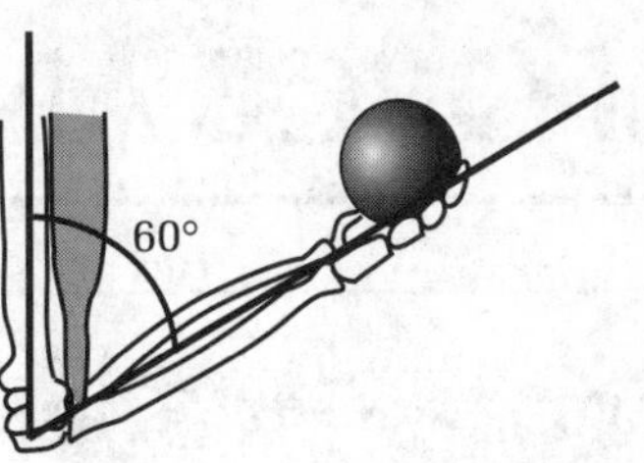

Fig 1.11

(iv) How much work has the athlete done in moving her arm, together with the shot?

(NICCEA June '93)

5. (a) The diagram below shows a 30 kg concrete mass, *M*, held in equilibrium by a light rope and a light rigid rod AB which is hinged at A. Sketch and label a free body diagram for the mass *M*.
Vectors which represent forces in equilibrium can be drawn end-to-end to form a closed polygon. Sketch and label the closed polygon which is formed by the forces acting on the mass *M*.
Find the tension in the rope and the compressive force in the rod.

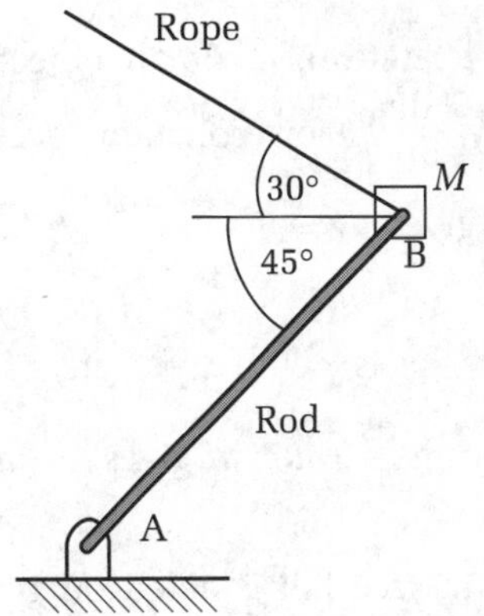

Fig 1.12

(b) Any force can be considered as either a *contact* force or a *distance* force. Explain, with reference to the forces acting on the mass *M* above, what you understand by the two terms in italics.

(c) Describe how, in a school physics laboratory, it is possible to demonstrate the existence of three kinds of large-scale distance force and relate them to three kinds of force field. Show how, in each case, the force on an object is calculated from an equation of the form

(Force on object) = (Physical property of object) × (Strength of field)

(d) Compare and contrast any *two* of the three kinds of force field.

(ULEAC June '89, Special Paper)

2 FORCE AND MOTION

What you need to know now

- ❑ The dynamics equations for constant acceleration.
- ❑ The rate of change of momentum of an object is proportional to the resultant force acting on it.
- ❑ The formulae for KE, PE, work and power.

What you need to know next

Motion at constant acceleration

❑ The acceleration, a, of an object is defined as its rate of change of velocity $\frac{dv}{dt}$. For constant acceleration, integrating the equation $a = \frac{dv}{dt}$ gives $v = u + at$.

❑ Velocity, v, is defined as rate of change of displacement $\frac{ds}{dt}$. Hence integrating $\frac{ds}{dt} = u + at$ gives $s = ut + at^2/2$ for constant acceleration.

An object in free fall is acted on by gravity only; hence its acceleration $a = -g$. Its horizontal component of velocity is therefore constant. Its vertical component of velocity changes at a constant rate of $-g$.

Using Newton's second law

For a mass m moving at instantaneous velocity v, its rate of change of momentum is $\frac{d}{dt}(mv)$. In the SI system of units, this is equal to the resultant force F.

1. **If the mass *m* is constant**, the rate of change of momentum $= m\frac{dv}{dt} = ma$. In other words, $F = ma$ for constant mass.

2. **If the rate of transfer of mass to or from the object is constant**, the rate of change of momentum is $v\frac{dm}{dt}$ where $\frac{dm}{dt}$ is the rate of transfer of mass and v is the velocity at which mass is transferred. Hence the resultant force $F = v\frac{dm}{dt}$.

Case study 1 Terminal speed

Consider a vehicle of mass M which is accelerated from rest by a constant force F_E from its engine, as shown in Fig 2.1(a). The resultant force is equal to $F_E - F_D$ where F_D is the drag force.

Using Newton's second law therefore gives

$$M\frac{dv}{dt} = F_E - F_D$$

Assuming the drag force increases with speed, the acceleration of the vehicle decreases gradually to zero as the speed reaches the terminal speed v_0. Fig. 2.1(b) shows how the speed and acceleration change with time.

Multiplying each term in the above equation by v gives

$$\frac{d}{dt}\left(\tfrac{1}{2}Mv^2\right) = F_E v - F_D v \qquad \text{since} \quad \frac{d}{dt}\left(\tfrac{1}{2}Mv^2\right) = Mv\frac{dv}{dt}$$

The first term represents the rate of change of kinetic energy. The equation shows that this is equal to (the work done per second by the engine) − (energy dissipated per second by the drag force).

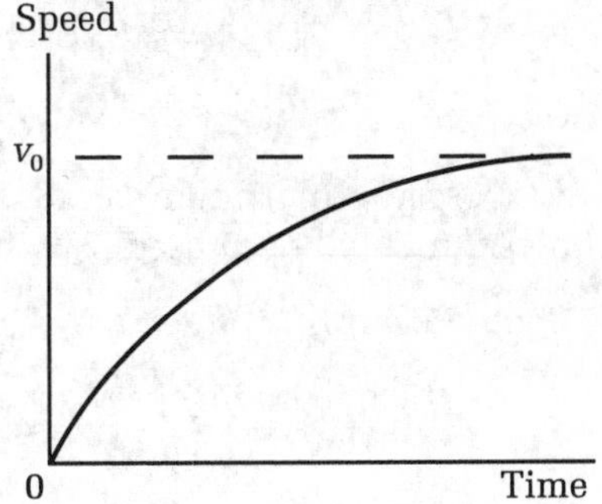

(a) Resultant force = $F_E - F_D$

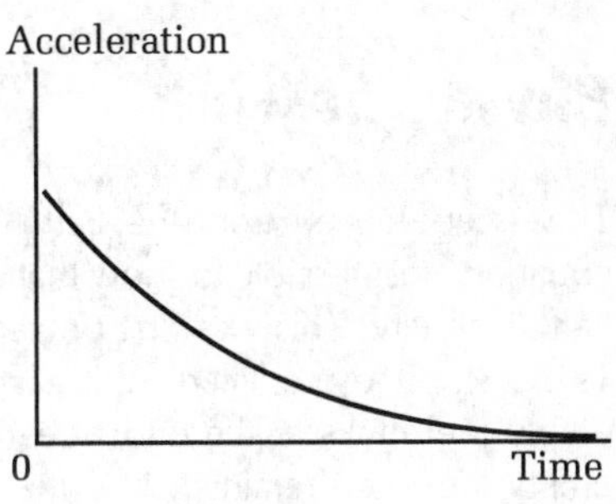

(b) Motion graphs

Fig 2.1

NOTE: The drag force at speed $v = \frac{1}{2}C_D A v^2 \rho$

where C_D = the drag coefficient of the vehicle,

ρ = the density of air,

A = the area of cross-section of the vehicle.

For a typical large truck where $A \approx 10\,\text{m}^2$, $\rho \approx 1\,\text{kg}\,\text{m}^{-3}$, $C_D \approx 0.5$, then $F_D = 2.5\,v^2$. At a speed of $30\,\text{m}\,\text{s}^{-1}$, the drag force is therefore about 2250 N and the energy dissipated per second due to drag is 67 500 W.

Physics at work

The European limit for the total mass of a loaded truck is 38 tonnes. The limit for engine power is 6 kW per tonne. The engine power of a 38 tonne truck must therefore not exceed 228 kW. Work out for yourself the top speed of a 38 tonne truck using the typical values given above.

Case study 2 Rockets and jets

In a rocket or a jet engine, mass is expelled at high speed at a constant rate. Hence the force due to such an engine is equal to $V\frac{dm}{dt}$ where $\frac{dm}{dt}$ is the mass loss per second and V is the speed of expulsion of the mass. Ignoring drag forces, the resultant force for a rocket moving vertically upwards is equal to the engine force $\left(V\frac{dm}{dt}\right)$ − weight (mg). This is a constant force since V and $\frac{dm}{dt}$ are both constant.

For a rocket using fuel at a constant rate k,

- its acceleration $\frac{dv}{dt}$ = resultant force/mass $= \frac{kV - mg}{m} = \frac{kV}{m} - g$
- at time t after ignition, its mass $m = M - kt$ where M is its total initial mass.

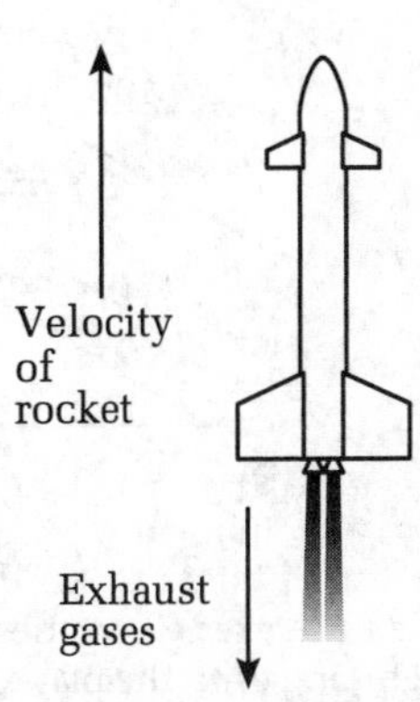

Fig 2.2 Lift off

Thus the acceleration increases as the rocket mass decreases until all the fuel is used.

Hence $\frac{dv}{dt} = \frac{kV}{(M - kt)} - g$.

NOTE: Rearranging and integrating gives

$$\int dv = \int \frac{kV}{(M - kt)} dt - \int g dt$$

Hence $v = V \ln [M/(M - kt)] - gt$.

Suppose the maximum speed is at time T after ignition when all the rocket fuel has been used.

Then $M - kT = M_0$, the rocket mass with no fuel in the tank.

Hence the maximum speed $v_{max} = V \ln (M/M_0) - gT$.

Physics at work

The escape speed from the Earth is approximately 11 km s^{-1}. Using the above equation, it is possible to show that a single-stage rocket could not escape from the Earth's gravity. This was first proved in 1895 by the Russian physicist Konstantin Tsiolovsky. He predicted multistage rockets using liquid fuel. By jettisoning the empty fuel tanks at the end of each stage, the final speed is greater than if the empty tanks are retained. Use the above formula to prove that a rocket of total initial mass 2750 tonnes including 2400 tonnes of fuel in fuel tanks of mass 300 tonnes with a speed of expulsion of 6 km s^{-1} and a total ignition time of 500 s would reach a speed of 7.4 km s^{-1} if it is a single-stage rocket whereas it would attain a speed of 11.5 km s^{-1} if launched in three equal stages.

Questions

1. A cable-car ascends a 30° slope at a constant speed of 2.0 m s^{-1}. The diagram shows the tension T in the cable and a resistive force F of constant magnitude opposing motion.

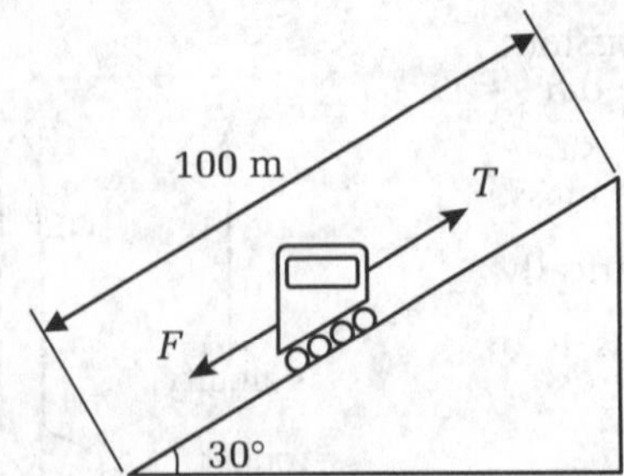

Fig 2.3

Two further forces act on the cable-car:
R, the force exerted on the cable car by the plane, acting at right angles to the plane, and W, the weight of the cable-car.

(a) Draw a labelled vector polygon showing how T, F, R and W are related.

(b) The weight of the car is 20 kN and, when moving up the slope at a constant speed of 2.0 m s^{-1}, the tension in the cable is 12 kN. The slope is 100 m long.
  (i) Using your vector polygon or otherwise, determine the magnitude of F.
  (ii) Calculate the power required to pull the car steadily up the slope at 2.0 m s^{-1}.
  (iii) Calculate the total work done during the ascent.

(AEB November '92)

2. (a) State the *law of conservation of linear momentum*. Hence explain how a rocket engine can develop a thrust.

(b) A toy rocket which contains water of density 1.0×10^3 kg m^{-3} and compressed air rests on the ground. At its base is a circular nozzle of diameter 2.5 mm, as shown in Fig 2.4.

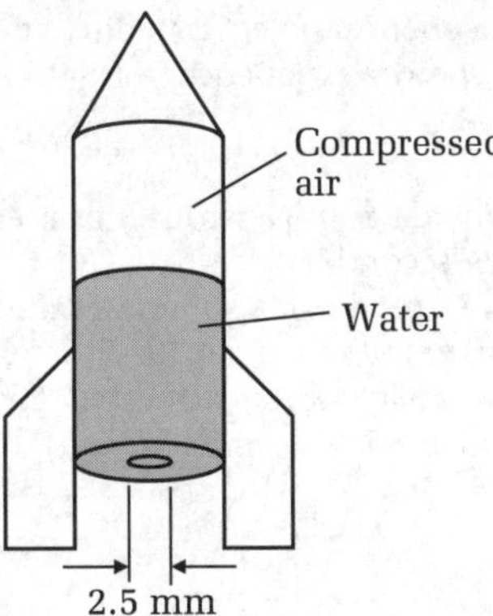

Fig 2.4

At the moment of lift-off, its total mass is 0.12 kg. Calculate the minimum speed with which water is ejected at this instant.

(c) Comment on the variation with time of
(i) the thrust,
(ii) the acceleration of the rocket described in (b) as the water is ejected.

(d) Briefly explain why a rocket can operate more efficiently when moving through a vacuum than through air.

(UCLES June '92)

3. (a) (i) Define *linear momentum*.
(ii) State *the principle of conservation of linear momentum* making clear the condition under which it can be applied.

(b) A spacecraft of mass 20 000 kg is travelling at 1500 m s^{-1}. Its rockets eject hot gases at a speed of 1200 m s^{-1} relative to the spacecraft. During one burn, the rockets are fired for a 5.0 s period. In this time the speed of the spacecraft increases by 3.0 m s^{-1}.
(i) What is the acceleration of the spacecraft?
(ii) Assuming that the mass of fuel ejected is negligible compared with the mass of the spacecraft determine the distance travelled during the burn. Give your answer to four significant figures.
(iii) What is the thrust produced by the rocket?
(iv) Determine the mass of gas ejected by the rocket during the burn.

(AEB June '92)

4. (a) A small rocket is fired vertically upwards from ground level. The graph below shows how the *upward speed* of the rocket changes with time. The rocket burns fuel at a constant rate for several seconds and then, as the fuel runs out, the rate of burning decreases to zero in a second or two. The rocket goes straight up.
(i) How would you find the acceleration of the rocket at any instant from this graph?
(ii) Sketch a graph to show approximately how the acceleration of the rocket varies during the time $t = 0$ to $t = t_D$.
(iii) Explain how it is possible for the acceleration to increase while the fuel is burning at a constant rate.

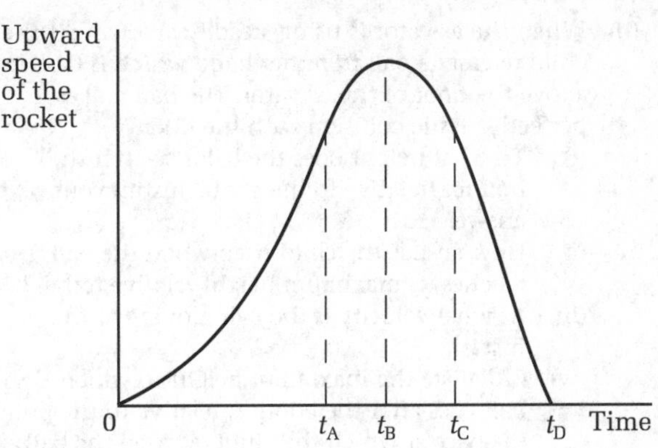

Fig 2.5

(iv) Why is the portion of the graph from time t_C to time t_D straight?
(v) At which of the times identified on the time axis was the resultant force on the rocket equal to zero? Explain your answer.

(b) Describe the apparatus you would use and state the measurements you would make to investigate the relationship between the force on a body and the acceleration that this force produces.

An engine and propeller of power output 48 kW can drive a boat at a maximum speed of 4 m s^{-1}. At the instant when the boat starts to move, the driving force from the propeller is the only horizontal force acting on the boat. Why is this so?

Calculate
(i) the force the propeller applies to the water when the boat is moving at maximum speed, and
(ii) the mass of the boat if the initial acceleration is 0.4 m s^{-2}.

(ULEAC June '91)

5. A child stands in a glass elevator in a shopping mall.

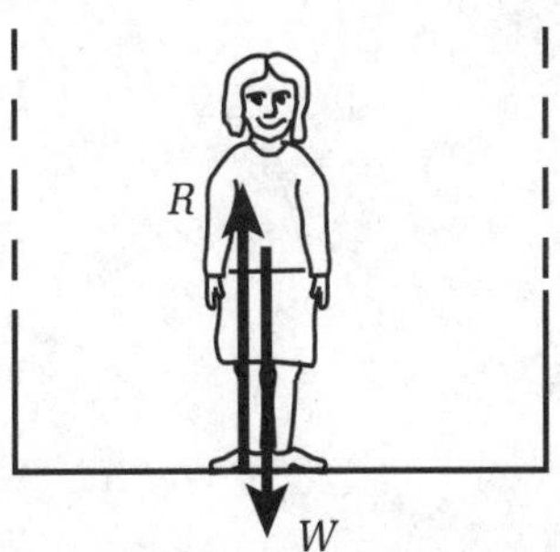

Fig 2.6

(a) Fig 2.6 is a simple diagram showing the two forces acting on her.
(i) When these forces are equal in magnitude, what can you say about the speed of the elevator? Justify your answer.
(ii) What is the value of R, in terms of W, when the elevator is accelerating upwards at 0.98 m s^{-2}?
(iii) What is the value of R, in terms of W, when the elevator is accelerating downwards at 0.98 m s^{-2}?

(b) When the elevator is rising steadily at $1.0\,\mathrm{m\,s^{-1}}$ the child releases a ball from her hand which is 0.50 m above the floor of the elevator. The ball makes a perfectly elastic collision with the floor.
(i) To what height does the ball rise after the bounce, relative to the child? Justify your answer.
(ii) How far has the child risen when the ball reaches its maximum height relative to her?
(iii) At what velocity is the ball moving at this instant?
(iv) Calculate the maximum height to which the ball rises after the bounce, relative to the point in space at which the child released the ball. This will be the height risen by the ball as seen by an observer in the shopping mall.

(O & C June '94)

6. (a) A ball is thrown into the air with an initial velocity at a direction of 45° to the horizontal. *By neglecting air resistance*, sketch,
(i) the variation of horizontal ball position with time,
(ii) the variation of vertical ball position with time.

(b) Repeat parts (a) (i) and (a) (ii) *without neglecting the effect of air resistance.*
(Sketch (a) (i) and (b) (i) on the same graph, with (a) (ii) and (b) (ii) on another graph.)

(c) *Neglecting air resistance*, where along the path of the ball described in part (a) is the speed of the ball,
(i) a maximum,
(ii) a minimum?
Justify your answer.

(d) A spherical object of radius r moving through air at a speed v experiences a frictional force

$$F = 340 \times 10^{-6} rv + 836 r^2 v^2$$

where F is in Newtons, r in metres and v in metres per second.
The speed v of a spherical raindrop of diameter 2.0 mm and mass 4.19×10^{-3} g falling from rest due to gravity varies with time t according to the sketch in Fig 2.7.

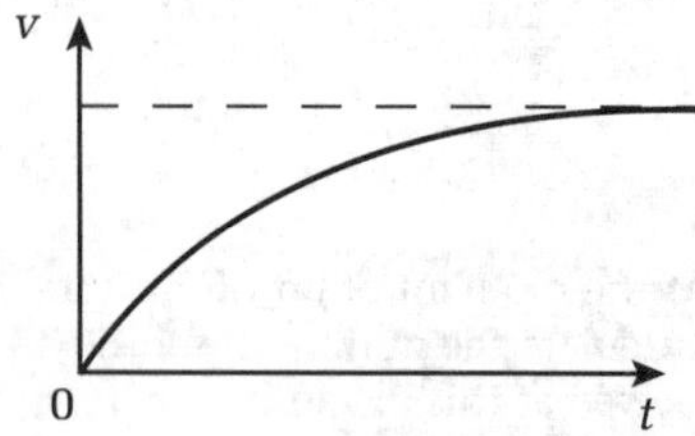

Fig 2.7

(i) Deduce the slope of the graph at time $t = 0$.
(ii) Estimate the value of v after a very long time has elapsed.
(Note that the value of v will be greater than $0.1\,\mathrm{m\,s^{-1}}$.)
(iii) Indicate without calculation how the total distance travelled in a certain time may be determined.

(c) The speed of fall of droplets in a fine mist is found to be $0.001\,\mathrm{m\,s^{-1}}$. Estimate the diameter of the droplets. (Note that the value of the diameter will be less than 0.02 mm.)
Density of water $= 1000\,\mathrm{kg\,m^{-3}}$.

(WJEC June '94, Special Paper)

3 COLLISIONS

What you need to know now

- Momentum is defined as mass x velocity.
- The impulse of a force acting for a given time is defined as force × time.
- Momentum is conserved in any collision or explosion.
- An elastic collision is defined as one in which the total kinetic energy is unchanged.
- A totally inelastic collision is where the bodies stick together on impact.

What you need to know next

Collisions in a straight line

When two bodies collide, momentum is transferred from one body to the other. The loss of momentum from one body is equal to the gain of momentum by the other body. Consider the collision shown in Fig 3.1 where body A collides with body B along a straight line.

The impulse of A on B equals $F_{AB}\,t$ where F_{AB} is the force of impact of A on B and t is the duration of the impact. According to Newton's second law, this is equal to the change of momentum of B

i.e. $F_{AB}\,t = m_B v_B - m_B u_B$

The impulse of B on A equals $F_{BA}\,t$ where F_{BA} is the force of impact of B on A and t is the duration of the impact, as before. According to Newton's second law, this is equal to the change of momentum of A

i.e. $F_{BA}\,t = m_A v_A - m_A u_A$

According to Newton's third law, $F_{AB} = -F_{BA}$ since the force of A on B is equal and opposite to the force of B on A. Hence $(m_B v_B - m_B u_B) = -(m_A v_A - m_A u_A)$. Rearranging this equation gives

$$m_A u_A + m_B u_B = m_A v_A + m_A v_B$$

i.e. total initial momentum equals the total final momentum.

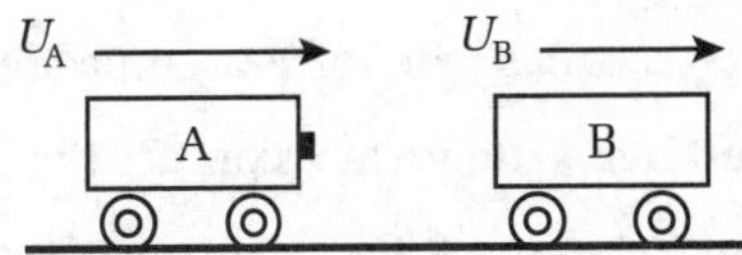

(a) Before impact

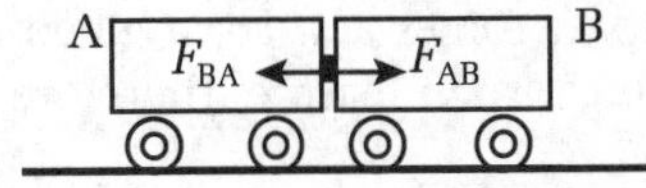

(b) At impact

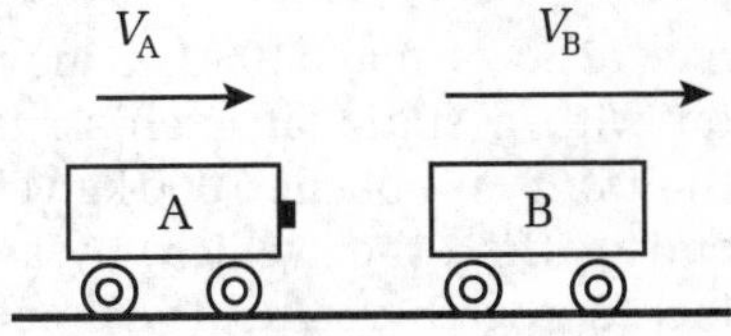

(c) After impact

Fig 3.1

Elastic collisions

Suppose Fig 3.1 represents an elastic collision. The total final kinetic energy is therefore equal to the total initial kinetic energy,

i.e. $\frac{1}{2}m_A u_A{}^2 + \frac{1}{2}m_B u_B{}^2 = \frac{1}{2}m_A v_A{}^2 + \frac{1}{2}m_B v_B{}^2$.

Also $m_A u_A + m_B u_B = m_A v_A + m_B v_B$ since momentum is conserved in any collision.

The two equations may be rearranged as below,

Equation 1 $\quad m_A u_A^2 - m_A v_A^2 = m_B v_B^2 - m_B u_B^2$

after cancelling $\frac{1}{2}$ from each term.

Equation 2 $\quad m_A u_A - m_A v_A = m_B v_B - m_B u_B$

Hence $\quad \dfrac{m_A u_A^2 - m_A v_A^2}{m_A u_A - m_A v_A} = \dfrac{m_B v_B^2 - m_B u_B^2}{m_B v_B - m_B u_B}$

which gives $\quad u_A + v_A = v_B + u_B \quad$ since $u^2 - v^2 = (u - v)(u + v)$.

Thus the relative velocity of approach = the relative velocity of separation.

Equation 3 $\quad v_B - v_A = u_A - u_B$

If $u_B = 0$, equations 2 and 3 may be combined to show that

$$v_A = \frac{(m_A - m_B)}{(m_A + m_B)} u_A$$

and

$$v_B = \frac{2 m_A u_A}{(m_A + m_B)}$$

If $m_A > m_B$ then $v_A > 0$ i.e. A does not reverse direction on impact.

If $m_A = m_B$ then $v_A = 0$ i.e. A stops completely and B carries away all the kinetic energy.

If $m_A < m_B$ then $v_A < 0$ i.e. A reverses direction due to the impact.

Impact forces

To calculate the force of impact of one body on another,

either use force × contact time = change of momentum

or use force × distance (over which the force acts) = change of kinetic energy

Safety features in vehicles such as seat belts and crumple zones are designed to increase the impact time and hence the distance over which impact forces act. For a given change of momentum or change of kinetic energy, such features therefore reduce the force of an impact.

Case study

A vehicle of mass 1000 kg moving at a speed of $30\,\mathrm{m\,s^{-1}}$ collides head-on with a stationary vehicle of mass 2000 kg. The impact compresses the front end of the 1000 kg vehicle by a distance of 0.60 m and the rear end of the other vehicle by a distance of 0.40 m. The vehicles remain locked together after the impact. Calculate (a) the speed of the two vehicles immediately after the impact force ceases to act, (b) the impact force and the impact time, (c) the acceleration of each vehicle due to the impact.

Fig 3.2

(a) Use the principle of conservation of momentum to calculate the speed v immediately after impact. Hence

$$(1000 + 2000)\,v = 1000 \times 30$$

$$v = 1000 \times 30/3000 = 10.0\,\mathrm{m\,s^{-1}}$$

(b) The impact force may be calculated from the total loss of kinetic energy ÷ total compression distance.

$$\text{The loss of kinetic energy} = \left(\tfrac{1}{2} \times 1000 \times 30^2\right) - \left(\tfrac{1}{2} \times 3000 \times 10.0^2\right)$$

$$= 300\,\mathrm{kJ}$$

$$\text{The total compression distance} = 0.60 + 0.40 = 1.00\,\mathrm{m}$$

$$\text{Hence the impact force} = 300\,\mathrm{kJ}/1.00\,\mathrm{m} = 300\,\mathrm{kN}$$

$$\text{The impact time} = \frac{\text{change of momentum}}{\text{impact force}}$$

$$= 2000 \times 10\,\mathrm{kg\,m\,s^{-1}}/300\,\mathrm{kN}$$

$$= 67\,\mathrm{ms}$$

(c) The acceleration of the 2000 kg vehicle = impact force/mass

$$= 300\,\mathrm{kN}/2000\,\mathrm{kg}$$

$$= 150\,\mathrm{m\,s^{-2}}$$

The acceleration of the 1000 kg vehicle $= -300\,\mathrm{kN}/1000\,\mathrm{kg}$

$$= -300\,\mathrm{m\,s^{-2}}$$

Safety at work

Acceleration of the human body can be expressed in terms of g, the acceleration due to gravity near the Earth's surface. The human body is incapable of withstanding a deceleration of more than about $20g$ for 0.1 s without serious injury. In the example above, an occupant in the 1000 kg vehicle without a seatbelt or airbag would experience the same deceleration as the vehicle which is 30 g, lasting 67 ms. Show for yourself that the vehicle travels 1.33 m in this time. Wearing a seatbelt which allows forward movement of 0.15 m would therefore allow the occupant to decelerate from $30\,\mathrm{m\,s^{-1}}$ to $10\,\mathrm{m\,s^{-1}}$ in a distance of 1.48 m, giving a deceleration of $27g$. An air bag to increase the contact area by a factor of ×5 would reduce the impact to the equivalent of $5.4g$ ($= 27g/5$).

Success at snooker

In an oblique collision, the vector nature of momentum must be considered. Fig 3.3 shows a collision between two snooker balls, one of which is initially at rest. Ball X transfers momentum to ball Y at the point of contact; assuming the surfaces are smooth so no angular momentum is transferred, ball Y therefore moves away from the point of impact along the line between their centres when in contact.

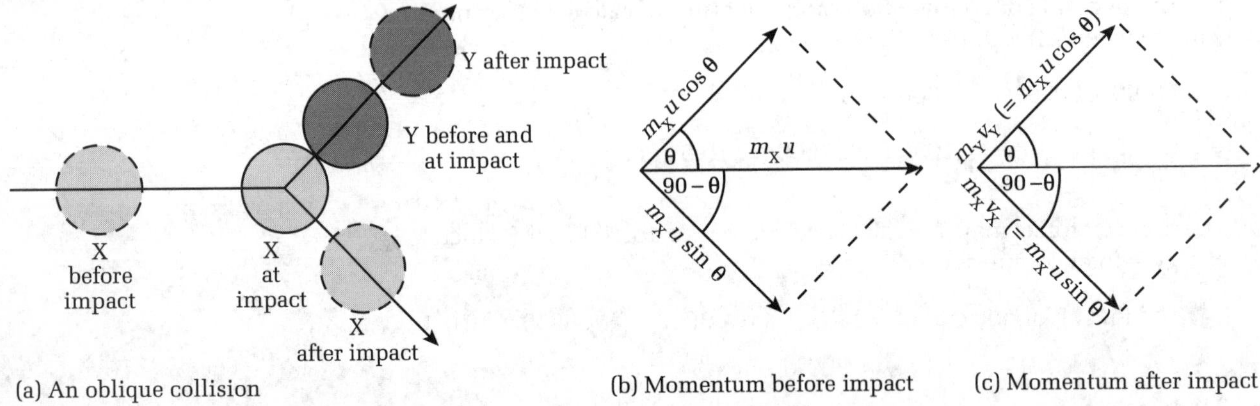

(a) An oblique collision (b) Momentum before impact (c) Momentum after impact

Fig 3.3

Resolving the initial momentum of ball X parallel and perpendicular to the line between the centres at impact therefore gives $m_X u \cos\theta$ as the parallel component and $m_X U \sin\theta$ as the perpendicular component, where θ is the angle between the initial direction of ball X and the line between the centres at impact.

The perpendicular component of ball X's momentum is unchanged by the impact. The parallel component is shared between X and Y just as in a head-on collision. Hence if the collision is elastic and the two balls have equal masses, X loses its parallel component of momentum completely which is transferred to Y. Thus two snooker balls (i.e. X and Y) move away from each other at right angles in an oblique collision provided the collision is elastic and the two spheres have equal masses. To check if two balls collide elastically, direct one head-on at the other one which should be stationary. If the first ball is stopped completely by the impact, the collision must be elastic.

Questions

1. (a) State the Law of Conservation of Momentum.

(b) A stationary radioactive nucleus disintegrates with the emission of an α-particle of mass m and a residual nucleus of mass M. If the kinetic energy of the α-particle is E prove that the kinetic energy of the residual nucleus is $\frac{m}{M}E$.

(c) A stationary nucleus of radium ($^{226}_{88}$Ra) spontaneously disintegrates to give radon ($^{222}_{86}$Rn) with the emission of an α-particle.

(i) Calculate the energy released by the disintegration.

(ii) If 98.0% of this energy appears as kinetic energy of the α-particle, use the result of part (b) to calculate the kinetic energy of the radon nucleus.

(iii) Find the total kinetic energy of the products of disintegration.

(d) (i) By comparing your answers for (c)(i) and (c)(iii), explain why a γ-ray photon is found to be emitted some time after the emission of the α-particle.

(ii) Calculate the wavelength of the γ-ray photon.

(Nuclear masses: $^{226}_{88}$Ra = 226.025360 u, $^{222}_{86}$Rn = 222.017500 u, α-particle = 4.002600 u. 1 u = 931 MeV.)

(WJEC June '94)

2. (a) (i) Define *linear* momentum.
(ii) State whether linear momentum is a vector or a scalar quantity.

(b) State the principle of conservation of momentum.

(c) The principle can be applied in different types of interaction. These are illustrated by the following examples.
(i) Inelastic collision: a piece of plasticine of mass 0.20 kg falls to the ground and hits the ground with a velocity of $8.0\ \mathrm{m\,s^{-1}}$ vertically downward. It does not bounce but sticks to the ground. Calculate the momentum of the plasticine just before it hits the ground.
State the transfers of momentum and of kinetic energy of the plasticine which occur as a result of the collision.
(ii) Elastic collision: a neutron of mass 1.00 u travelling with velocity $6.50 \times 10^5\ \mathrm{m\,s^{-1}}$ collides head on with a stationary carbon atom of mass 12.00 u. The carbon atom moves off in the same direction with velocity $1.00 \times 10^5\ \mathrm{m\,s^{-1}}$. Calculate the velocity of the neutron after the collision.
State what happens to the total kinetic energy as a result of this collision.
(iii) There is a third type of interaction: this happens when two strong magnets are held stationary with the north pole of one pushed against the north pole of the other. On letting go, the magnets spring apart. It is apparent that the kinetic energy of the magnets has increased. Explain how the law of conservation of momentum applies in this case.

(UCLES June '94)

3. (a) The diagram shows a collision between two bodies, A and B, equal in size but unequal in mass. The collision occurs on a horizontal, flat and friction-free surface. Body A, of mass 200 g and moving with speed $0.80\ \mathrm{m\,s^{-1}}$, strikes the stationary body B of mass 100 g. Their new speeds are v_A and v_B respectively. The collision is perfectly elastic and lasts for a time Δt. The graph illustrates how the force F_{AB}, applied by A to B, varies with time.

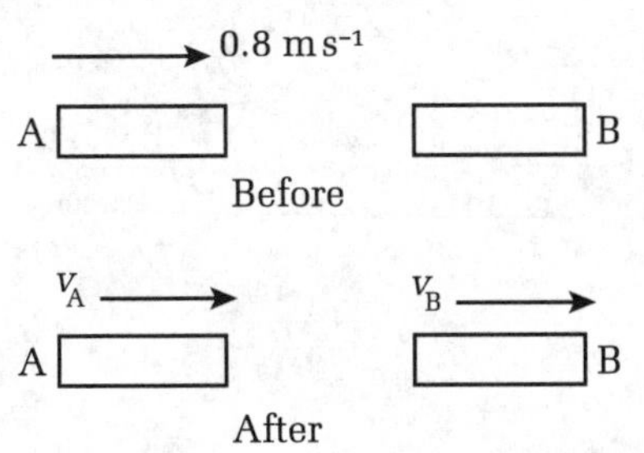

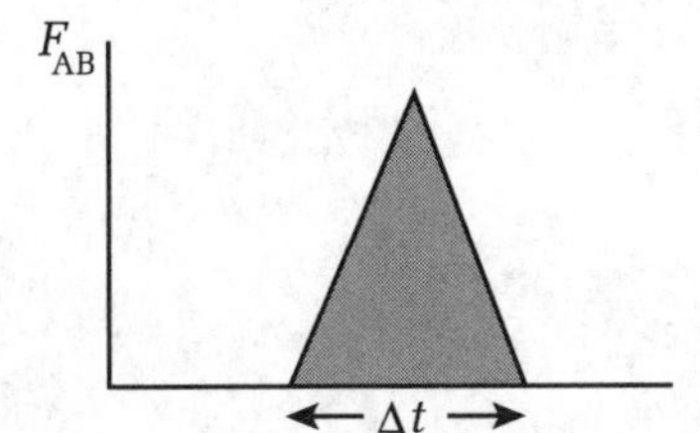

Fig 3.4

(i) Draw two free-body force diagrams, one for A and one for B, at the same instant during the collision.
(ii) Describe how Newton's third law of motion applies to this collision. Use this law to explain why

$$0.1v_B = 0.16 - 0.2v_A$$

(iii) What is meant by a perfectly elastic collision? Find the values of v_A and v_B.
(iv) Evaluate the shaded area of the graph.

(b) Discuss the relevance of Newton's third law of motion to the assertion that linear momentum is conserved in all collisions, whether or not they are elastic.

(c) A glass cylinder filled with transparent oil stands resting on a top-pan balance. The total mass is exactly one kilogram. A 50 g steel ball is dropped through the surface of the oil; it slows down to its constant final speed halfway down the cylinder. It stops at the bottom without bouncing.
Discuss, with the aid of a sketch graph, how the balance reading varies with time during the course of the ball's descent.

(ULEAC June '94, Special Paper)

4. An α-particle with a kinetic energy of 5.7 MeV makes a head-on collision with a gold nucleus which has proton number 79.

(a) If the gold nucleus is assumed not to move during the collision what will be the distance of closest approach?
Another α-particle of the same kinetic energy makes a head-on collision with a carbon nucleus of proton number 6 and nucleon number 12 which is free to move during the collision.

(b) What will be the relative velocity of the two particles at the point of closest approach? Explain your reasoning.

(c) Find the distance of closest approach in this case.

(O & C Nuffield June '92, Special Paper)

5. State briefly the conditions under which momentum, kinetic energy and total energy are conserved during a collision between two particles.

(a) Calculate the velocity of a proton of energy 1.2 MeV (i.e. a proton accelerated from rest though a potential difference of 1.2×10^6 V).

(b) The proton undergoes a head-on collision with an α-particle which is initially at rest. Consider the total kinetic energy of the two particles during the collision. Show that this total kinetic energy is a minimum at the instant when both particles have the same velocity. Calculate this minimum kinetic energy. Hence show that the closest separation of the two particles equals 3.0×10^{-15} m. Explain your reasoning.

(c) Calculate the final velocities of the α-particle and the proton after the collision.

(d) In another collision, a 1.2 MeV proton interacts with a stationary α-particle, after which the proton leaves at exactly 90° to its original direction. By applying conservation of momentum along the initial direction of the proton and also perpendicular to it, prove that the angle θ between the initial proton direction and the final α-particle direction satisfies $\cos^2 \theta = 5/8$. Hence find the final velocities in this case. Discuss whether you expect the closest separation to be greater or less than 3.0×10^{-15} m.

(O & C June '91, Special Paper)

4 FAIRGROUND CIRCLES

What you need to know now

- ❏ The velocity of an object moving along a circular path continually changes direction.
- ❏ Angular speed $\omega = \frac{v}{r}$ where v is the speed and r is the radius of curvature of its path.
- ❏ Centripetal acceleration $a = -\frac{v^2}{r}$ where the minus sign signifies 'towards the centre'.
- ❏ For uniform circular motion, the speed and radius are constant. Hence $v = \frac{2\pi r}{T}$ where T is the time for one complete rotation.
- ❏ The centripetal force on an object in circular motion $= -\frac{mv^2}{r}$.

What you need to know next

Centripetal and tangential acceleration

An object moving with uniform circular motion has zero tangential acceleration because it moves along its path at constant speed. However, because its direction is continually changing, it experiences a centripetal acceleration towards the centre of the circle.

Consider a point object P moving with speed v at distance r from a fixed point O, as in Fig 4.1, where O is the origin of the coordinate system shown. The coordinates of point P are $x = r\sin\theta$, $y = r\cos\theta$ where θ = angle YOP.

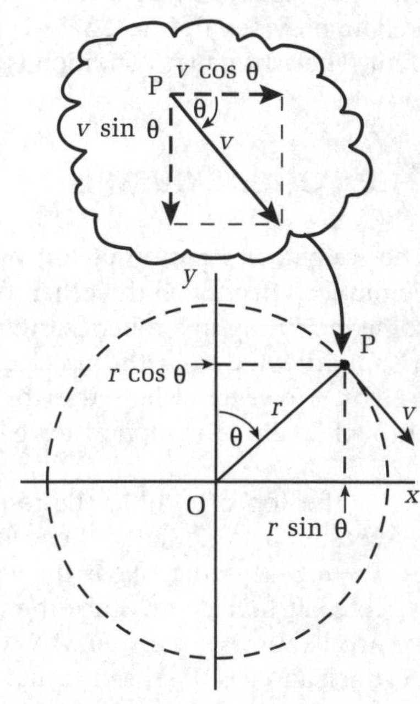

Fig 4.1

- ❏ The position vector of P in the coordinate system is therefore

$$\boldsymbol{r} = r\sin\theta\,\mathbf{i} + r\cos\theta\,\mathbf{j},$$

where $\mathbf{i}$ and $\mathbf{j}$ represent unit vectors along OX and OY respectively.

- ❏ The velocity vector of P, $\boldsymbol{v} = \frac{d\boldsymbol{r}}{dt} = r\cos\theta\frac{d\theta}{dt}\,\mathbf{i} - r\sin\theta\frac{d\theta}{dt}\,\mathbf{j}$

since $\frac{d}{dt}(\sin\theta) = \cos\theta\frac{d\theta}{dt}$ and $\frac{d}{dt}(\cos\theta) = -\sin\theta\frac{d\theta}{dt}$.

Hence $\boldsymbol{v} = r\omega(\cos\theta\,\mathbf{i} - \sin\theta\,\mathbf{j})$

where the angular speed of P, $\omega = \frac{d\theta}{dt}$.

1. Velocity $\boldsymbol{v}$ has a component $r\omega \cos\theta$ along the x-axis and a component $-r\omega \sin\theta$ along the y-axis. Therefore velocity $\boldsymbol{v}$ is perpendicular to position vector $\boldsymbol{r}$, as shown in Fig 4.1.

2. The speed of P, $v = r\omega$.

❑ The acceleration of P, $\boldsymbol{a} = \frac{d\boldsymbol{v}}{dt} = \frac{d}{dt}(r\omega \cos\theta\,\mathbf{i} - r\omega \sin\theta\,\mathbf{j})$; hence using the differentiation rules as before gives

$$\boldsymbol{a} = -r\omega \sin\theta \frac{d\theta}{dt}\mathbf{i} - r\omega \cos\theta \frac{d\theta}{dt}\mathbf{j}$$

Thus $\boldsymbol{a} = -\omega^2 \boldsymbol{r}$ since $\frac{d\theta}{dt} = \omega$ and $\boldsymbol{r} = r\sin\theta\,\mathbf{i} + r\cos\theta\,\mathbf{j}$.

1. Centripetal acceleration therefore has magnitude $\omega^2 r$ and its direction is always towards O.

2. The above proof assumes a constant radius and speed. In situations where the speed is changing at constant radius, show for yourself that the above method gives the same formula for the velocity but the acceleration has a tangential component $r\frac{d^2\theta}{dt^2}$ as well as a radial component equal to $-\omega^2 r$.

3. Since $\omega = v/r$, the centripetal acceleration $a = -\omega^2 r = -v^2/r$. Hence the centripetal force $F = mv^2/r$ towards the centre of the circle.

Weight and weightlessness

Weight is defined as the force of gravity on an object. A space vehicle in orbit about the Earth moves on a circular path because the force of gravity provides the necessary centripetal force. An astronaut floating around inside the space vehicle is unsupported but not weightless. The astronaut's weight provides the necessary centripetal force to keep the astronaut in orbit. The astronaut's condition is 'unsupported' rather than 'weightless'.

The roller coaster

The weight of a person at rest or in uniform motion is balanced by the combined effect of all the other forces acting on that person. For example, someone sitting in a roller coaster moving at constant velocity experiences a support force from the roller coaster equal and opposite to his or her weight. However, when the roller coaster goes over a 'hill' or passes through a 'dip', the support force is no longer equal to the weight.

1. At the top of a 'hill', the resultant force F on a person in the roller coaster acts towards the centre of curvature of the track. Hence $F = mg - S$, where mg is the weight of the person and S is the support force at that point. Since the resultant force F provides the centripetal acceleration, $mv^2/r = mg - S$, where r is the radius of curvature of the track and v is the speed at that point.

   Hence the support force $S = mg - mv^2/r$. In other words, the support force is less than the weight by an amount equal to mv^2/r.

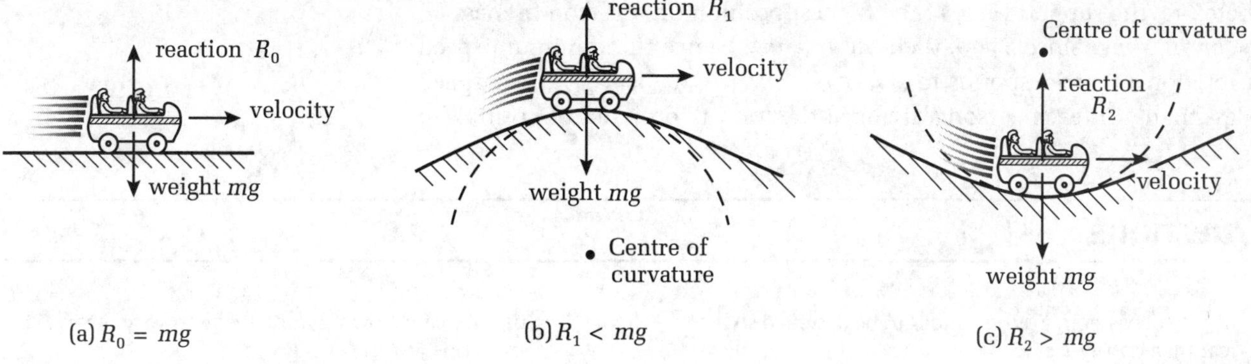

Fig 4.2 Roller coasting

2. When passing through the middle of a dip in the track, the support force exceeds the weight. The resultant force F acting towards the centre of curvature is $S - mg$. Since the resultant force is equal to mv^2/r, it therefore follows that the support force $S = mg + mv^2/r$ in this case.

The difference between the support force and the weight equals mv^2/r. The extra support force is therefore equal to mv^2/r. This is equivalent to increasing g by an amount equal to v^2/r. The human body is incapable of withstanding an extra support force of more than about three times its weight without loss of consciousness.

Over the top

Fig 4.3 shows another type of fairground ride. The wheel rotates in a vertical plane at a steady angular speed, pinning the occupants against its perimeter 'wall'. A person at the **highest** position experiences a support force S acting downwards from the perimeter wall. The combined effect of this support force and the person's weight combine to provide the centripetal force. Hence $S + mg = mv^2/r$ where r is the radius of rotation and v is the speed of a person at the wall in the wheel.

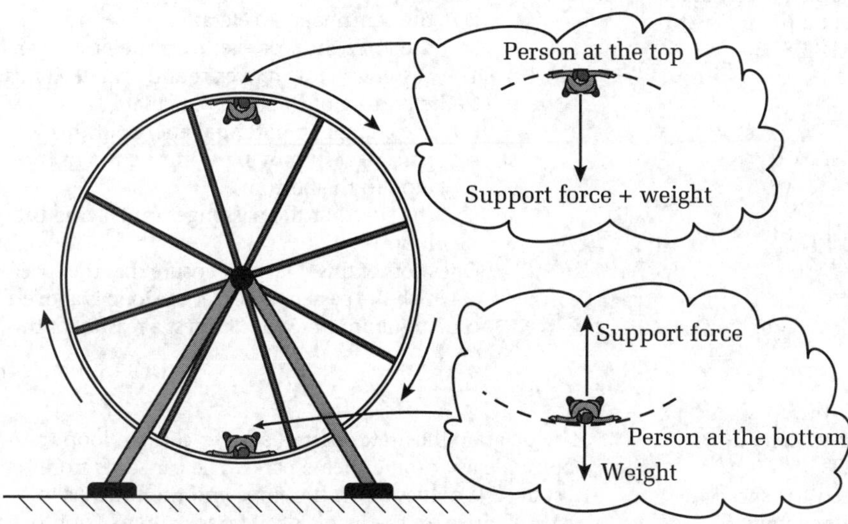

Fig 4.3 Defying gravity

Therefore, the support force at the highest position on a person of mass m, $S = mv^2/r - mg$. Since $S \geqslant 0$, then $mv^2/r \geqslant mg$. Hence the minimum speed of rotation $v_{\min}$ corresponds to $mv_{\min}{}^2/r = mg$, i.e. $v_{\min} = \sqrt{gr}$. If the speed is less than $\sqrt{gr}$, each person arriving at the top will drop out of position!

Questions

1. A roller coaster in a fairground is to be designed so that a car travels unpowered along the track shown in the diagram starting from rest at A which is 20 m above the ground. The point B is 5.0 m above the ground.

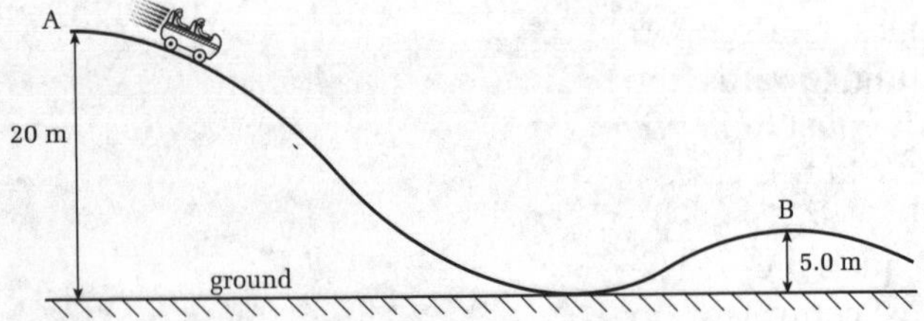

Fig 4.4

For safety purposes the car must always remain in contact with the track.

(a) Estimate the speed of the car as it reaches B. Explain why the speed can only be estimated.

(b) Estimate the minimum safe value for the radius of curvature of the track at B.

(c) State and explain the effect on the time taken to reach B of
(i) increasing the slope at the top of the track
(ii) increasing the mass of the car and passengers.

(Acceleration of free fall, $g = 10\,\text{m}\,\text{s}^{-2}$.)

(AEB June '90)

2. (a) State what is meant by *angular velocity*.

(b) A stone is tied to one end of a cord and then made to rotate in a horizontal circle about a point C with the cord horizontal, as shown in Fig 4.5.

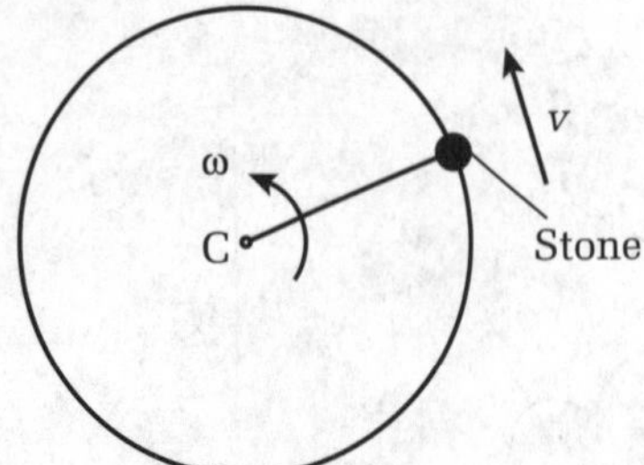

Fig 4.5

The stone has speed v and angular velocity ω about C.

(i) Write down a relation between the speed v, the length r of the cord and the angular velocity ω.

(ii) Explain how v can be made to vary when ω is constant.

(iii) Explain why there needs to be a tension in the cord to maintain the circular motion.

(iv) Write down an expression for the acceleration of the stone in terms of v and r. Hence, if the stone has mass m, show that the tension T in the cord is given by

$$T = mv\omega$$

(c) On one particular ride in an amusement park, passengers 'loop-the-loop' in a vertical circle, as illustrated in Fig 4.6.

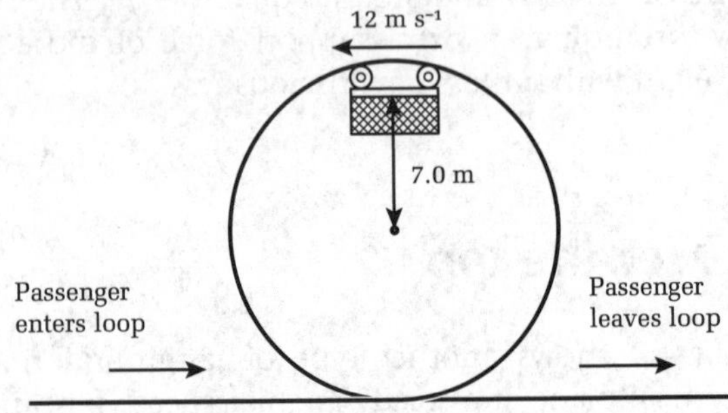

Fig 4.6

The loop has a radius of 7.0 m and a passenger, mass 60 kg, is travelling at $12\,\text{m}\,\text{s}^{-1}$ when at the highest point of the loop. Assume that frictional forces may be neglected.

(i) Calculate, for the passenger when at the highest point,
(1) the centripetal acceleration,
(2) the force the seat exerts on the passenger.

(ii) The passenger now moves round and descends to the bottom of the loop. Calculate
(1) the change in potential energy of the passenger in moving from the top of the loop to the bottom,
(2) the speed of the passenger on leaving the loop.

(iii) Operators of this ride must ensure that the speed at which the passengers enter the loop is above a certain minimum value. Suggest a reason for this.

(UCLES June '94)

3. The diagram illustrates part of a roller-coaster 'loop-the-loop' ride as at some theme parks. The car starts from rest at A. It moves down the slope and then travels in a vertical circle on the inside of the track and exits onto the incline at the right hand side of the diagram.

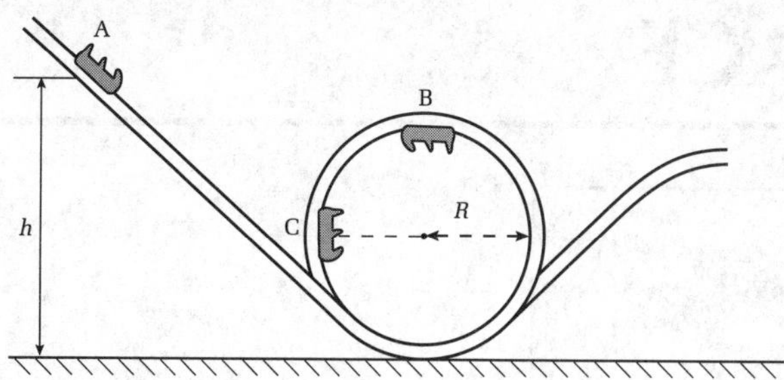

Fig 4.7

Treat the car as a particle of mass m sliding on a frictionless track. The radius of the loop is R.

(a) (i) The speed of the car is v when it reaches B, the highest point of the loop. Show that the *minimum* value of v for the car to remain in contact with the track is $\sqrt{gR}$.

(ii) Obtain an expression in terms of m, g and R for the minimum kinetic energy of the car at B.

(b) (i) State the law of conservation of energy. What can you deduce about the sum of the kinetic energy and the potential energy of the car at any point in its motion?

(ii) The point A, from which the car is released, is a vertical height h above the lowest point of the track and $R = 12.0$ m. Use the law of conservation of energy to find the minimum value of h which allows the car to loop-the-loop in contact with the track.

(c) The car has $m = 150$ kg. It is now released from rest at $h = 3R$.

(i) Calculate the magnitude of the horizontal force acting on the car when it passes point C, which lies on a horizontal diameter of the loop.

(ii) Calculate the magnitude of the total force on the car as it passes C.

(O & C June '93)

4. A boy ties a string around a stone and then whirls the stone so that it moves in a horizontal circle at constant speed.

(a) Draw a diagram showing the forces acting on the stone, assuming that air resistance is negligible. Use your diagram to explain

(i) why the string cannot be horizontal,

(ii) the direction of the resultant force on the stone and

(iii) the effect that the resultant force has on the path of the stone.

(b) The mass of the stone is 0.15 kg and the length of the string between the stone and the boy's hand is 0.50 m. The period of rotation of the stone is 0.40 s. Calculate the tension in the string.

(c) The boy now whirls the stone in a vertical circle, but the string breaks when it is horizontal. At this instant, the stone is 1.0 m above the ground and rising at a speed of 15 m s^{-1}. Describe the subsequent motion of the stone until it hits the ground and calculate its maximum height.

(O & C June '91)

5. The design of a space station looks like a giant rotating bicycle wheel with the laboratory area for the crew housed within the 'bicycle tyre'. See Fig 4.8. The radius of the wheel, that is, from the hub to the floor of the laboratories, is 200 m. The crew's living quarters are situated halfway to the hub of the station and are connected to the laboratories by a radial tunnel.

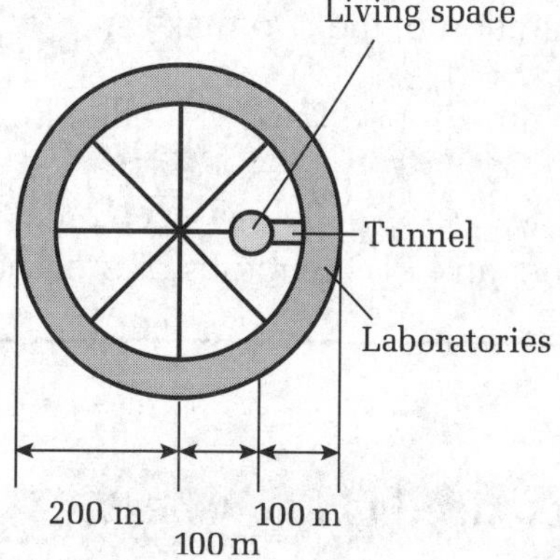

Fig 4.8

(a) Why does the rotation of the space station about the hub produce artificial gravity for the crew?

(b) Find the rate of rotation for the crew to experience artificial gravity equal to $g\,(= 9.8\,\text{m s}^{-2})$ in the laboratories.

(c) What is the value of artificial gravity on the floor of the crew's quarters 100 m from the hub of the station?

(d) Sketch a graph of the strength of the artificial gravitational field felt by an astronaut in the radial tunnel between the laboratory and the living quarters. Label your axes appropriately.

(e) Find the minimum energy required for a man of mass 70 kg to move from the laboratory to the living quarters.

(O & C June '94)

5 GRAVITY AND SPACE

What you need to know now

- ❑ Gravitational field strength g is the force per unit mass on a small mass.
- ❑ Gravitational potential V is the PE per unit mass of a small mass, zero PE being defined when the small mass is at infinity. This is equal to the work done per unit mass to move a small mass from infinity into the field.
- ❑ The gravitational force F between two point masses m_1 and m_2 is given by the equation $F = \frac{Gm_1 m_2}{r^2}$ where r is the separation of the two masses.
- ❑ The time period T for a satellite in an orbit about a spherical planet is given by $T^2 = \frac{4\pi^2}{GM} r^3$ where M is the mass of the planet and r is the radius of orbit of the satellite.

What you need to know next

Uniform and radial fields

A **uniform** field is one in which the gravitational field strength g is the same in magnitude and direction at all points. The gravitational field in a room is effectively the same throughout the room since the difference in the magnitude of g between the floor and the ceiling is negligible and so too is the difference in direction of a vertical line at either side of the room. The lines of force of a uniform field are parallel to each other. The dimensions of the room are insignificant compared with the radius of the Earth so g is effectively the same throughout the room. The lines of force of a uniform field are parallel to each other. However, in a space of dimensions not insignificant compared with the Earth, g would change according to position. The field in such a space cannot therefore be considered uniform. The gravitational field surrounding the Earth may be described as **radial** because its lines of force always point towards the centre of the Earth.

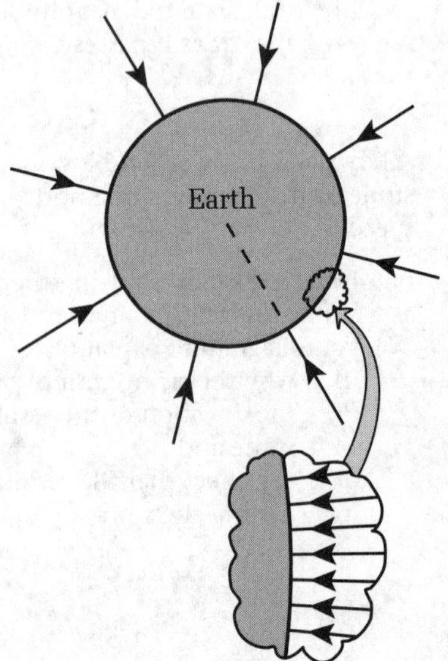

Fig 5.1 A radial field

Potential gradients

Suppose a small mass m moves a distance δr along the direction of a line of force in a gravitational field. The work done by the field on the mass is equal to $mg\,\delta r$ because the force of the field on the mass is mg and it moves distance δr in the direction of the force.

Hence change of potential energy $\delta(\text{PE}) = -mg\,\delta r$

and change of potential $\delta V = \delta(\text{PE})/m = -g\,\delta r$.

Rearranging this equation gives $g = -\dfrac{\mathrm{d}V}{\mathrm{d}r}$ in the limit $\delta r \to 0$.

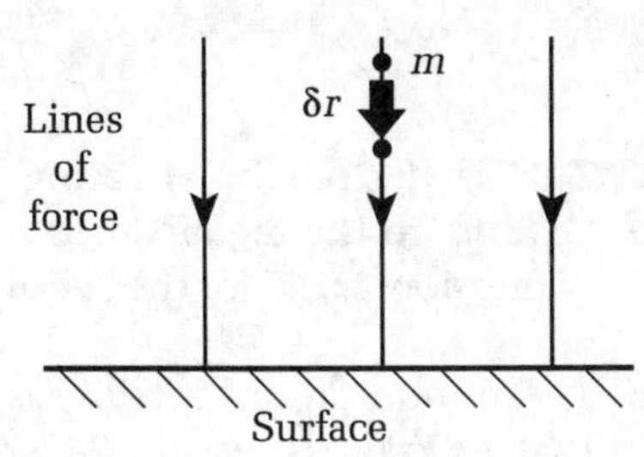

Fig 5.2 Gravity at work

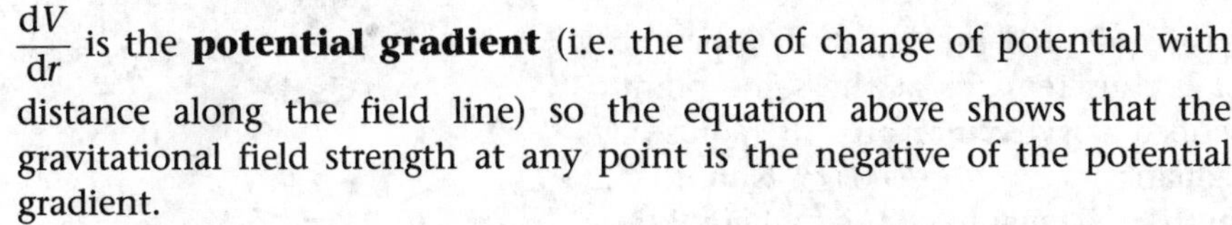

$\dfrac{\mathrm{d}V}{\mathrm{d}r}$ is the **potential gradient** (i.e. the rate of change of potential with distance along the field line) so the equation above shows that the gravitational field strength at any point is the negative of the potential gradient.

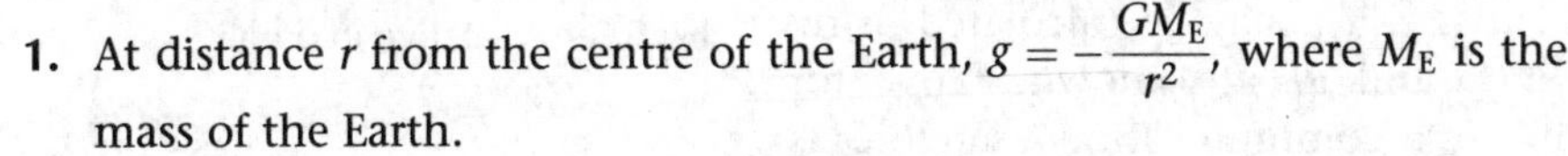

1. At distance r from the centre of the Earth, $g = -\dfrac{GM_E}{r^2}$, where M_E is the mass of the Earth.

   Hence $-\dfrac{\mathrm{d}V}{\mathrm{d}r} = -\dfrac{GM_E}{r^2}$.

   Thus $V = \displaystyle\int_\infty^r \mathrm{d}V = \int_\infty^r \frac{GM_E}{r^2}\mathrm{d}r = -\frac{GM_E}{r}$.

2. If a small mass is to be moved to infinity from distance r from the centre of a planet, its PE must be increased to zero from $-\dfrac{GM_E}{r}$. For a projectile, its increase of PE is from its initial kinetic energy, hence its escape speed v_{esc} is given by equating its minimum KE for escape to the necessary increase of PE,

   $$\tfrac{1}{2}mv_{esc}^2 = \frac{GM_E}{r}$$

   Hence $v_{esc} = \left(\dfrac{2GM_E}{r}\right)^{1/2} = \sqrt{2gr}$

   since $\dfrac{GM_E}{r^2} = g$ and $M_E \gg m$.

Black holes

Nothing can escape from a black hole, not even light. The **event horizon** of a black hole is where an object entering a black hole disappears, never to be seen again. The radius of the event horizon is called the Schwartzschild radius R_S. This is given by the above formula with the speed of light c as the escape speed,

$$R_S = \frac{2GM}{c^2}$$

The derivation of this formula is beyond the scope of this book but the outcome is exactly as described above. Prove for yourself that for a sphere to be a black hole, its actual radius must be less than $\left(\dfrac{3c^2}{8G\pi\rho}\right)^{1/2}$ where ρ is the density of the sphere.

Satellite dynamics

1. For a satellite of mass m in a circular orbit of radius r about a planet of mass M, the time period T is given by the equation,

$$T^2 = \frac{4\pi^2}{GM} r^3$$

This is derived by equating the gravitational force on the satellite GMm/r^2 to the required centripetal force mv^2/r and substituting in the expression $2\pi r/T$ for the speed v.

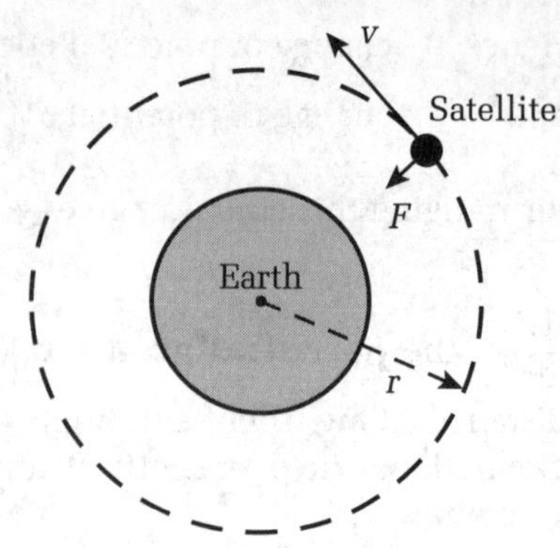

Fig 5.3 A satellite in orbit

2. A communications satellite is in an equatorial orbit at such a height that its orbit is exactly 24 hours. It thus remains at the same point above the equator. Its orbit is described as **synchronous**. Its radius of orbit can be calculated from the equation $T^2 = (4\pi^2/GM)\,r^3$. Note that the surface gravitational field strength g_s is equal to $GM/R_E{}^2$ where R_E is the Earth's radius. Hence the radius of orbit r may be calculated using the equation $T^2 = (4\pi^2/g_s R_E{}^2)\,r^3$ if g_s and R_E are known. Prove for yourself that the radius of orbit of a communications satellite is approximately $6.6\,R_E$.

3. Weather satellites need to be considerably closer to the Earth than communications satellites to provide useful images. A weather satellite in a polar orbit (i.e. passing over both poles) with a time period of two hours would cross the equator 30° further West each successive transit. Prove for yourself that its radius of orbit is approximately $1.26\,R_E$. A satellite in an orbit significantly lower than this would experience atmospheric drag which would reduce its speed and make it fall to the ground.

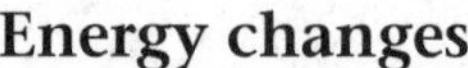

Energy changes

The total energy of a satellite in a circular orbit far above the Earth's atmosphere is constant. The gravitational force does no work on the satellite because the force direction (towards the centre of the Earth) is perpendicular to the velocity direction at any point on the satellites's path.

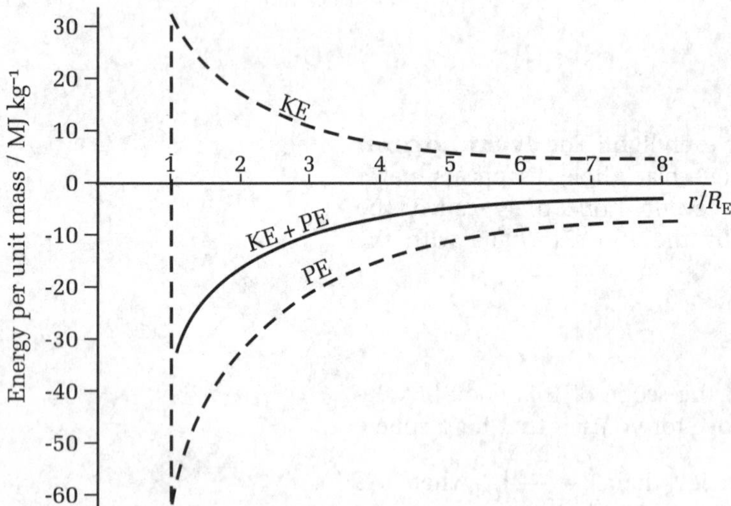

Fig 5.4 Energy versus distance for a satellite

For a satellite of mass m in circular orbit of radius r,

- its potential energy $= -\dfrac{GmM_E}{r}$ where M_E is the mass of the Earth

- its kinetic energy $= \frac{1}{2}mv^2 = \dfrac{GmM_E}{2r}$ since $\dfrac{mv^2}{r} = \dfrac{GmM_E}{r^2}$
(Note its potential energy is $-2\times$ its kinetic energy.)

- the total energy $E =$ potential energy + kinetic energy $= -\dfrac{GmM_E}{2r}$.

Fig 5.4 shows how the energy of a satellite varies with its radius of orbit. The energy ΔE required to move a satellite of mass m from the Earth's surface into a circular orbit of radius r is the difference between its total energy in orbit and its total energy at the surface, i.e.

$$\Delta E = \left(-\frac{GmM_E}{2r}\right) - \left(-\frac{GmM_E}{R_E}\right) = \left(\frac{GmM_E}{R_E}\right) - \left(\frac{GmM_E}{2r}\right)$$

where M_E is the mass of the Earth and R_E is the Earth's radius. The above expression assumes the kinetic energy of the rocket on the ground is negligible.

Atmospheric drag

The Earth's atmosphere extends several hundred kilometres into space, becoming less and less dense with increased height. At the surface, the density of the atmosphere is approximately $1.2\,\text{kg}\,\text{m}^{-3}$. At a height of 300 km above the surface, its density is about $10^{-11}\,\text{kg}\,\text{m}^{-3}$. Even this extremely small density is sufficient to bring a satellite down to Earth eventually.

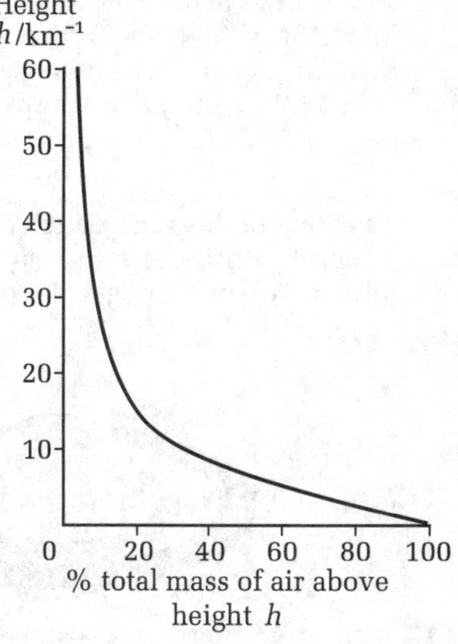

Fig 5.5 Atmospheric mass

For a satellite moving at speed v through the atmosphere, the drag force $F \approx \rho A v^2$ where ρ is the density of the atmosphere and A is the effective area of cross section of the satellite. Show for yourself that the speed of a satellite in orbit 300 km above the Earth is approximately $7.7\,\text{km}\,\text{s}^{-1}$ and its time period is approximately 90 minutes. The drag force at this height on a satellite of effective cross-sectional area $10\,\text{m}^2$ is therefore of the order of 6 mN. Thus the work done against drag per orbit is approximately 0.25 MJ (= force $\times$ circumference). The total energy of a satellite of mass 500 kg at this height is approximately 5000 MJ. The energy of this satellite would therefore be reduced by 1% in 200 orbits which is about 12.5 days.

What effect does this energy change have on the radius of orbit r? Since the total energy $E = k/r$ where $k = -GmM_E/2$, then a slightly different radius $r + \delta r$ corresponds to total energy $E + \delta E = k/(r + \delta r)$. Hence the change of the total energy $\delta E = \dfrac{k}{(r+\delta r)} - \dfrac{k}{r} = \dfrac{-k\delta r}{r(r+\delta r)} = \dfrac{-k\delta r}{r^2}$, since $r(r+\delta r)$ is effectively equal to r^2 provided $\delta r \ll r$. Hence $\dfrac{\delta E}{E} = -\dfrac{\delta r}{r}$ so the radius decreases by 1% because the energy changes by 1%.

NOTE: For two variables y and x linked by the formula $y = kx^n$, $\dfrac{\delta y}{y} = n\dfrac{\delta x}{x}$ so the % change of y equals $n \times$ the % change of x for small changes.

Questions

1. The gravitational field close to the Earth's surface is often described as uniform. Explain, with the aid of a diagram, what is meant by a *uniform gravitational field*.

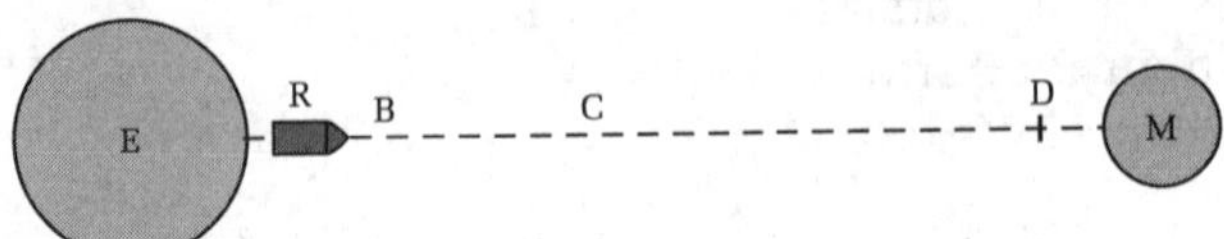

Fig 5.6

The diagram above shows a space rocket R which relies on the kinetic energy it gains in the first few minutes of its flight to carry it from the Earth to the Moon.

(i) As it moves further away from the Earth and into the region BC, the decrease in kinetic energy per kilometre of path gets less. Why is this?

(ii) The force of the rocket is zero at D, 346×10^3 km from the centre of the Earth and 38×10^3 km from the centre of the Moon. Find the ratio of the Earth's mass to the Moon's mass.

(iii) The radius of the Earth is 3.66 times the radius of the Moon. Find a value for the ratio of the density of the Earth to the density of the moon.

(ULEAC June '93)

2. The rings of the planet Saturn consist of a vast number of small particles, each in a circular orbit about the planet. Two of the rings are shown in the diagram.

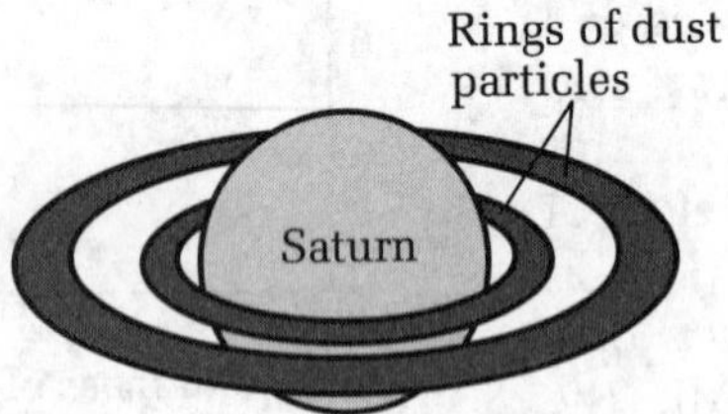

Fig 5.7

The inner edge of the inner ring is 70 000 km from the centre of the planet and the outermost edge of the outer ring is 140 000 km from the centre. The speed of the outermost particles is $17\,\text{km}\,\text{s}^{-1}$.

(a) Show that the speed, v, of a particle in an orbit of radius r around a planet of mass M is given by

$$v = \sqrt{\frac{GM}{r}}$$

where G is the universal gravitational constant, $6.7 \times 10^{-11}\,\text{N}\,\text{m}^2\,\text{kg}^{-2}$.

(b) Determine the mass of Saturn.

(c) How long does it take for the outermost particles to complete an orbit?

(d) Calculate the orbital speed of the particles nearest to Saturn.

(AEB Summer '94)

3. Many of the objects which we see in the sky are binary stars. A binary star consists of two stars rotating about a common centre of mass.

(a) What evidence would lead you to believe that two neighbouring stars were part of a binary system rather than two stars with a wide separation in approximately the same line of sight?

(b) One of the stars in a binary system is thought to be a 'black hole'. What evidence would support this suggestion?

(c) The separation of two stars in a particular binary system is 1.0×10^{10} m with the centre of mass of the system 9.0×10^9 m from the visible star. The visible star has mass 1.0×10^{30} kg. The other star is a black hole of mass M.

(i) Draw a sketch of the binary system, incorporating the above data.

(ii) Suggest a reason why the mass M of the black hole is of the order 9×10^{30} kg.

(iii) Calculate the density ρ of the black hole, given that

$$\rho = \frac{c^6}{4.2\,G^3M^2}$$

where c is the speed of light in a vacuum.

(iv) Comment on your answer to (c) (iii) in relation to your knowledge of black holes.

(UCLES June '92)

4. For this question consider the motion of the planets around the Sun to be circular. Take the distance from the Earth to the Sun to be 1.5×10^8 km and 1 year to be 3.1×10^7 s.

(a) Show how Kepler's third law of planetary motion relating the period of any planet around the Sun to its distance from the Sun, i.e. $T \propto R^{3/2}$, can be derived from Newton's law of gravitation.

(b) Hence, or otherwise, find a value for the mass of the Sun.

(c) The distance of Mars from the Sun is 1.524 times that of the Earth from the Sun. Find how many Earth years are equal to one Martian year.

(d) It is proposed to send a spacecraft of mass 50 000 kg from the Earth to Mars. Find the *minimum* energy which is required by the spacecraft to be able to travel to the orbit of Mars and to have the same orbital speed as Mars. Consider only the gravitational attraction of the Sun on the spacecraft. Neglect the gravitational attraction on the spacecraft of the Earth and Mars, that is, the energy changes in lift-off and landing on a planet.

(O & C June '93)

5. (a) State Newton's law of gravitation, defining any symbols you use.

(b) A satellite of mass M_S in a circular orbit of radius r about the Earth behaves as though the Earth's mass M_E were concentrated at its centre. The satellite's potential energy is

$$E_P = -\frac{GM_E M_S}{r}$$

(i) Use this relationship to show that

$$E_P = -2E_K$$

where E_K is the satellite's kinetic energy.

(ii) As a result of atmospheric friction, the radius of the satellite's orbit about the Earth decreases by 0.1% in a week. Assuming that the orbit remains circular, find the percentage change in the orbital speed in one week.

(iii) Given that $r = 6.60 \times 10^6$ m, $M_S = 2.00 \times 10^3$ kg and $M_E = 5.98 \times 10^{24}$ kg, find the change in the satellite's total energy (kinetic plus potential) in one week.

(iv) Hence show that the frictional force on the satellite is approximately 0.01 N.

(v) In fact, the satellite carries a small booster motor to compensate for the effect of atmospheric friction. The force exerted by the motor is equal to uz where z is the rate at which fuel is burnt (mass per unit time), and u has a value of 2.00×10^3 N s kg^{-1}. If the satellite carries 30 kg of fuel, for how long can it maintain its orbit?

(UCLES June '94, Special Paper)

6. An Earth satellite of mass 70 kg is launched into a circular orbit 350 km above the surface of the Earth.

(a) Calculate the potential energy of the satellite:

(i) relative to the surface of the Earth

(ii) relative to infinity. (Ignore the effect of the Sun, other planets, etc.)

Comment upon the significance of the signs of these two figures.

(b) (i) Find the period of the satellite orbit.

(ii) Find the kinetic energy of the satellite in this orbit.

(c) Find the *total* energy of the satellite using the zero of potential energy as defined in (a) (ii) above.

(d) After some time the satellite has fallen to a new circular orbit at an altitude of 345 km because of the effects of atmospheric drag.

(i) Find the magnitude and sign of the change in its potential energy.

(ii) Find the magnitude and sign of the change in its kinetic energy.

(iii) Find the magnitude and sign of the change in its total energy.

(e) The drag force on the satellite can be estimated by assuming that it undergoes an elastic collision with each air molecule that it meets.

(i) Show that the force is given approximately by $F = 2A\rho v^2$ where A is the cross-sectional area of the satellite in the direction in which it is moving, ρ is the atmospheric density and v is the velocity of the satellite.

(ii) In practice the drag force is about one half of this. Suggest reasons why this is so.

(f) Making a reasonable assumption about the value of A, estimate how long the satellite takes to move from an altitude of 350 km to an altitude of 345 km.

(g) In practice the density of the upper atmosphere can be studied by observing the decay of a satellite orbit. An easy measurement to make is the rate of decrease of the orbital period. Estimate the initial rate of change of the period when the satellite is at an altitude of 350 km. Express your answer in seconds per day.

Data: The radius of the Earth = 6350 km; the mass of the Earth = 6.0×10^{24} kg; the atmospheric density at 350 km is close to 1×10^{-11} kg m^{-3}.

(O & C Nuffield June '92, Special Paper)

6 STRESS AND ITS LIMITS

What you need to know now

- ❑ Hooke's Law states that the tension T in a spring is proportional to its extension e, i.e. $T = ke$ where k is a constant.
- ❑ Stress is defined as the force per unit area acting normal to that area.
- ❑ Strain is defined as extension per unit length.
- ❑ The Young modulus of a solid is defined as $\frac{\text{stress}}{\text{strain}}$.

What you need to know next

Keeping within limits

For a material under tension or compression, strain is proportional to stress up to the *limit of proportionality*. Provided this limit is not exceeded, stress/strain is a constant defined as the Young modulus of the material. Beyond the limit of proportionality, the strain is no longer proportional to the stress. The material will return to its original length when the applied forces are removed provided it is not stretched beyond its *elastic limit*. For some materials such as steel, the elastic limit is very close to the limit of proportionality. For other materials such as rubber, this is not so.

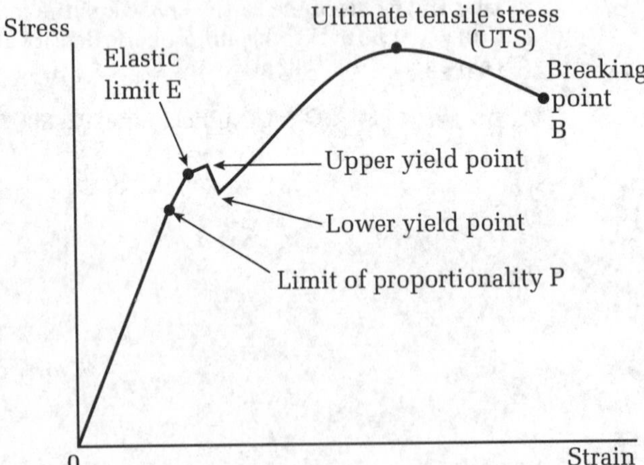

Fig 6.1 Stress versus strain for a metal

Case study 1

How much does a cable stretch due to its own weight? Cables used to support or lift objects must be sufficiently strong to withstand stress changes. Steel is the most commonly used material because its Young modulus is high. For a vertical cable, its extension e when carrying a load of weight W is calculated directly from the Young modulus equation,

$$\text{Young modulus } E = \frac{\text{stress}}{\text{strain}} = \frac{T/A}{e/l_0} = \frac{Tl_0}{Ae}$$

where A is the area of cross section of the cable, l_0 is its initial length and T is the tension in the cable.

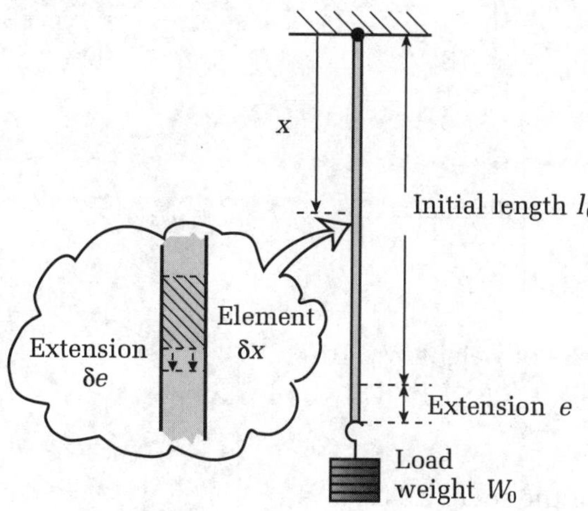

Fig 6.2 Stretching a cable

1. If the weight of the cable itself is negligible, tension T is equal to the weight W_0 supported by the cable.

2. In general, the tension T at distance x below the top of the cable $= W_0 + \dfrac{w\,(l_0 - x)}{l_0}$ where w is the weight of the cable itself.

Consider the extension of an element of length δx at distance x below the top. This is given by

$$\delta e = \frac{T\mathrm{d}x}{AE} = \frac{\mathrm{d}x}{AE}\left(W_0 + w - \frac{wx}{l_0}\right)$$

$$\text{The total extension } e = \int_{x=0}^{x=l_0} \mathrm{d}e = \frac{1}{AE}(W_0 + w)\int_{x=0}^{x=l_0} \mathrm{d}x - \frac{w}{AEl_0}\int_{x=0}^{x=l_0} x\,\mathrm{d}x.$$

$$\text{Hence} \qquad e = \frac{1}{AE}(W_0 + w)\,l_0 - \frac{w}{AEl_0}\frac{l_0^{\,2}}{2} = \frac{(W_0 + 0.5w)}{AE}l_0.$$

Thus the extra extension due to the cable's own weight w is equal to the extension caused by increasing the load weight W_0 by $0.5\,w$. Clearly if $w \ll W_0$, the extra extension due to the cable's own weight is insignificant.

Case study 2

How much does a horizontal cable fixed at both ends 'give' when loaded at its centre?

Consider the cable of length l_0 as in Fig 6.3(a) stretched between two fixed points on the same horizontal level at a separation also equal to l_0.

Assuming the cable's own weight is negligible, there is no tension in the cable under zero load conditions.

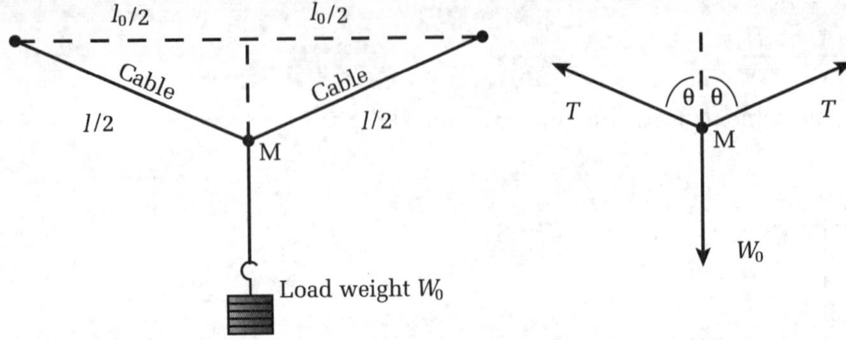

(a) Loading a horizontal cable (b) Force diagram at M

Fig 6.3 Loading a horizontal cable

Suppose the cable is now loaded at its centre with a load of weight W_0. To calculate the weight the cable can support for a given 'drop' y of the midpoint M of the cable

- ❑ Use Pythagoras' theorem to calculate the length l of the stretched cable

  $$(l/2)^2 = (l_0/2)^2 + y^2$$

- ❑ The next stage is to calculate the total extension of the cable from the increase of its length and then use the Young modulus equation to determine the tension in the cable, i.e. tension $T = \dfrac{A(l - l_0)E}{l_0}$.

- ❑ Finally, consider the relationship between the tension T and the load weight W_0. The vertical component of the tension in the two halves of the cable supports the weight as in Fig 6.3(b). Hence $W_0 = 2T\cos\theta$ where θ is the angle of each half of the cable to the vertical. Note that $\sin\theta = l_0/l$.

Worked example

A steel cable is to be used to accelerate a loaded lift of mass 1500 kg upwards at a constant acceleration of $1.2\,\text{m s}^{-2}$. The Young modulus of steel is 2.0×10^{11} Pa and the limit of proportionality is at a stress of 2.4×10^{8} Pa.

(a) (i) Show that the tension in the cable is 16.5 kN.

(ii) The safe maximum working stress is one third of the limit of proportionality. Calculate the minimum diameter of the cable.

(iii) Calculate the extension of 100 m of steel cable of this minimum diameter when it is used to accelerate the loaded lift at $1.2\,\text{m s}^{-2}$ upwards. 7 marks

(b) The density of steel is $7850\,\text{kg m}^{-3}$. Calculate the weight per unit length of the cable in (a)(iii) and hence discuss whether or not this cable extends significantly due to its own weight. 3 marks

Solution

(a) (i) Consider the forces acting on the lift, as shown in Fig 6.3. Using Newton's second law gives

resultant force $T - mg = ma$ ✓

where a = acceleration, m = mass, T = tension.

Hence $T = mg + ma = 1500g + (1500 \times 1.2) = 16\,500\,\text{N}$ ✓ (using $g = 9.8\,\text{m s}^{-2}$).

(ii) Safe maximum working stress $= \frac{1}{3} \times 2.4 \times 10^8 = 8.0 \times 10^7$ Pa. ✓

Hence the minimum area of cross section A = tension T/safe maximum stress

$$A = \frac{1500g}{8.0 \times 10^7} = 1.83 \times 10^{-4}\,\text{m}^2 \quad ✓$$

Thus the minimum diameter d_{min} is given by $\pi {d_{min}}^2/4 = 1.83 \times 10^{-4}$, giving $d_{min} = 15.3$ mm. ✓

(iii) Strain e/l_0 = stress/$E = \dfrac{8.0 \times 10^7}{2.0 \times 10^{11}} = 4.0 \times 10^{-4}$. ✓

Hence extension e = strain × length $= 4.0 \times 10^{-4} \times 100 = 4.0 \times 10^{-2}$ m. ✓

(b) Mass = density × volume = density × area of cross section × length. ✓

Hence mass per unit length = density × area of cross section $= 7850 \times 1.83 \times 10^{-4} = 1.44\,\text{kg m}^{-1}$. ✓

Therefore, the weight of a length of 100 m of this cable is 1410 N ($= 1.44 \times 100 \times g$). This is less than one tenth of the load weight and would cause an extra extension of approximately 2 mm which is not significant. ✓

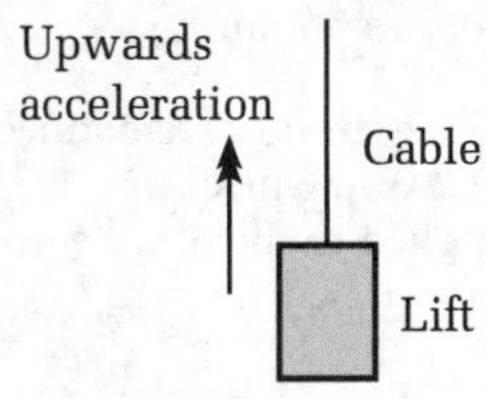

(a) Cable support

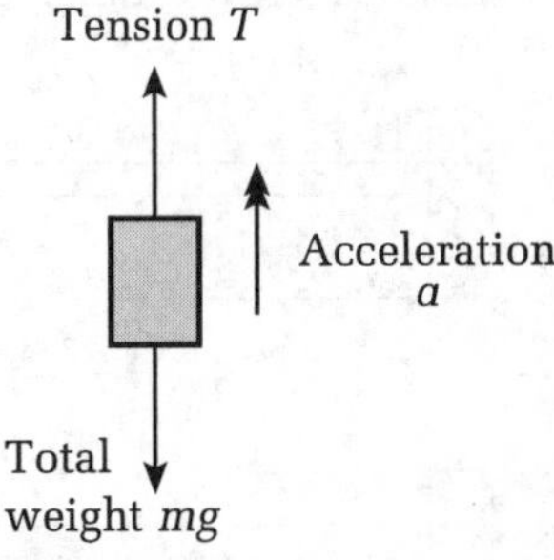

(b) Free body force diagram of lift

Fig 6.4 An accelerating lift

Questions

1. A cylindrical copper wire and a cylindrical steel wire, each of length 1.000 m and having equal diameters are joined at one end to form a composite wire 2.000 m long. This composite wire is subjected to a tensile stress until its length becomes 2.002 m. Calculate the tensile stress applied to the wire.
(The Young modulus for copper $= 1.2 \times 10^{11}$ Pa and for steel $= 2.0 \times 10^{11}$ Pa.)

(WJEC June '91)

2. A catapult is made of rubber cord of total unstretched length 150 mm and of square cross section of side 1.5 mm. The cord is stretched to a length of 180 mm and then released to propel a mass of 6.0 g horizontally. The Young modulus for rubber is 2.0×10^7 Pa.
Calculate
(i) the tension in the stretched cord,
(ii) the energy stored,
(iii) the speed of the mass leaving the catapult.
State **two** assumptions made in your calculations.

(NEAB June '93)

3. The graph shows force against extension for a length of steel wire.

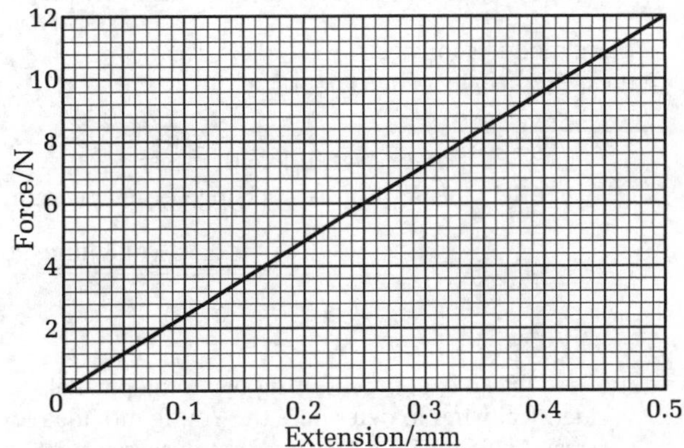

Fig 6.5

(a) The wire has diameter 0.40 mm and its unstretched length is 1.0 m. Find the value of the Young modulus for the steel wire.

(b) A second wire made of the same steel and having the same unstretched length has *twice* the diameter. Draw the force against extension graph for this wire **carefully** on a copy of the diagram above. Explain your reasoning.

(c) The two wires are connected to form a wire length of 2.0 m. One end is fixed and a force of 8.0 N applied to the other end. Find the total extension of the wires.

(O & C June '93)

4. The diagrams show an apparatus designed to demonstrate the resistance to shear of a new material.

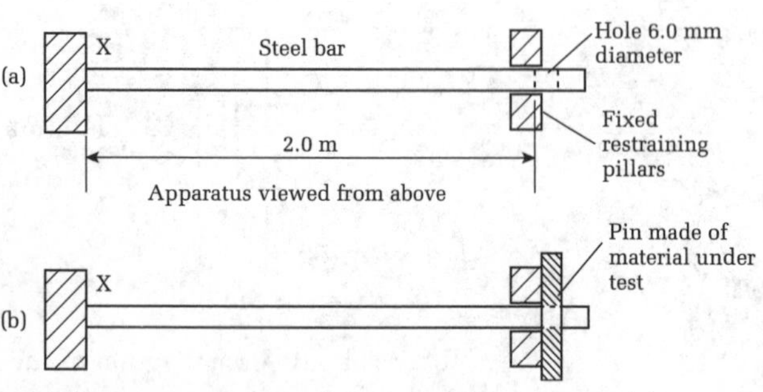

Fig 6.6

One end X of the steel bar is fixed. The other end has a hole of diameter 6 mm drilled in it. When the room temperature is 20 °C, the distance between the fixed end of the bar and the nearer edge of the hole is 2.0 m as shown in Fig 6.6(a). At this temperature half of the hole protrudes beyond the restraining pillars.
The bar is heated in a constant temperature enclosure until the hole just clears the restraining pillars. A pin, which just fits the hole and made of the material under test, is then inserted through the hole as shown in Fig 6.6(b).

(a) Calculate the temperature of the enclosure.

(b) Given that the bar does not extend beyond its limit of proportionality, calculate the tensile stress in the steel bar when the temperature returns to 20 °C.

Young modulus for steel $= 1.2 \times 10^{11}$ Pa.
Linear expansivity of steel $= 1.5 \times 10^{-6}\,\mathrm{K}^{-1}$.
Linear expansivity =

$$\frac{\text{change in length of bar}}{\text{original length of bar} \times \text{change in temperature}}.$$

(AEB June '90)

5. (a) Describe an experiment using two long, parallel, identical wires to determine the Young modulus for steel. Explain why it is necessary to use two such wires. Indicate what quantities you would measure and what measuring instrument you would use in each case. State what graph you would plot, and show how it is used to calculate the Young modulus.

(b) A light rigid bar is suspended horizontally from two vertical wires, one of steel and one of brass, as shown in Fig 6.7. Each wire is 2.00 m long. The diameter of the steel wire is 0.60 mm and the length of the bar AB is 0.20 m. When a mass of 10.0 kg is suspended from the centre of AB the bar remains horizontal.

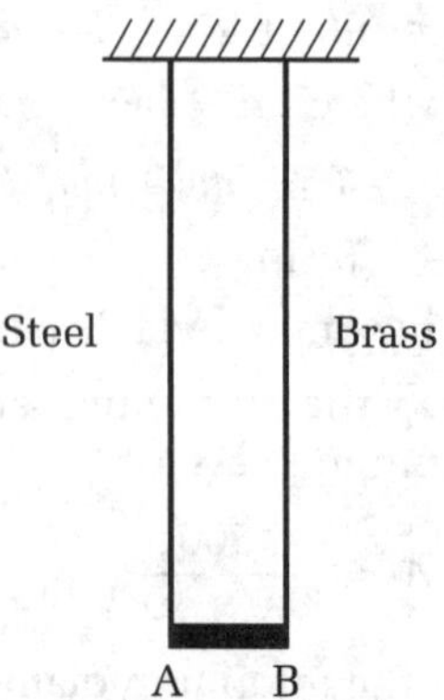

Fig 6.7

(i) What is the tension in each wire?
(ii) Calculate the extension of the steel wire and the energy stored in it.
(iii) Calculate the diameter of the brass wire.
(iv) If the brass wire were replaced by another brass wire of diameter 1.00 mm, where should the mass be suspended so that AB would remain horizontal?

(The Young modulus for steel $= 2.0 \times 10^{11}$ Pa; the Young modulus for brass $= 1.0 \times 10^{11}$ Pa.)

(NEAB June '91)

6. Some polymeric materials, like polyethylene for example, consist partly of crystalline material and partly of amorphous, or disordered material. They are sometimes referred to as two-phase materials although this is, of course, a considerable simplification of the real structure. Such a material can be modelled formally by a linked combination of 'blocks' of the two phases. There are two simple varieties which are referred to as the 'parallel model' (Fig 6.8(a)) and the 'series model' (Fig 6.8(b)). The crystalline component is labelled 'C' and the amorphous component 'A'.

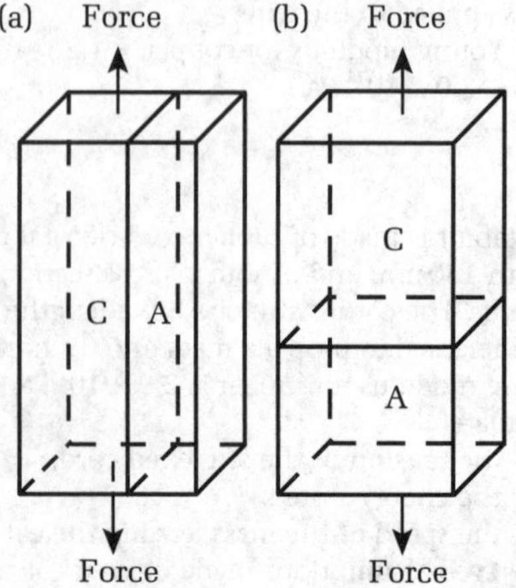

Fig 6.8

Consider first the parallel model. The blocks have the same length but different cross-sectional areas. If the material is extended along the direction of the arrows, both blocks extend by the same amount and the total force on the whole block is the sum of the forces on the individual components. This model behaves like two different springs in parallel.

In the series model however the situation is different and the blocks have the same cross-sectional area but different lengths. Both blocks now experience the same force but extend by differing amounts. This model behaves like two different springs in series.

Use the data given below and the definition of the Young modulus to calculate the Young modulus of the composite block for

(i) the parallel model, and

(ii) the series model.

Data: the Young modulus of the crystalline material $= 2.4 \times 10^{11}$ Pa; the Young modulus of the amorphous material $= 5.0 \times 10^{9}$ Pa; fraction of the A component present in the parallel model = 45%; fraction of the A component present in the series model = 35%.

(O & C Nuffield June '91, Special Paper)

7 CALCULATIONS FOR KEEPING COOL

What you need to know now

- The internal energy of a system may be changed as a result of work done or heat transfer. Work is done when a force moves its point of application in the direction of the force. Heat is energy transferred by means other than work.
- For mass m of material in a given state, the heat supplied or removed $Q = mc\,\Delta\theta$ where c = specific heat capacity and $\Delta\theta$ = temperature change.
- For mass m of material to change state without change of temperature, the heat supplied or removed $Q = ml$, where l = specific latent heat of the material.

What you need to know next

Heat capacity

When work is done on an isolated system or heat is supplied to it, the internal energy of the system increases. This increase of internal energy causes the temperature to rise or the state of the material to change or both. Provided the state of the material doesn't change and no heat is lost to the surroundings, the temperature rise $\Delta\theta$ can be calculated for a given transfer of energy if the **heat capacity** of the system is known. This is the energy needed to raise the temperature of the system by 1 K. For example, for a system which consists of two different materials of masses m_1 and m_2 which have specific heat capacities c_1 and c_2 respectively, its heat capacity $C = m_1c_1 + m_2c_2$.

$$\text{Energy transferred} = C\,\Delta\theta = (m_1c_1 + m_2c_2)\,\Delta\theta$$

Electrical heating

Consider a system with perfect insulation heated electrically at a constant rate. The rate of transfer of energy $= IV$ where I is the heater current and V is the heater PD.

Hence $IV = C\dfrac{d\theta}{dt}$ where $\dfrac{d\theta}{dt}$ is the rate of change of temperature of the system.

Hence $\dfrac{d\theta}{dt} = \dfrac{IV}{C}$.

Thus the rate of change of temperature is constant provided the heater power is constant. In other words, the temperature rises at a constant rate in this situation.

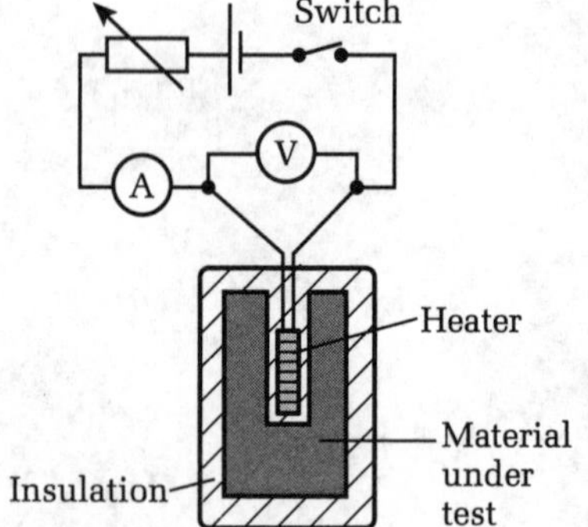

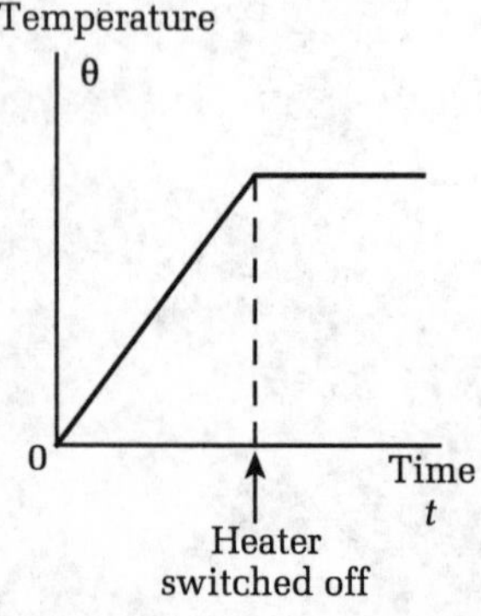

Fig 7.1 Perfect thermal insulation

Continuous flow

There are many situations where a fluid is used to transfer heat. Examples include water flowing through a passive solar panel heated by solar radiation, water flowing through an electrically heated shower, carbon dioxide gas as a coolant pumped through the core of a nuclear reactor and steam passed through a heat exchanger. In all these situations, the inlet and outlet are at different temperatures. The temperature at any point in the fluid is constant provided the flow rate is steady. The heat supplied or removed by the fluid in time t is equal to $mc\,\Delta\theta$ where m is the mass of fluid passing through in time t, c is the specific heat capacity of the fluid and $\Delta\theta$ is the difference of temperature between the inlet and the outlet. Hence the rate of supply or removal of heat $\dfrac{Q}{t} = \dfrac{m}{t} c\,\Delta\theta$.

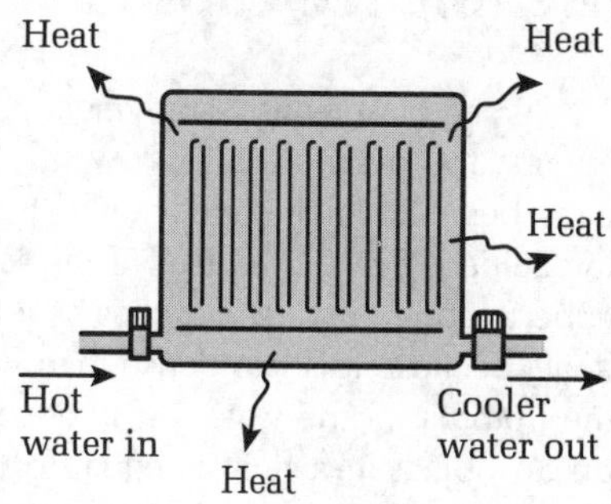

Fig 7.2 Continuous flow

Preventing meltdown

The heat produced in a nuclear reactor is used to generate electricity. A cooling fluid is pumped through the core in a sealed 'circuit'. Water is used for this purpose in the pressurised water reactor. The hot cooling fluid from the core is used to raise steam in a heat exchanger. The steam is then used to drive turbines. Cooling water is pumped through the turbine block to prevent the turbines overheating. If the pumps failed, the reactor core would need to be shut down rapidly or it would meltdown. A 1000 MW nuclear power station operating at an efficiency of 35% would produce 350 MW of electrical power and 650 MJ s^{-1} of heat. Prove for yourself that cooling water entering the turbine block at 20 °C would need to be pumped through at a rate of over 1500 kg s^{-1} to remove heat at a rate of 650 MJ s^{-1} if the turbine temperature is to be kept below 120 °C.

Natural cooling

Consider a system being allowed to cool naturally with no electrical power supplied. Heat loss from the system will increase the internal energy of the *surroundings*. Provided the system is not subjected to forced convection, the rate of heat loss to the surroundings is proportional to the excess temperature of the system (i.e. the difference between the temperatures of the system and the surroundings). This relationship is known as Newton's law of cooling. For a system of heat capacity C being allowed to cool naturally,

$$\text{rate of heat loss } C\frac{d\theta}{dt} = -\alpha(\theta - \theta_0)$$

where θ_0 = the temperature of the surroundings and α = a constant for the system.

You ought to have met this *type* of equation in the form $\dfrac{dN}{dt} = -\lambda N$ in your studies on radioactivity. Its solution is similar to the equation $N = N_0\,e^{-\lambda t}$ for radioactive decay. Hence $(\theta - \theta_0) = (\theta_1 - \theta_0)\,e^{-\lambda t}$ where $\lambda = \alpha/C$ in this case. The temperature difference $(\theta - \theta_0)$ therefore decreases exponentially from the initial temperature θ_1 (see Fig 7.3). Test Newton's law of cooling for yourself by measuring the temperature of a hot solid as it cools. A graph of $\ln(\theta - \theta_0)$ against time t should give a straight line if the decrease is exponential.

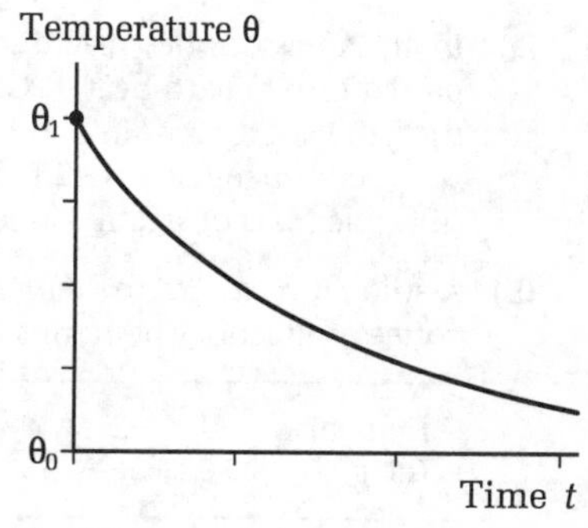

Fig. 7.3

Melting ice caps

The work of scientists studying the effects of global warming is of particular interest to governments of low level nations. It is thought that if the polar ice caps begin to melt significantly, the coastlines of low level countries will be threatened. See for yourself if the level of water in a beaker containing an ice cube floating in water changes as a result of the ice cube melting. The ice cube floats because it is less dense than water. The weight of the ice cube is equal to the upthrust of the water on it; according to Archimedes principle, the upthrust on an object in a fluid is equal to the weight of fluid displaced by the object. Hence the ice cube displaces its own weight of water. When it melts, it therefore makes no difference to the level of water in the beaker. However, this is only true for pure water since ice is frozen pure water. Salt water is more dense than pure water. Prove for yourself that the fractional increase of volume when pure ice melts in salt water is equal to $(\rho_s - \rho_w)/\rho_w$ where ρ_s and ρ_w are the densities of salt water and pure water respectively.

Questions

1. A deep-frying vessel holds 20 litres of cooking oil. The oil has to be heated from 15 °C to 200 °C in 30 minutes. Calculate
(i) the mass of cooking oil in the vessel,
(ii) its heat capacity, and
(iii) the average rate at which energy must be transferred to the oil.
(1 litre = 1000 cm^3, density of cooking oil = 920 $kg\,m^{-3}$, specific heat capacity of cooking oil = 1850 $J\,kg^{-1}\,K^{-1}$.)
In practice, the rate of energy supply has to be about 30% higher than is needed to heat the oil. Give *two* possible reasons for this.
The rate at which the temperature of the oil rises is higher at the beginning of the heating process than at the end. Why should this be so?

(ULEAC June '92)

2. (a) In an espresso coffee machine, steam at 100 °C is passed into milk to heat it. Calculate
(i) the energy required to heat 150 g of milk from room temperature (20 °C) to 80 °C,
(ii) the mass of steam condensed.

(b) A student measures the temperature of the hot coffee as it cools. The results are given below:

Time/min	0	2	4	6	8
Temp/°C	78	66	56	48	41

A friend suggests that the rate of cooling is exponential.
(i) Show quantitatively whether this suggestion is valid.
(ii) Estimate the temperature of the coffee after a total of 12 min.

(Specific heat capacity of milk = 4.0 $kJ\,kg^{-1}\,K^{-1}$; specific heat capacity of water = 4.2 $kJ\,kg^{-1}\,K^{-1}$; specific latent heat of steam = 2.2 $MJ\,kg^{-1}$.)

(O & C June '91)

3. In the hair drier shown in Fig 7.4 air is drawn through the system by a fan. The air is warmed as it passes the heating elements.

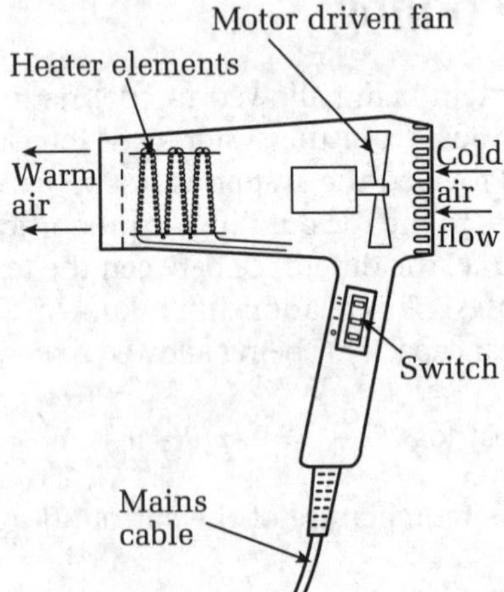

Fig 7.4

The hair drier has the option of using one heating element on its own or two heating elements in parallel. Each element provides 600 W when operated at 240 V. There are also two fan speeds, the volume flow rate automatically increasing when both heating elements are used.
The effective specific heat capacity of the air is 990 $J\,kg^{-1}\,K^{-1}$. The density of air is 1.25 $kg\,m^{-3}$ at 60 °C.

(a) In one case the ambient temperature is 20 °C. When one 600 W element is used and the fan is run at its slower speed, the temperature of the air leaving the drier is 60 °C. Calculate:
(i) the mass flow rate; (ii) the volume flow rate.

(b) When the second element is switched on the temperature of the air from the drier rises to 75 °C. Calculate the new mass flow rate of the air.

(c) Explain why it would be unwise to design the drier so that both heating elements are used without an increase in the volume flow rate.

(d) Determine the supply current when both heating elements are on, neglecting the current in the fan.

(e) The heating element is cooled by the process of *forced convection*.
  (i) How does *forced convection* differ from *natural convection*?
  (ii) The equation which relates to cooling by forced convection is

$$\frac{d\theta}{dt} = -k(\theta - \theta_0)$$

  State in your own words what this equation expresses in mathematical terms.
  (iii) Use the equation to explain what happens to the hot air temperature when the hair drier is used in colder conditions.

(f) State and explain what would happen if the fan were to stop working.

(AEB Summer '94)

4. (a) During a change of phase (melting or boiling), what is the value of the rate of change of temperature with energy input?

(b) Define *specific latent heat*, and explain briefly in molecular terms why you would expect the specific latent heat of fusion of ice to be less than the specific latent heat of vaporisation of water.

(c) (i) Calculate the energy input required to convert 0.500 kg of ice at −20 °C to 0.500 kg of water vapour at 100 °C.
  (ii) A thermally isolated beaker contains 1.000 kg of water at 20 °C. A mass M of ice at −20 °C is dropped into it. When the system reaches thermal equilibrium, a mass m of ice remains unmelted. Show that

$$m = 1.123M - 0.252$$

  where M and m are measured in kg.
  (iii) Use the result in part (c)(ii) to calculate the largest mass of ice at −20 °C that can be completely melted by 1.000 kg of water, initially at 20 °C.

(Specific heat capacity of ice = 2.05 kJ kg^{-1} K^{-1};
specific heat capacity of water = 4.19 kJ kg^{-1} K^{-1};
specific latent heat of fusion of ice = 333 kJ kg^{-1};
specific latent heat of vaporisation of water = 2.26 MJ kg^{-1}.)

(UCLES June '94, Special Paper)

5. As part of an environmental project, a group of pupils investigated how the melting of icebergs and polar ice-caps affects the level of the sea. Their determinations were based on laboratory experiments and reference-book data.

(a) An initial experiment modelled the melting of an iceberg. A cube of ice was placed in a beaker of cold tap-water (density 1000 kg m^{-3}). The following observations were made:
  (1) The ice cube, of side 30 mm and mass 25 grams, floated with most of its volume beneath the surface of the water.
  (2) As the cube melted, the surrounding water-level remained unchanged.
  (i) Calculate the fraction of the floating ice cube that was beneath the water surface in the beaker when the experiment began.
  (ii) Explain the second observation.
  (iii) The pupils deduced that if salt-water (of greater density than tap-water) had been used in the experiment, the water level **would** have risen. State their reasoning.

(b) To investigate the thermal properties of ice, 10 grams of crushed ice at 0 °C were placed in a vacuum flask of negligible thermal capacity containing 200 grams of tap-water at 20 °C. The mixture was then heated with a small 40 W immersion heater. After 110 s, the temperature of the mixture returned to 20 °C.
Take the specific heat capacity of tap-water as 4.2 kJ kg^{-1} K^{-1}.
  (i) How much heat was required to transform 1 gram of ice at 0 °C to water at 0 °C? Assume there was no heat transfer between the vacuum flask and the surroundings during the investigation.
  (ii) State and explain whether the result of this experiment would have been different if the flask had an appreciable thermal capacity.

(c) A reference book gave the mean radius of the Earth in polar regions as 6350 km and stated that the polar ice-caps covered $\frac{1}{30}$th of the Earth's surface. The long-term mean rate of arrival of solar energy at high latitudes was estimated at 7.5 W m^{-2} and one-quarter of this was thought to cause ice to melt. Calculate estimates for:
  (i) the total area of the Earth covered by the ice-caps;
  (ii) their yearly absorption of solar energy resulting in the melting of ice.

(d) Using your results from (b)(i) and (c)(ii), find the volume of pure water produced by the melting ice-caps each year. Hence predict the annual rate of rise of the level of the sea from this cause. Assume the sea covers two-thirds of the Earth's surface.

(UODLE June '94, Special Paper)

8 USING THE KINETIC THEORY OF GASES

What you need to know now

- An ideal gas is one that obeys Boyle's Law.
- The equation of state for an ideal gas is $pV = nRT$.
- The assumptions and proof of the kinetic theory equation $pV = \frac{1}{3}Nmc_{rms}^{2}$.
- The internal energy of an ideal gas $U = \frac{3}{2}nRT$.
- For any gas, work done $= p\Delta V =$ the area under a p–V curve.

What you need to know next

Mathematical modelling of an ideal gas

The kinetic theory of gases is a very successful model because it gives a theoretical equation which agrees with the ideal gas laws and the equation of state for an ideal gas. You should already know where the assumptions of the kinetic theory equation (i.e. point molecules, elastic collisions, random motion, no intermolecular attractions and insignificant impact times) fit into the proof of the equation. You should also know the meaning of *root mean square speed* and *the Avogadro constant*, and be able to use the kinetic theory equation and the ideal gas law to prove that the mean kinetic energy of an gas molecule is $\frac{3}{2}kT$, where $k\,(= R/N_A)$ is the Boltzmann constant. Further aspects of the kinetic theory of gases are developed below to help you develop a deeper understanding of this important topic.

Distribution of molecular speeds

The molecules in an ideal gas move about at random. The distribution of molecular speeds in an ideal gas is shown in Fig 8.1. Because the y-axis represents the number of molecules per unit speed range, the area under the curve from speed v to $v + dv$ represents the number of molecules in the speed range from v to $v + dv$. Thus the total area under the curve represents the total number of molecules.

- The root mean speed c_{rms} is higher than the mean speed $\bar{c}$ because molecules moving faster than the mean speed contribute more significantly to the r.m.s. speed than molecules moving slower than the mean.
- The higher the temperature, the more the distribution curve spreads out. Since the total number of molecules is constant, the area under the curve is constant; hence it is flatter and more spread out at higher temperature.

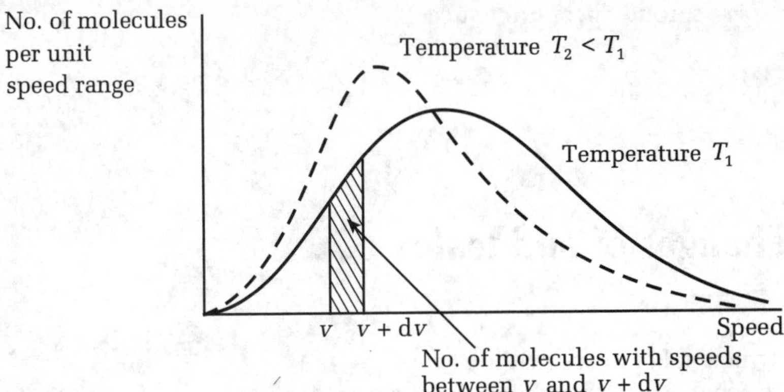

Fig 8.1 Distribution of molecular speeds

- This type of curve is called a normal or gaussian distribution curve. Since there is a continuous distribution of speeds, there is also a continuous distribution of kinetic energies. The mean kinetic energy of an ideal gas molecule is $\frac{3}{2}kT$. Hence the r.m.s speed is proportional to $\sqrt{T}$.

Planetary atmospheres

The escape speed from the surface of a planet of radius R is $\sqrt{2g_s R}$ where g_s is the surface gravitational field strength. Gas molecules released at the surface will escape if the r.m.s. speed is not insignificant compared with the escape speed from the planet. The r.m.s. speed depends on temperature which in general decreases with distance from the Sun. For example, Mercury is smaller than the Earth and is the closest planet to the Sun. Hence gas molecules released on Mercury would easily attain speeds comparable with the escape speed from Mercury. In comparison, Mars is only a little smaller than the Earth and is further from the Sun than is the Earth. As a result, Mars has retained an atmospheric because its escape speed is comparable to that of the Earth and the r.m.s speed of its atmospheric molecules is less than on Earth.

Collision rates

The rate of molecular impacts per unit area on a surface exposed to a gas depends on the gas density. There are many situations where it is necessary to know the collision rate to ensure a solid surface is not over exposed to a gas. For example, a semiconductor is 'doped' with donor or acceptor atoms by exposure to the atoms in the vapour state.

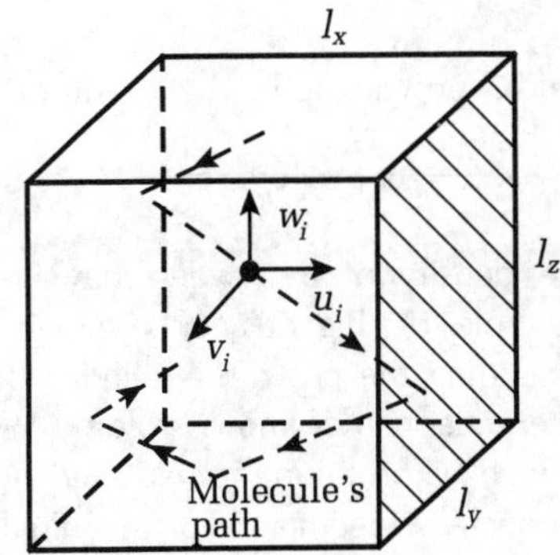

Fig 8.2 Collision rates

Consider the impacts of a single molecule on one face of a rectangular box, as shown in Fig 8.2. The time between two successive collisions is $2l_x/u_i$ where u_i represents the x-component of the molecule's velocity. Hence the number of collisions per second made by the molecule is $u_i/2l_x$. Since the area of the face is $l_y\,l_z$, the number of collisions per second per unit area is $u_i/2V$ where $V = l_x\,l_y\,l_z$ = volume of the box. For all N molecules in the box, the total number of collisions per second per unit area on this face is therefore $\sum_{i=1}^{i=N} \frac{u_i}{2V}$ which may be written $\frac{N\bar{u}}{2V}$ where $\bar{u} = \sum_{i=1}^{i=N} u_i/N$.

Thus the total number of collisions per second per unit area is proportional to

1. the number of molecules per unit volume N/V, and
2. the mean value of the x-component of velocity $\bar{u}$.

Adiabatic and isothermal changes of an ideal gas

- An **adiabatic** change is a change which takes place without heat transfer. For an ideal gas, an adiabatic change is represented by the equation $pV^{\gamma} = \text{constant}$, where γ is the ratio of molar heat capacities of the gas. You will find the proof of this equation in your textbook. The value of γ depends on the atomicity of the gas, as explained on p41.
- An **isothermal** change is a change which takes place at constant temperature. For an ideal gas, an isothermal change is represented by the equation $pV = \text{constant}$.

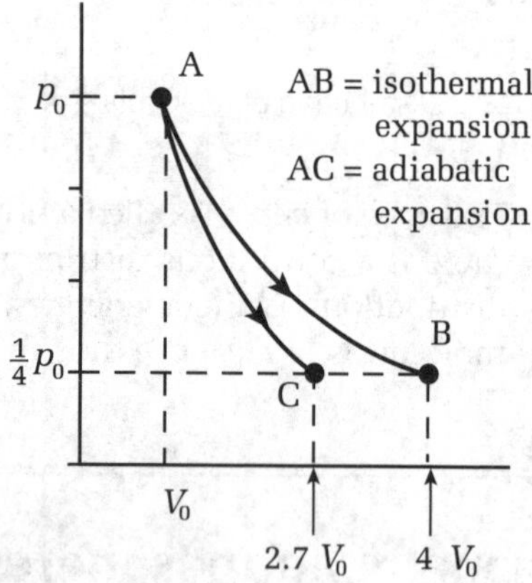

Fig 8.3 Ideal gas changes

Physics at work

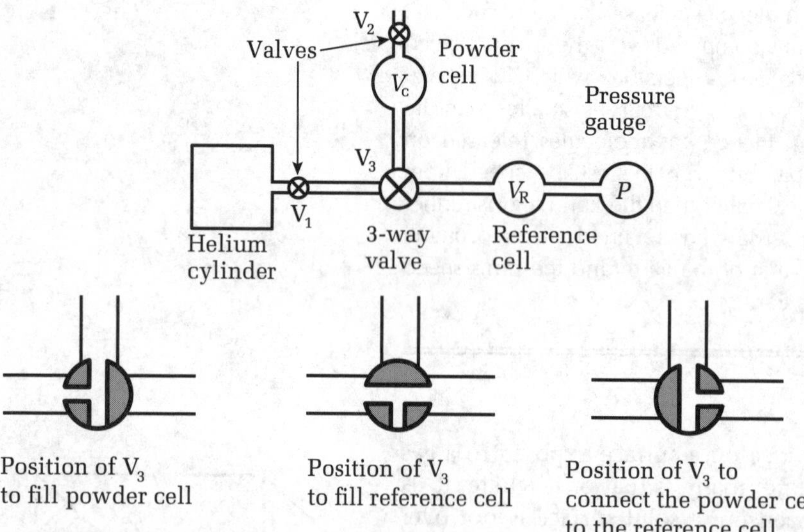

Fig 8.4 A gas pycnometer

The density of a powder may be measured using a **gas pycnometer**. The principle of this device is shown in Fig 8.4. A cell of known volume V_c containing the powder is filled with helium at ambient pressure p_A. A second 'reference' cell of known volume V_R without powder at the same temperature T is filled with helium at measured pressure p_1 above p_A. The two cells are then connected together and the final pressure p_2 is measured at the same temperature T. Prove for yourself using the ideal gas equation that the powder volume $V_p = V_c - \frac{(p_1 - p_2)}{(p_2 - p_A)}V_R$. By measuring the pressure differences $(p_1 - p_2)$ and $(p_2 - p_A)$, the powder volume can be determined if V_c and V_R are known.

Degrees of freedom and atomicity

- A **monoatomic** molecule may be considered to be a point molecule provided the average intermolecular spacing is much greater than the molecule's diameter. It possesses three degrees of freedom. This means it can move in any one of three perpendicular directions without changing more than one of its positional coordinates. Boltzmann proved that the mean KE of an ideal gas molecule associated with each degree of freedom is $\frac{1}{2}kT$, thus giving $\frac{3}{2}kT$ for all three degrees of freedom. Hence the internal energy for n moles of an ideal gas is $\frac{3}{2}nRT$.
- A **diatomic** molecule possesses two more degrees of freedom than a point molecule. This is because it requires two rotational coordinates as well as three positional coordinates. Since a diatomic molecule possesses five degrees of freedom, its mean kinetic energy is $\frac{5}{2}kT$. Hence the internal energy of n moles of a diatomic gas is $\frac{5}{2}nRT$.
- A molecule comprising three or more atoms is referred to as **polyatomic**. Such a molecule possesses six degrees of freedom, corresponding to an extra rotational coordinate in comparison with a diatomic molecule. Hence the mean kinetic energy of a polyatomic molecule is $3kT\,(=6\times\frac{1}{2}kT)$ and the internal energy of n moles is therefore $3nRT$.

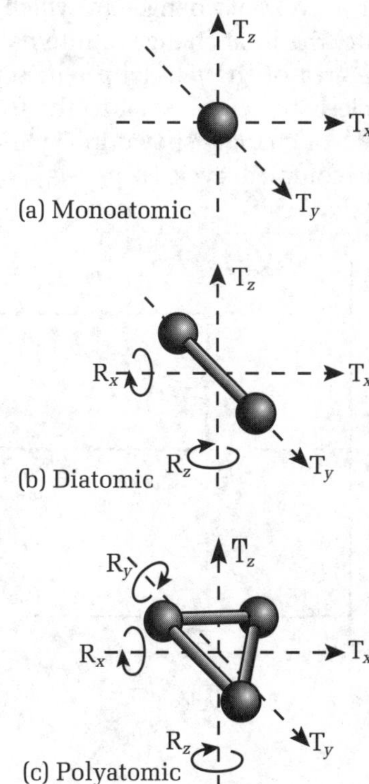

Fig 8.5 Atomicity

1. When a gas at **constant volume** is heated, the gain of internal energy ΔU is equal to the heat supplied Q. If the temperature change is ΔT for n moles of monoatomic gas, $\Delta U = \frac{3}{2}nR\,\Delta T$; hence $Q = \frac{3}{2}nR\,\Delta T$. Therefore the molar heat capacity of a monoatomic gas at constant volume, $C_v = \frac{3}{2}R$. Prove for yourself that $C_v = \frac{5}{2}R$ for a diatomic gas and $3R$ for a polyatomic gas.

2. When a gas is heated at **constant pressure**, the gain of internal energy ΔU is equal to the heat supplied $Q - W$, where W is the work done by the gas to expand. Since $W = p\Delta V$ and $p\Delta V = nR\,\Delta T$ at constant pressure, prove for yourself that the molar heat capacity of an ideal gas at constant pressure $C_p = C_v + R$. Hence show that C_p and γ are respectively equal to $\frac{5}{2}R$ and 1.67 for a monoatomic gas, $\frac{7}{2}R$ and 1.4 for a diatomic gas and $4R$ and 1.33 for a polyatomic gas.

p–V diagrams for an ideal gas

Ideal gas changes for a fixed mass of gas may be represented on a graph of pressure against volume. For any change from initial pressure p_1, volume V_1 and temperature T_1 to a final pressure p_2, volume V_2 and temperature T_2,

- The area under the curve is equal to the work done W.

  For a small change of volume δV at pressure p, the work done is $p\delta V$. When the volume changes from V_1 to V_2, the total work done

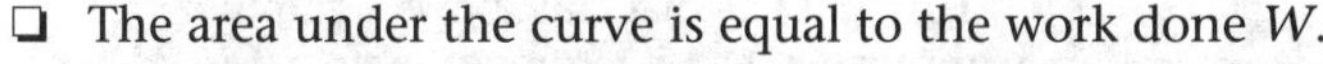

  $W = \int_{V_1}^{V_2} p\,dV$ = area under the *p–V* curve from V_1 to V_2. Note that the gas does work to expand (i.e. for $V_2 > V_1$) and work is done on the gas when it is compressed (i.e. for $V_2 < V_1$).

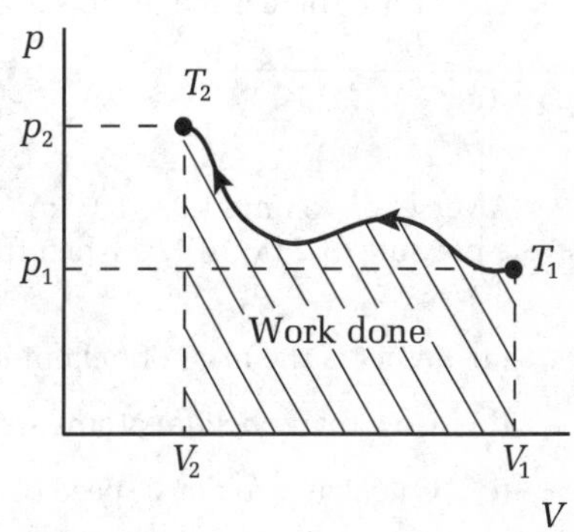

Fig 8.6 A *p–V* diagram

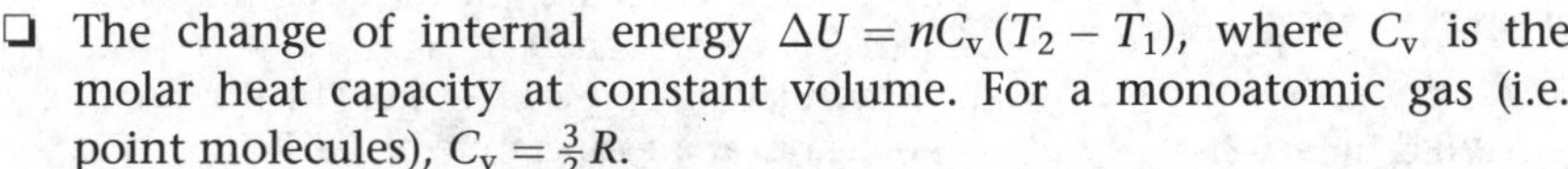

- The change of internal energy $\Delta U = nC_v(T_2 - T_1)$, where C_v is the molar heat capacity at constant volume. For a monoatomic gas (i.e. point molecules), $C_v = \frac{3}{2}R$.

❑ The heat transfer Q to the gas $= \Delta U + \int_{V_1}^{V_2} p\,\mathrm{d}V$.

For a cycle of changes in which the final state is the same as the initial state, the total change of internal energy is zero and the total work done is the area of the p–V loop representing the cycle. The heat transfer in one cycle is therefore equal to the total work done. For example, consider the cycle of changes shown in Fig 8.7. Prove for yourself that the work done in one complete cycle is $(p_2 - p_1)(V_2 - V_1)$.

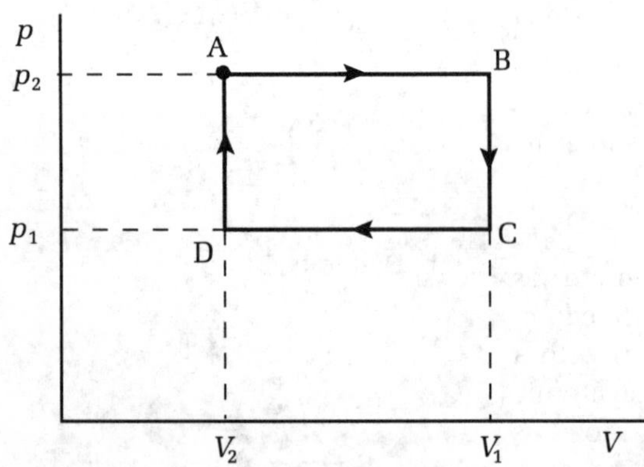

	A → B	B → C	C → D	D → A
Q	$nC_p(T_B - T_A)$	$nC_v(T_C - T_B)$	$nC_p(T_D - T_C)$	$nC_v(T_A - T_D)$
W	$p_2(V_1 - V_2)$	0	$p_1(V_2 - V_1)$	0
ΔU	$nC_v(T_B - T_A)$	$nC_v(T_C - T_B)$	$nC_v(T_D - T_C)$	$nC_v(T_A - T_D)$

Fig 8.7 A p–V cycle

Questions

1. (a) Calculate the root-mean-square speed of nitrogen molecules at 400 °C.
Molar gas constant, $R = 8.3\,\mathrm{J\,K^{-1}\,mol^{-1}}$; mass of one mole of nitrogen $= 2.8 \times 10^{-2}$ kg.

(b) Calculate the escape velocity from the surface of a spherical planet of radius 4.8×10^5 m and mean density $5.0 \times 10^3\,\mathrm{kg\,m^{-3}}$.
Gravitational constant $= 6.7 \times 10^{-11}\,\mathrm{N\,m^2\,kg^{-2}}$.

(c) Using your answers to (a) and (b) discuss whether such a planet could retain nitrogen in its atmosphere if the mean surface temperature were 400 °C.

(NEAB June '91)

2. A vessel of volume $1.0 \times 10^{-3}\,\mathrm{m^3}$ contains helium gas at a pressure of 2.0×10^5 Pa when the temperature is 300 K.

(a) What is the mass of helium in the vessel?

(b) How many helium atoms are there in the vessel?

(c) Calculate the r.m.s. speed of the helium atoms.

Take: Relative atomic mass of helium = 4; the Avogadro constant $= 6.0 \times 10^{23}\,\mathrm{mol^{-1}}$; the molar gas constant $R = 8.3\,\mathrm{J\,mol^{-1}\,K^{-1}}$.

(WJEC June '92)

3.

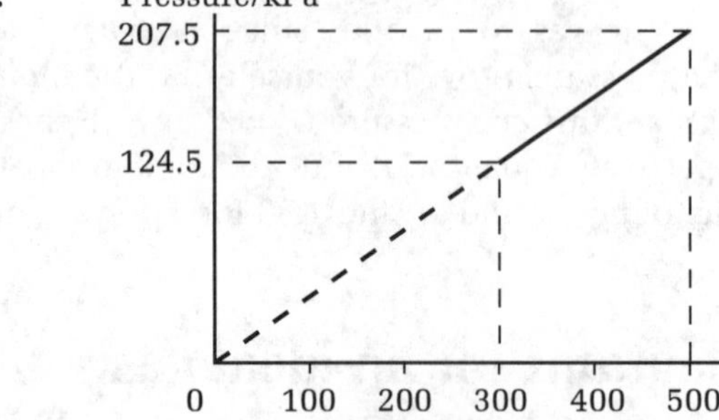

Fig 8.8

(a) A fixed mass of helium gas is enclosed in a container which has a fixed volume of $1.0 \times 10^{-3}\,\mathrm{m^3}$. The diagram shows a graph of pressure against temperature for temperatures between 300 K and 500 K.
Calculate
(i) the number of moles of gas present,
(ii) the mass of gas present.

(b) A second container, identical to that described in (a), contains a mixture consisting of equal masses of hydrogen and helium, the total mass being the same as the original mass in (a).
(i) Calculate the pressure exerted by this mixture of gases at a temperature of 300 K.

(ii) State how you would expect the gradient of a pressure against temperature graph for this mixture of gases to differ from that shown in the diagram.
Explain your answer.

Molar gas constant, $R = 8.3\,\mathrm{J\,mol^{-1}\,K^{-1}}$; molar mass of hydrogen = 2.0 g; molar mass of helium = 4.0 g.

(NEAB June '94)

4. An ideal gas is contained in a hollow cylinder, sealed at one end, with a frictionless piston at the other. Initially the gas occupies a volume of $1.0 \times 10^{-3}\,\mathrm{m^{-3}}$ at a pressure of 200 kPa and at a temperature of 300 K.

(a) The gas is heated isothermally. How is the thermal energy Q supplied related to the change in internal energy ΔU and the work W done by the gas? Explain your answer. Does the gas expand or must the piston be pushed in?

(b) How many moles of gas does the cylinder contain?

(c) The cylinder is used as a Stirling engine by suitable coupling to the piston. The gas undergoes the following cycle of changes:
(i) compressed isothermally to half its initial volume,
(ii) heated at constant volume to 450 K,
(iii) expanded isothermally back to the original volume,
(iv) cooled at constant volume to the initial condition.
Calculate the pressure at the end of each stage.
Draw a p–V diagram showing the gas undergoing these four processes.

(d) Explain how you could use the p–v diagram to find the thermal efficiency of the Stirling engine, which can be defined as

$$\frac{\text{(work done by the gas)} - \text{(work done on the gas)}}{\text{work done by the gas}}$$

(O & C June '93)

5. (a) (i) What assumptions are made about the properties of ideal gas molecules?
(ii) Explain why the behaviour of all gases at very low pressures can be considered 'ideal'.

(b) The collisions of ideal gas molecules are assumed to be perfectly elastic.
(i) What aspect of a perfectly elastic collision distinguishes it from other types of collision?
(ii) Discuss briefly how collisions between gas molecules can sometimes be inelastic.

(c) The behaviour of an ideal gas can be summarised algebraically by the equation $pV = nRT$. Use this expression and the data below to calculate the density of air at room temperature. Assume that air behaves as an ideal gas.
Atmospheric pressure = 103 kPa; molar mass of air = $0.029\,\mathrm{kg\,mol^{-1}}$; room temperature = 17 °C; ideal gas constant = $8.3\,\mathrm{J\,mol^{-1}\,K^{-1}}$.

(AEB Summer '94, Special Paper)

6. (a) (i) Explain how molecular movement causes a pressure to be exerted by a gas.
(ii) Use a simple model to derive the expression $p = \frac{1}{3}\rho\langle c^2\rangle$ for the pressure exerted by an ideal gas.

(b) By using the ideal gas law show that $\langle c^2\rangle = \dfrac{3RT}{M}$, and calculate the value of the root mean square velocity for the molecules of oxygen gas at 20 °C. (Relative molecular mass of oxygen = 32)

(c) Specialised processes used in the fabrication of microelectronic devices require conditions where the number of molecules colliding with a solid surface per unit area per second, N, is less than some critical value, in order to keep the surface free from contamination. By using the simple model used in part (a), show that

$$N = \frac{nc_x}{2}$$

where c_x is the average molecular velocity along the x-direction and n is the number of molecules per unit volume.

(d) Use your answer to part (b) as an approximate value for c_x, and therefore estimate the pressure such that N is less than 1×10^{13} collisions $\mathrm{m^{-2}\,s^{-1}}$.
$\left(\text{Note that } n = \dfrac{N_A p}{RT}.\right)$

(e) Estimate the time for the surface to become essentially covered with oxygen. (Note that the spacing between the atoms of a solid surface is of the order of 3×10^{-9} m.)

(WJEC June '94, Special Paper)

9 FLOW PROCESSES

What you need to know now

- The rate of flow of heat through a material of length L and cross-sectional area A,

$$\frac{dQ}{dt} = kA\frac{\Delta\theta}{L}$$

where $\Delta\theta$ is the temperature difference across the material and k is its thermal conductivity.

- The rate of flow of charge (i.e. current I) through a material of length L and cross-sectional area A,

$$I = \frac{AV}{\rho L}$$

where V is the p.d. across the material and ρ is the electrical resistivity of the material.

- For a sample of material of length L and cross-sectional area A,

its thermal resistance $R_{th} = \dfrac{L}{kA}$

where k is the thermal conductivity of the material,

its electrical resistance $R = \dfrac{\rho L}{A}$

where ρ is the electrical resistivity of the material.

What you need to know next

Resistor combination rules

Problems involving thermal conductors in series or parallel can be solved by using methods from electric circuit theory. The table in Fig 9.1 (below) compares electrical and thermal conduction.

Electrical conduction	Thermal conduction
Rate of flow of charge (i.e. current) I	Rate of flow of heat $\dfrac{dQ}{dt}$
Potential difference V	Temperature difference $\Delta\theta$
Electrical resistance $R = V/I$	Thermal resistance $R_{th} = \dfrac{\Delta\theta}{dQ/dt}$
Electrical resistivity $\rho = 1/\text{electrical conductivity } \sigma$	Thermal resistivity $\rho = 1/\text{thermal conductivity } k$
Electrical resistance $R = \rho L/A$	Thermal resistance $R_{th} = L/kA$
Potential gradient V/L	Temperature gradient $\Delta\theta/L$

Fig 9.1 Comparison of electrical and thermal conduction

1. **For two thermal conductors in series,**

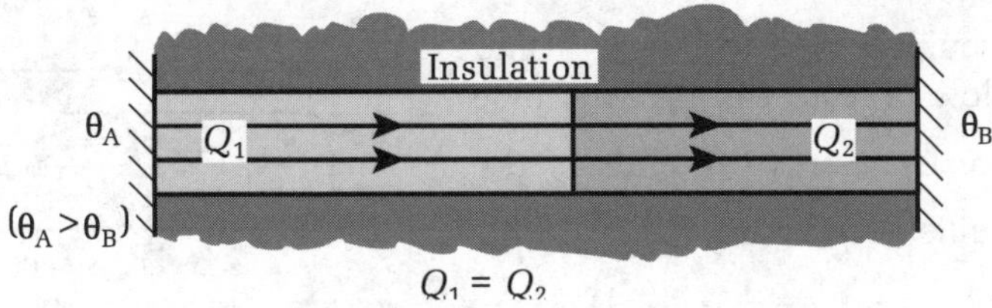

Fig 9.2 Two thermal conductors in series

- ❑ the total thermal resistance = the sum of the individual thermal resistances,
- ❑ the rate of flow of heat through each conductor is the same, equal to $\dfrac{\text{the overall temperature difference}}{\text{total thermal resistance}}$,
- ❑ the temperature difference across a conductor = rate of flow of heat × thermal resistance of the conductor.
- ❑ the overall temperature difference is equal to the sum of the individual temperature differences.

2. **For two thermal conductors in parallel,**

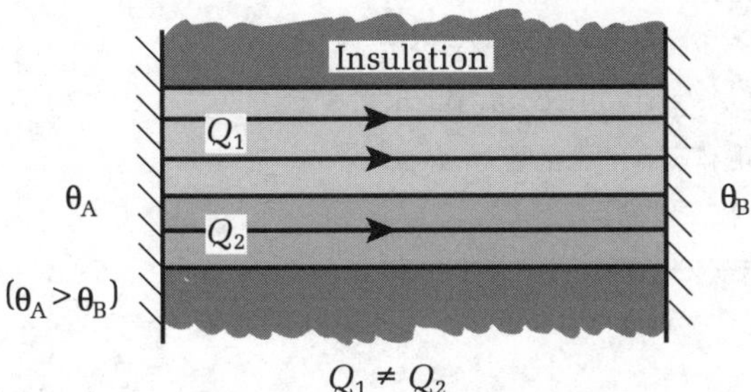

Fig 9.3 Two thermal conductors in parallel

- ❑ $\dfrac{1}{\text{the total thermal resistance}} = \dfrac{1}{R_1} + \dfrac{1}{R_2}$, where R_1 and R_2 are the individual thermal resistances,
- ❑ the temperature difference across each conductor is the same,
- ❑ the rate of flow of heat through a conductor is equal to $\dfrac{\text{the temperature difference}}{\text{thermal resistance of the conductor}}$,
- ❑ the total rate of flow of heat is equal to the sum of the individual heat flow rates.

Rewrite the above two paragraphs for electrical conductors with as little change as possible. No more than three words need to be changed.

Fluid resistance

Consider a viscous fluid flowing steadily through a pipe of length L and uniform cross-sectional area A. The rate of flow of fluid through the pipe $\frac{dV}{dt}$ is proportional to the pressure difference Δp across the ends of the pipe. The exact relationship is given by Poiseuille's equation,

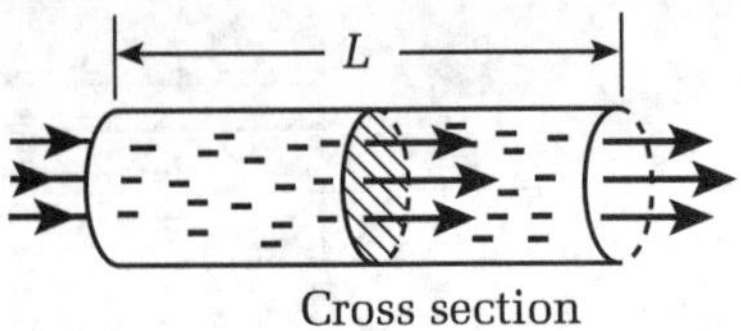

Fig 9.4 Pipe flow

$$\frac{dV}{dt} = \frac{\pi r^4}{8\eta}\frac{\Delta p}{L}$$

where r is the pipe radius and η is the viscosity of the fluid.

Comparison with electrical conduction gives $8\eta L/\pi r^4$ for the pipe resistance $R_p\left(= \Delta p \Big/ \frac{dV}{dt}\right)$ and $8\eta/r^2$ for the 'resistivity'. Clearly the comparison with resistivity is limited since it gives a quantity which depends on the pipe radius whereas electrical resistivity is a material property independent of the dimensions of the conductor. The smaller the pipe radius, the greater the fluid's 'resistivity' which is to be expected because the pipe surface drags on the fluid.

Physics at work

Blood flow through the arteries is severely affected by deposition of solids on the inner walls of the arteries. Such depositions narrow the arteries and restrict the blood flow. A 5% reduction of the radius of an artery causes a 20% reduction of the flow rate. This is because the flow rate through a pipe of radius r is given by Poiseuille's equation $\frac{dV}{dt} = kr^4$ where k is a constant. As explained on p. 25, for a relationship of the form $y = kx^n$, the % change of $y = n \times$ the % change of x.

More about heat flow

Consider an insulated bar of uniform cross-sectional area A and length L with a constant temperature $\Delta\theta$ across its ends. Assuming it conducts heat at a steady rate, the temperature gradient is constant ($= \Delta\theta/L$) because the rate of flow of heat is the same at all points along the bar. If the bar was not insulated or if its cross-sectional area was not constant, the temperature gradient would not be constant at all points along the bar. In general, the temperature gradient along a bar can be written as $\frac{d\theta}{dx}$ where $\frac{d}{dx}$ means 'rate of change with distance x'.

The direction of heat flow in a conductor is opposite to the direction of the temperature gradient. In other words, a positive temperature gradient is from cold to hot whereas the heat flow is in the opposite direction. Hence the thermal conductivity equation ought to include a minus sign, i.e.

$$\frac{dQ}{dt} = -kA\frac{d\theta}{dx}$$

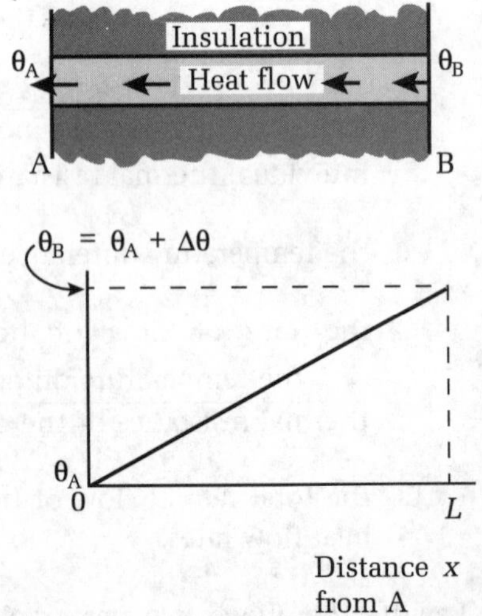

Fig 9.5 Temperature gradient

Case study

A uniform conducting rod of thermal conductivity k is heated by the passage of a constant electric current through it. The ends of the rod are maintained at constant temperature θ_0 and its sides are insulated. Show that the temperature at the midpoint is equal to $\theta_0 + \frac{PL}{8kA}$ where P is the electrical power supplied to the bar, L is its length and A is its area of cross section.

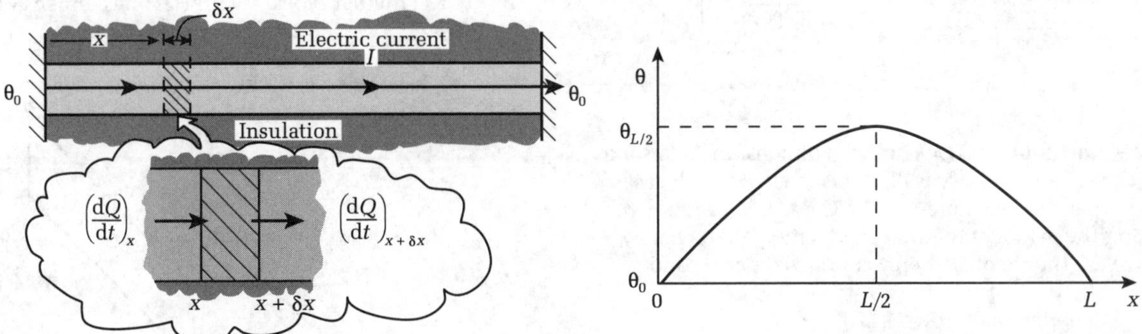

Fig 9.6 Electrical heating of a bar

Solution

Assuming uniform dissipation of power in the bar, the rate of production of heat in an elementary disc of thickness δx is $\frac{P\delta x}{L}$. If the rate of heat flow at distance x from one end is $\left(\frac{dQ}{dt}\right)_x$ then the rate of flow of heat at $x + \delta x$, $\left(\frac{dQ}{dt}\right)_{x+\delta x} = \left(\frac{dQ}{dt}\right)_x + \frac{P\delta x}{L}$.

Since $\frac{dQ}{dt} = -kA\frac{d\theta}{dx}$, then $\left(\frac{d\theta}{dx}\right)_{x+\delta x} = \left(\frac{d\theta}{dx}\right)_x - \frac{P\delta x}{kAL}$.

$$\frac{d^2\theta}{dx^2} = \frac{\left(\frac{d\theta}{dx}\right)_{x+\delta x} - \left(\frac{d\theta}{dx}\right)_x}{\delta x} \quad \text{as } \delta x \to 0$$

So $\frac{d^2\theta}{dx^2} = -\frac{P}{kAL}$.

Because $\frac{P}{kAL}$ is constant, $\frac{d\theta}{dx} = \int \frac{d^2\theta}{dx^2}dx = -\frac{P}{kAL}\int dx = -\frac{P}{kAL}x + c_1$

where c_1 is a constant.

Repeating the integration procedure gives

$$\theta = -\frac{P}{2kAL}x^2 + c_1 x + c_2$$

where c_2 is a constant.

Since $\theta = \theta_0$ at $x = 0$ and at $x = L$, then it follows by substitution that $c_2 = \theta_0$ and $c_1 = \frac{P}{2kA}$.

Hence $\theta = \theta_0 + \frac{P}{2kAL}x(L - x)$.

The variation of θ against x is shown in Fig 9.6. At the midpoint $x = L/2$, the temperature is $\theta_{x=L/2} = \theta_0 + \frac{PL}{8kA}$.

Questions

1. 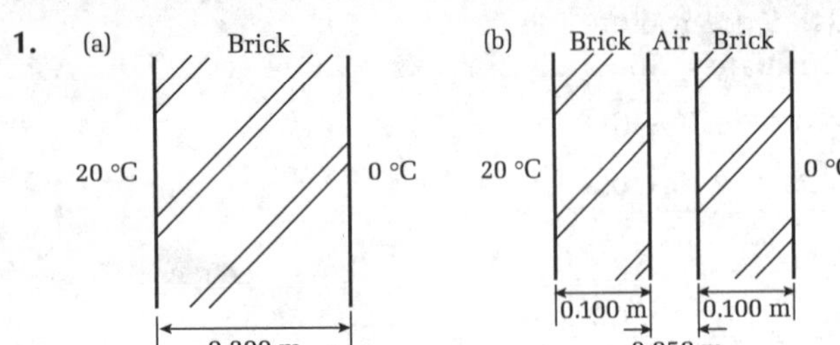

Fig 9.7

Fig 9.7(a) and Fig 9.7(b) show the dimensions of a solid brick wall and a cavity wall, respectively. In each case the surface temperatures are 20 °C and 0 °C, as shown. Using the values of thermal conductivity given below, calculate the thermal energy conducted per second through 10 m^2 of

(i) the brick wall shown in Fig 9.7(a),
(ii) the cavity wall shown in Fig 9.7(b).

You may assume that the temperature at the centre of the cavity is 10 °C.
Thermal conductivity of brick = 0.60 W m^{-1} K^{-1}; thermal conductivity of air = 2.4 × 10^{-2} W m^{-1} K^{-1}.

(NEAB June '93)

2. (a) Why is a good conductor of heat also a good conductor of electricity?

(b) Explain how heat is conducted through
(i) a good conductor,
(ii) a poor conductor.

(c) Write down equations for
(i) the rate of flow of charge (current) through a conductor,
(ii) the rate of flow of heat through a substance.
Name the symbols in these equations.

(d) By comparing the equations in part (c) above, find an expression for the quantity which is the thermal equivalent of electrical resistance.

(e) Using this idea of 'thermal' resistance, or otherwise, calculate the heat passing per second through 1 m^2 of glass of thickness 2 mm when its faces are maintained at 20 °C and 5 °C respectively. (Thermal conductivity of glass = 1.2 W m^{-1} K^{-1}.)

(f) Two such sheets of glass are now placed 4 mm apart and sealed so as to trap air in the space between them forming a 'sandwich' of thickness 8 mm. Given that the thermal conductivity of air is 0.024 W m^{-1} K^{-1}, calculate the rate of heat conduction per m^2 when the outside faces of the glass are again maintained at 20 °C and 5 °C respectively.

(g) Give **one** application of such a 'sandwich' and briefly explain why, in practice, the rate of heat transfer will be different from that calculated.

(WJEC June '91)

3. (a) (i) Define the *electrical resistivity* of a material.
(ii) The unit of electrical resistivity is the ohm metre (Ω m).
Express this unit in terms of the SI base units m, kg, s and A.

(b) A rectangular block ABCDEFGH has dimensions x, $2x$ and $3x$, as shown in Fig 9.8.

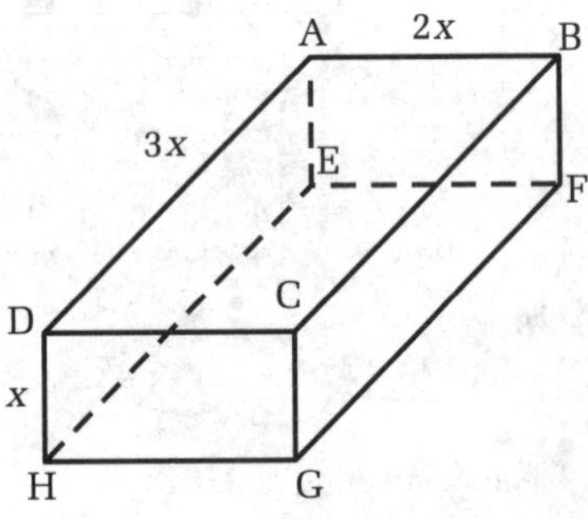

Fig 9.8

Electrical contact can be made to the block between opposite pairs of faces (for example, between ABCD and EFGH). Between which pair of faces would the *maximum* resistance be obtained? Show clearly how you arrive at your conclusion. If the material has resistivity ρ, what is this maximum resistance?

(c) (i) The equation for thermal conduction may be given as

$$\frac{Q}{t} = \lambda A \frac{\theta_1 - \theta_2}{x}$$

Making reference to a well-lagged metal bar in which a steady state exists, explain what the quantities $\frac{Q}{t}$, λ, A and $\frac{\theta_1 - \theta_2}{x}$ represent.

(ii) There is a close analogy (or similarity) between the equations describing thermal conduction and electrical conduction. What quantities in the thermal conduction equation are analogous to the electrical quantities *current* and *potential difference*?

(iii) In applying the thermal conduction equation, you considered a well-lagged bar in which a steady state existed. Why is it important to state these conditions? Explain why similar conditions are never emphasised in the case of electrical conduction.

(d) A teapot rests on a wooden stand on a table (Fig 9.9). The wooden stand is a circular disc of radius 120 mm and thickness 20 mm. The heat capacity (the product of mass and specific heat capacity) of the teapot and its contents is 4.0 × 10^3 J K^{-1}. The base of the teapot is in good thermal contact with the top of the wooden stand.

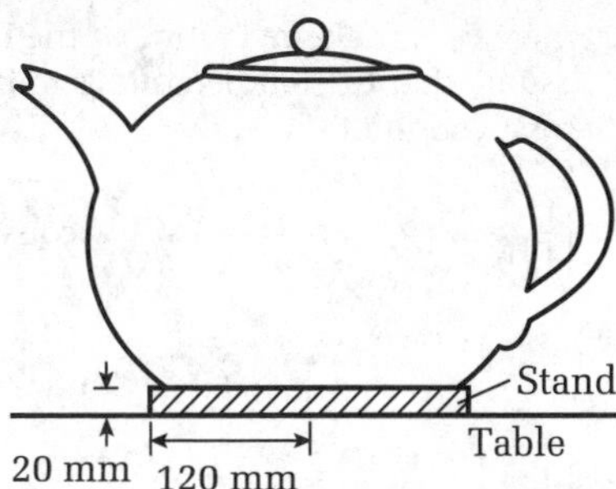

Fig 9.9

At a certain instant, the teapot and its contents are at a temperature of 68 °C, and the temperature is falling at a rate of 3.5×10^{-2} °C s^{-1}.

(i) At this instant, at what rate is the teapot losing heat?

(ii) Assuming that 10% of the heat lost from the teapot passes through the wooden stand, what is the temperature of the lower face of the stand (in contact with the table) at the instant when the upper face is at 68 °C? Assume that the heat flow through the stand is steady and parallel.

(Thermal conductivity of wood = 0.16 W m^{-1} K^{-1}.)

(NICCEA June '93)

4. (a) (i) What is meant by the *internal energy* of a system?

(ii) When a liquid freezes at a constant temperature there is a change of internal energy. State and explain whether the change is a gain or a loss.

The deposit of frost on the surfaces of the freezer unit of a refrigerator reduces efficiency and results in wasted energy.

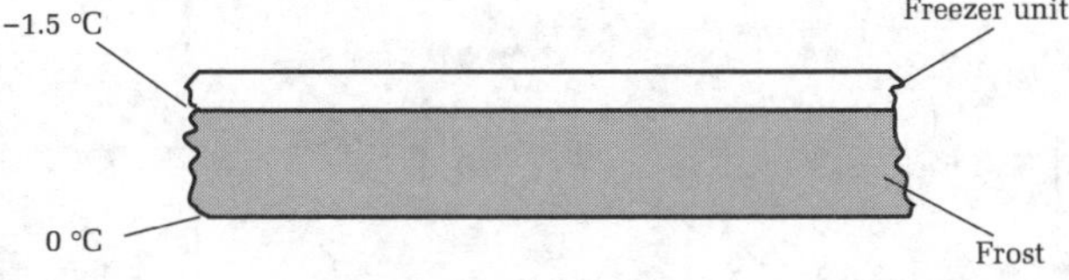

Fig 9.10

The following data apply to the frost and a typical freezer unit (Fig 9.10).

Density of the frost: $\rho = 720$ kg m^{-3}.

Specific latent heat of fusion of frost: $l = 340$ kJ kg^{-1}.

Surface temperature of freezer unit: $\theta = -1.5$ °C.

Temperature of air/frost surface: 0 °C.

(b) The frost accumulates continuously after the refrigerator is first switched on. After time t of working, the frost thickness on the surfaces of the freezer unit is y.

Show that the rate of increase in thickness can be expressed as

$$\frac{dy}{dt} = -\frac{k\theta}{\rho l}\left(\frac{1}{y}\right)$$

where k is the thermal conductivity of the frost.

(c) Measurements were made of the thickness, y, of frost after it first began to form and corresponding times t. The results are represented in the following graph.

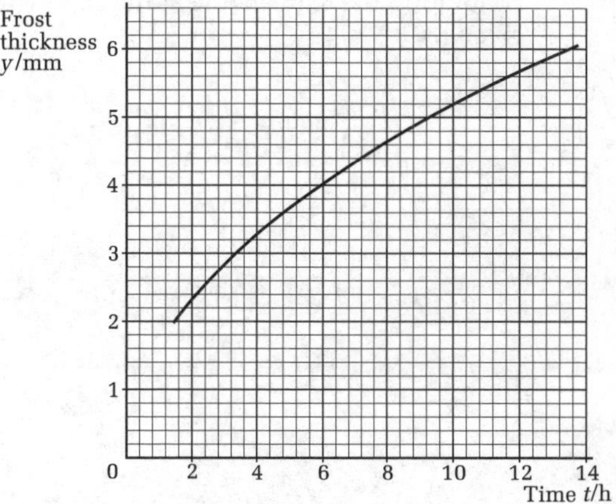

Fig 9.11

Using the expression from (b) and the numerical data above, deduce from this graph a value for k.

(AEB Summer '94, Special Paper)

5. Distinguish, briefly, between *conduction*, *convection* and *radiation* as mechanisms of thermal energy transfer.

(a) Explain why measurements of the thermal conductivity of gases are especially difficult and suggest how the difficulties might be overcome practically.

(b) Discuss the two principal mechanisms by which thermal energy is conducted in a metal. Explain why one of these mechanisms predominates at room temperature.

(c) A thin circular disc of radius r and thickness δx consists of a material of thermal conductivity k. One face is maintained at a temperature $\delta\theta$ higher than the other. Write down an expression for the rate of thermal energy transfer between the faces in the direction of increasing temperature.

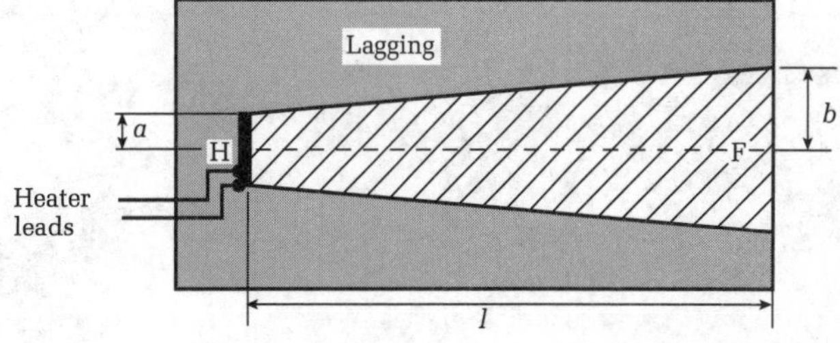

Fig 9.12

(d) A solid bar of metal of thermal conductivity k has the shape shown in Fig 9.12. Its length is l. The cross section is circular, the radius increasing from a at the narrow end, to b at the wide end. It is surrounded by effective lagging which prevents all energy loss except at the exposed face F. An electric heater H is attached to the narrow end face and is supplied with power P. Use the expression you have quoted in (c) to show that, under steady-state conditions, the temperature at the exposed face F is given by

$$\theta = \theta_0 - \frac{Pl}{k\pi ab}$$

where θ_0 is the temperature at the heater end. Assume that the temperature is uniform over any cross section of the bar.

$$\left[\int \frac{\mathrm{d}x}{(p+qx)^2} = -\frac{1}{q(p+qx)} + \text{constant}\right]$$

(O & C June '91, Special Paper)

10 ADVANCED ELECTROSTATICS

What you need to know now

- ❏ The definitions of electric field strength and potential.
- ❏ Coulomb's law of force between two point charges.
- ❏ The formulae for E and V near a point charge and between parallel plates.
- ❏ The effect of a dielectric in an electric field.
- ❏ The relative permittivity of a dielectric is the ratio of its permittivity to the absolute permittivity of free space.

What you need to know next

Electric field strength and potential

A point charge q in an electric field experiences a force qE due to the field where E is the electric field strength at the point charge. If the charge moves a distance δx in the direction of the field, the work done by the field on the charge is equal to $qE\,\delta x$. Hence the change of potential energy $\delta(\text{PE})$ of the charge in the field is $-qE\,\delta x$. Therefore the change of potential $\delta V = -E\,\delta x$ since $\delta V = \dfrac{\delta(\text{PE})}{q}$. Hence the electric field strength $E = -\dfrac{dV}{dx}$ since $\dfrac{dV}{dx} = \dfrac{\delta V}{\delta x}$ in the limit $\delta x \to 0$. Since $\dfrac{dV}{dx}$ is the potential gradient, the electric field strength $E = -$the potential gradient $\dfrac{dV}{dx}$ at any position.

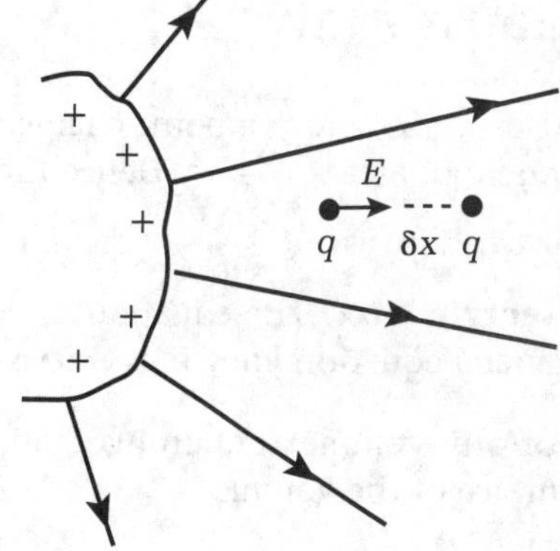

Fig 10.1 Work done

1. At distance r from a point charge Q, the electric potential $V = \dfrac{Q}{4\pi\varepsilon_0\,\varepsilon_r\,r}$ where ε_r is the relative permittivity of the medium. Hence the potential gradient $\dfrac{dV}{dr} = \dfrac{d}{dr}\left(\dfrac{Q}{4\pi\varepsilon_0\,\varepsilon_r\,r}\right) = -\dfrac{Q}{4\pi\varepsilon_0\,\varepsilon_r\,r^2}$ which gives

$$E = \frac{Q}{4\pi\varepsilon_0\,\varepsilon_r\,r^2} = -\frac{dV}{dr}$$

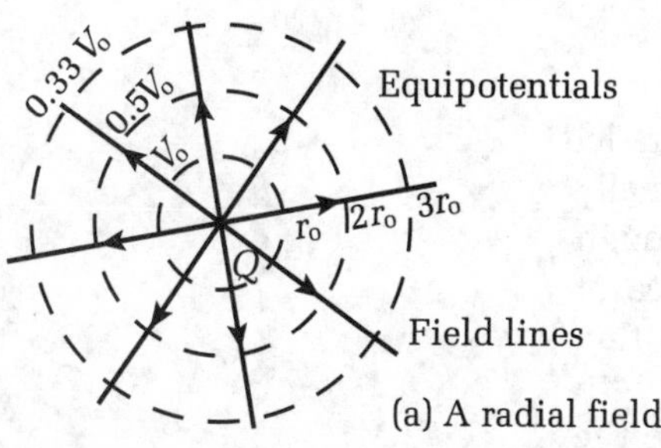

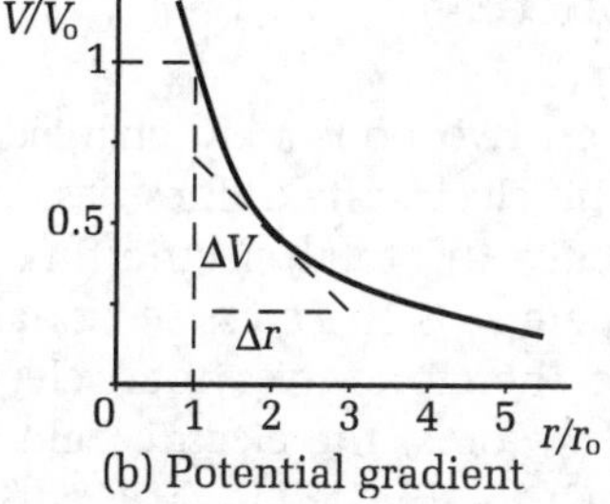

Fig 10.2 Near a point charge

2. At distance x from the earthed plate in a charged parallel plate system, the electric potential $V = \frac{V_p}{d}x$ where V_p is the p.d. between the plates and d is the plate spacing. Hence $E = -\frac{dV}{dx} = -\frac{V_p}{d}$. Thus the magnitude of the electric field strength is V_p/d and its direction is towards the earthed plate if the other plate is positive and away from the earthed plate if the other plate is negative.

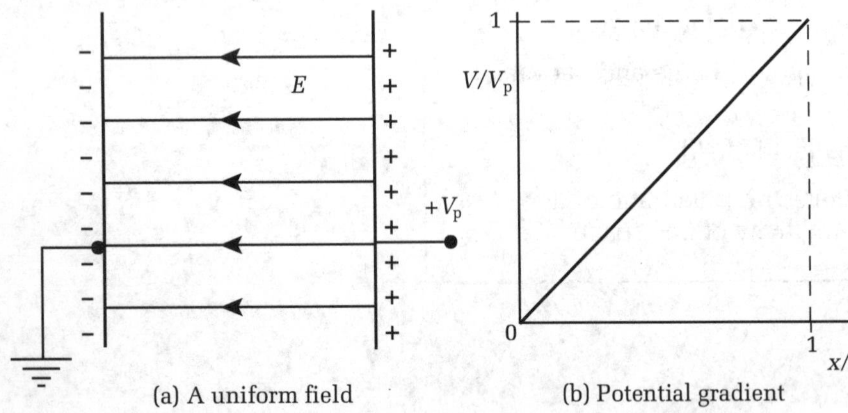

Fig 10.3 Between parallel plates

Gauss's law

At distance r from a point charge Q, the electric field lines pass through a sphere of area $A = 4\pi r^2$. Hence the equation for electric field strength may be written as $E = \frac{Q}{A\varepsilon_0\,\varepsilon_r}$ or $EA = Q/\varepsilon_0\,\varepsilon_r$. The product EA is called the **electric flux**. The equation $EA = Q/\varepsilon_0\,\varepsilon_r$ is a specific example of a more general equation known as **Gauss's law**.

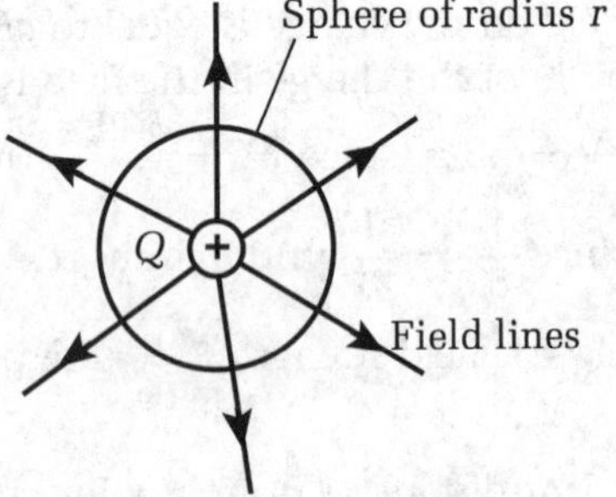

Fig 10.4 Gauss's law for a point charge

For any volume containing charge Q, the total electric flux through the surface of the volume

$$\int E_n \,dA = Q/\varepsilon_0\,\varepsilon_r$$

where E_n is the normal component of the electric field passing through an element of surface area dA.

Case study 1 Parallel plates

Consider a cylindrical volume between two oppositely charged parallel plates in air, as shown in Fig 10.5. The electric field lines pass normally through one end of the cylinder. Hence the total electric flux through the surfaces of the cylinder is EA where A is the cross-sectional area of the cylinder. Using Gauss's theorem therefore gives total electric flux $EA = Q/\varepsilon_0$ since $\varepsilon_r = 1$ for air. In other words, the electric field strength at any point between the plates, $E = Q/A\varepsilon_0$. Hence $Q = \varepsilon_0 AV/d$ since the magnitude of $E = V/d$ where V is the plate p.d. and d is the plate spacing.

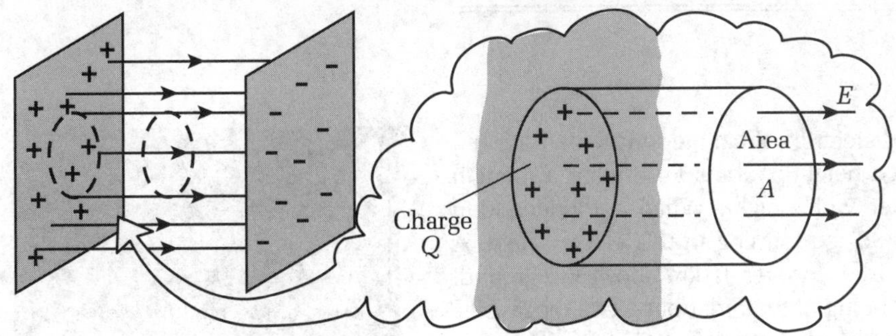

Fig 10.5 Gauss's law for parallel plates

- Capacitance $C = \frac{Q}{V} = \frac{A\varepsilon_0\,\varepsilon_r}{d}$ for a pair of parallel plates.
- Energy stored $= \frac{1}{2}CV^2 = \frac{A\varepsilon_0\,\varepsilon_r V^2}{2d}$.

NOTE: Coulomb's law of force between two point charges q_1 and q_2 at separation r is $F = k\frac{q_1 q_2}{r^2}$ where $k = 1/4\pi\varepsilon_0\,\varepsilon_r$. By defining the constant of proportionality k as $1/4\pi\varepsilon_0\,\varepsilon_r$, Gauss's law then has the form as on p. 52. Hence for a vacuum between the plates, $\varepsilon_r = 1$ and ε_0 may then be seen as the constant of proportionality in the parallel plates equation $Q = \varepsilon_0 AV/d$. The value of ε_0 may therefore be confirmed by making measurements using a parallel plates system. Using air between the plates makes no significant difference to the accuracy of such an experiment since ε_r is effectively 1 for air.

Case study 2 Charged spheres

Consider an isolated hollow conducting sphere carrying a charge Q. The charge is uniformly distributed on its outer surface. The electric field lines radiate from the centre of the sphere. At distance r from the centre, the electric field lines pass through a sphere of area $4\pi r^2$. The total electric flux passing through this sphere is $4\pi r^2 E$ where E is the electric field strength at this distance.

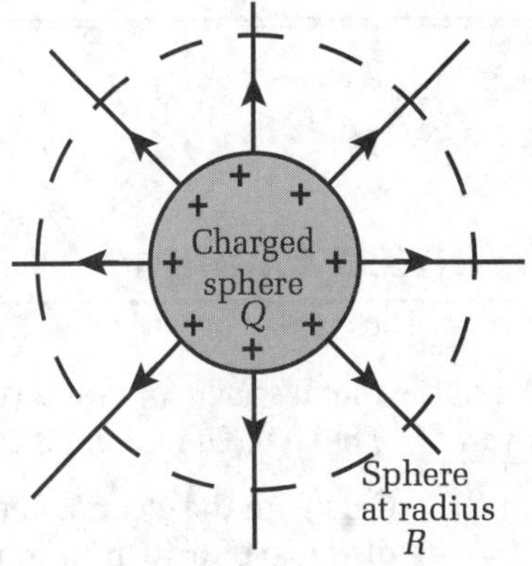

Fig 10.6 Gauss's law applied to a charged sphere

Using Gauss's theorem gives

$$\text{total electric flux} \quad 4\pi r^2 E = Q/\varepsilon_0\,\varepsilon_r$$

where ε_r is the relative permittivity of the medium in which the charged sphere is placed.

Hence the electric field strength is the same as for a point charge Q at the centre, i.e. $E = \frac{Q}{4\pi\varepsilon_0\,\varepsilon_r r^2}$.

- Inside a hollow charged sphere, $E = 0$ and $V =$ surface potential.
- At the surface, $E = \frac{Q}{4\pi\varepsilon_0\,\varepsilon_r R^2}$ and $V = \frac{Q}{4\pi\varepsilon_0\,\varepsilon_r R}$ where R is the radius of the sphere. Hence the capacitance $C = \frac{Q}{V} = 4\pi\varepsilon_0\,\varepsilon_r R$.
- The electrostatic potential energy of a charged hollow sphere $= \frac{1}{2}CV^2$.

Atmospheric electricity

When the sky is clear, there is a downward electric field at the surface of the Earth. This field, originating in the ionosphere at a height of about 50 km, has a strength of about $100\,\mathrm{V\,m^{-1}}$ and becomes weaker with height. When a thundercloud forms, the cloud becomes electrified due to ice forming in this electric field. A typical thundercloud extends from about 2 km to over 10 km above the ground, the p.d. between the base and the ground being of the order of several megavolts. When a lightning flash occurs, a 'step leader' of charge from the cloud meets a 'streamer' from the ground about 50 m above the ground. A continuous conducting path is thus opened between the ground and the cloud and a 'return' stroke at a speed of more than $30\,000\,\mathrm{km\,s^{-1}}$ travels between the cloud and the ground. A single lightning flash may consist of several return strokes in less than a second. Each stroke transfers up to 10 C or more of charge in less than 0.2 ms, corresponding to an average current up to 50 kA or more.

Fig 10.7 Lightning

A lightning conductor provides a point of origin for the streamer and usually conducts the stroke to ground safely. Lightning conductors on very tall buildings may cause sufficient ionisation to prevent return strokes. Without a lightning conductor, the streamer and hence the return strokes can originate at any exposed earthed point above the ground. In a thunderstorm, charge tends to accumulate at such points or at the tip of a lightning conductor if present because this is where the surface is most curved and hence where the surface electric field strength is greatest. If the electric field strength exceeds the dielectric strength of the surrounding air, air molecules become ionised and the air becomes conducting, allowing charge to flow.

A lightning stroke can damage an installation without actually striking the installation. The massive current in the stroke spreads out when it hits the ground. The ground is not a perfect conductor and therefore a potential gradient exists along the ground. This can be sufficient to damage installations or harm animals.

Worked example

A hollow metal sphere of radius 0.10 m is supported on an insulating rod as shown in Fig 10.8. The sphere is charged to a potential of +1000 V in air.

(a) (i) Calculate the electric field strength and potential at a distance of 0.40 m from the surface of the sphere. **4 marks**

(ii) Sketch graphs to show the variation of electric field strength and potential from the centre of the sphere to a distance of 0.60 m from the centre of the sphere. **4 marks**

(b) An uncharged metal rod of length 0.10 m on a insulating support is placed pointing towards the centre of the sphere, with its near end 0.40 m from the centre.

(i) Without further calculations, explain how the metal rod affects the electric field. **5 marks**

(ii) On each of your graphs, sketch a further curve to show the effect of the metal rod on the field. **3 marks**

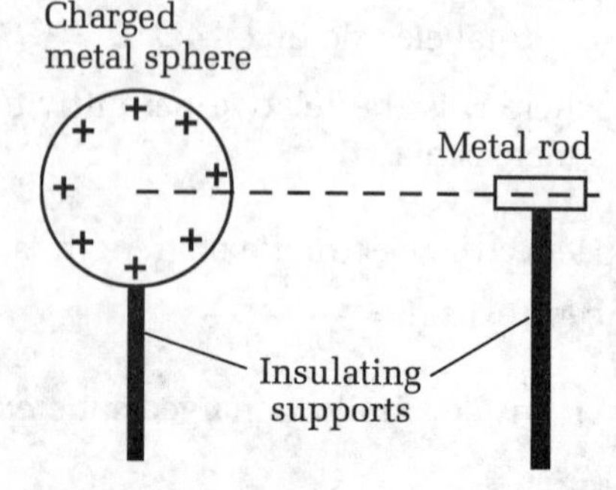

Fig 10.8

Solution

(a) (i) At the surface of the sphere, $V = \dfrac{Q}{4\pi\varepsilon_0 R}$ where R is the radius of the sphere. Hence $Q = 4\pi\varepsilon_0 RV = 4\pi\varepsilon_0 \times 0.1 \times 1000 = 400\pi\varepsilon_0$. ✓

At distance r from the centre $V = \dfrac{Q}{4\pi\varepsilon_0 r} = \dfrac{400\pi\varepsilon_0}{4\pi\varepsilon_0 r} = \dfrac{100}{r}$ and $E = \dfrac{400\pi\varepsilon_0}{4\pi\varepsilon_0 r^2} = \dfrac{100}{r^2}$. ✓

Therefore for $r = 0.40\,\text{m}$, $V = 100/0.4 = 250\,\text{V}$ ✓ and $E = 100/0.4^2 = 625\,\text{V m}^{-1}$. ✓

(ii) See Fig 10.9.

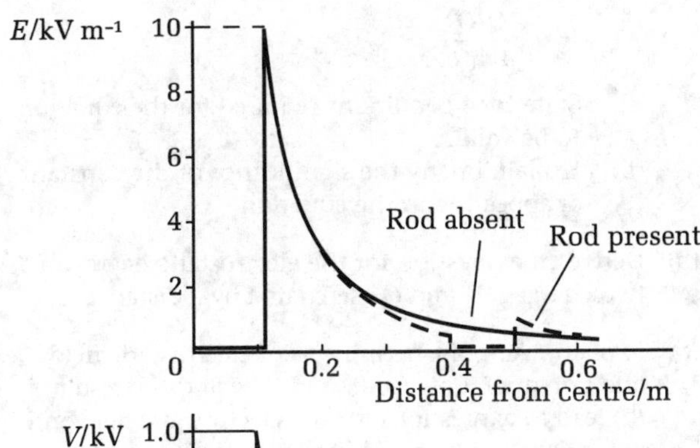

Fig 10.9

(a)(ii) **E vs r curve**

✓ E = 10 kV at r = 0.1 m plotted; E, r values correct at one more point outside sphere

✓ E = 0 for r < 0.1 m

V vs r curve

✓ V = 1 kV at r = 0.1 m; V, r values correct at one more point outside sphere

✓ V = 1.0 kV for r < 0.1 m

(b)(ii) **E vs r curve**

✓ E = 0 from r = 0.4 to 0.5 m

V vs r curve

✓ V = constant from r = 0.4 to 0.5 m

✓ Correct general shape of E or V curve

(b) (i) Free electrons move towards the end of the rod near the sphere. Hence that end becomes negative and the other end becomes positive. ✓
As a result, the potential at 0.4 m from the centre is reduced. ✓
The rod is at constant potential ✓ and therefore the potential at the other end is higher than before. ✓
The electric field between the sphere and the rod is stronger because the potential gradient is steeper. ✓

(ii) See Fig 10.9.

Questions

1. Two point charges of $+5\,\mu C$ and $-3\,\mu C$ are placed at the points A and B as shown in Fig 10.10.

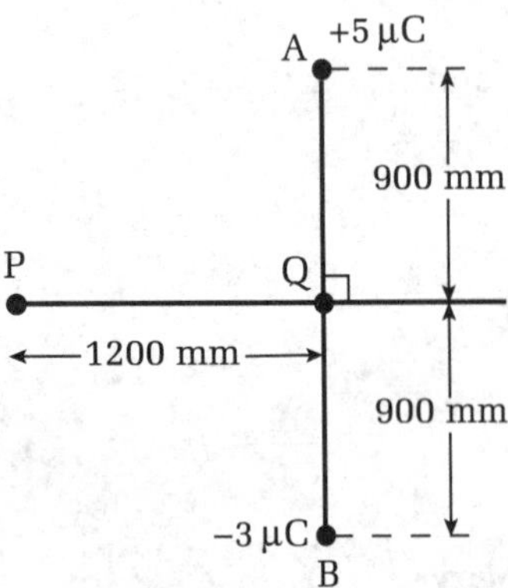

Fig 10.10

Calculate the work done in moving a charge of $-3\,\mu C$ from P to Q.

$\left[\text{Take } \frac{1}{4\pi\varepsilon_0} = 9 \times 10^9\ F^{-1}\,m.\right]$

(WJEC June '91)

2. (a) For each of the following, state whether it is a scalar or a vector and give an appropriate unit:
   (i) electric potential,
   (ii) electric field strength.

   (b) Points A and B are 0.10 m apart. A point charge of $+3.0 \times 10^{-9}$ C is placed at A and a point charge of -1.0×10^{-9} C is placed at B.
   (i) X is the point on the straight line through A and B, between A and B, where the electric potential is zero. Calculate the distance AX.
   (ii) Show on a diagram the approximate position of a point, Y, on the straight line through A and B where the electric field strength is zero. Explain your reasoning, but no calculation is expected.

(NEAB June '92)

3. (a) Show that the electrostatic potential energy of an isolated conducting sphere of radius a carrying a charge Q is given by

$$\frac{Q^2}{8\pi\varepsilon_0 a}$$

   (b) The vertical electric field below a thundercloud is roughly 10 000 V m^{-1}.
   (i) Show that the smallest charge a water drop of radius 0.001 m would have to carry for it not to fall under gravity in this field is 4.2×10^{-9} C.
   (ii) Is it likely that the drop could carry such a charge? Support your answer with a calculation. (The breakdown strength of air is roughly 3×10^6 V m^{-1}.)

   (c) If a drop of radius 0.001 m were to split into two smaller equal drops there would be an increase in the surface energy of 0.25 μJ.
   (i) Explain qualitatively the reason for this increase of surface energy.
   (ii) Discuss quantitatively whether the energy conditions are favourable for a drop of this size carrying a charge of 4.2×10^{-9} C to split into two halves.

(NEAB June '94, Special Paper)

4. (a) Coulomb's law for the force between two electric charges can be stated in the form

$$F = \frac{Q_1 Q_2}{4\pi\varepsilon_0 r^2}$$

   (i) State **two** conditions required for the equation to be valid.
   (ii) Explain briefly the significance of the constant ε_0 appearing in the equation.

   (b) Derive an expression for the electrostatic energy of two charges Q_1 and Q_2 separated by a distance r.

   (c) Explain, using the definitions of electrostatic field and potential, how Coulomb's law and the result of (b) lead to expressions for the electrostatic field and potential at a distance r from a charge Q.

   (d) Four charges of magnitude Q, three positive and one negative, are situated at the corners of a square of side a.
   (i) Obtain the magnitude and direction of the force exerted by the three positive charges on the negative one.
   (ii) Show that the electrostatic energy of the four charges is zero.

   (e)

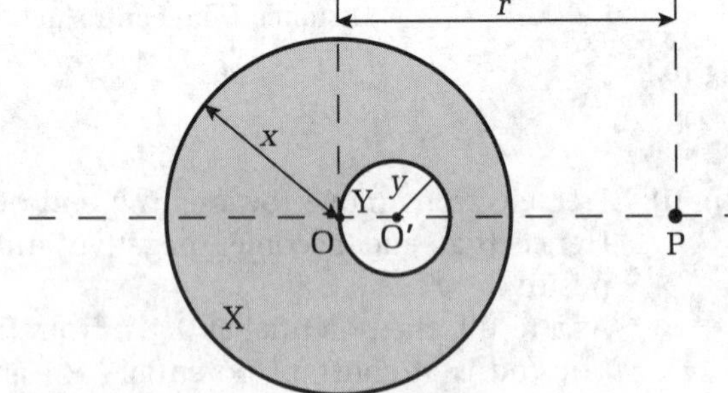

Fig 10.11

X is a spherical region of centre O and radius x. Y is a spherical cavity, within X, of centre O′ and radius y. The shaded region is uniformly charged with a charge density σ (C m^{-3}). The cavity Y is free of charge. Derive an expression for the electric field at P where OP = r given that O, O′ and P are collinear. Explain clearly your reasoning.

(O & C June '92, Special Paper)

5. (a) The electric potential at a distance x from an isolated charge Q in a vacuum is given by

$$V = \frac{Q}{4\pi\varepsilon_0 x}$$

(i) State the unit of all the physical quantities in the expression above.
(ii) Where will V be zero?
(iii)

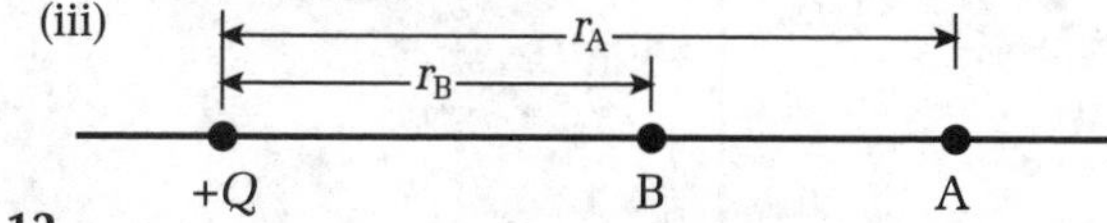

Fig 10.12

With reference to the Fig 10.12, explain how the equation may be used to determine:
(I) the potential difference between A and B.
(II) the difference in potential energy of a charge $+q$ placed at A from that placed at B.

(b) (i) Write down an expression for the gravitational potential at a distance r from an isolated mass M.
(ii) Calculate the change in potential energy of a satellite of mass 500 kg if it moves from an orbit at a height of 20 000 km to an orbit at a height of 15 000 km above the Earth's surface.

(c) A hydrogen atom can be assumed to have the following structure:

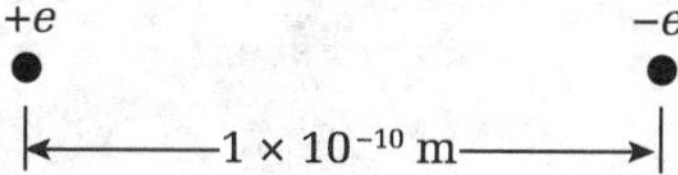

Fig 10.13

Calculate the potential energy of the atom due to electrostatic forces.

(d) Calculate the potential energy of a helium atom (due to electrostatic forces), assuming the following model:

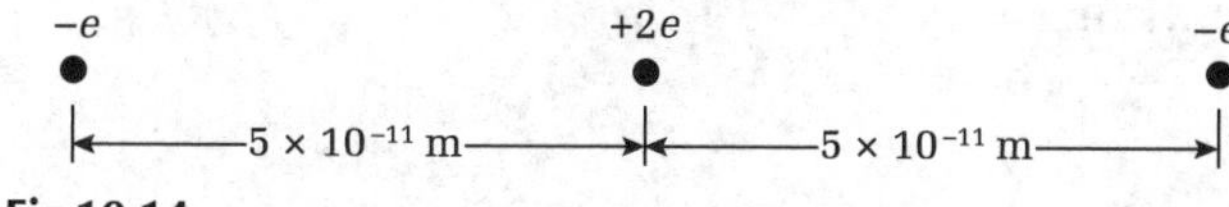

Fig 10.14

(WJEC June '94, Special Paper)

6. (a) What is meant by the term *electric field strength*?

(b) Calculate the force exerted on a proton, which has a charge of $+1.6 \times 10^{-19}$ C, when it is in a uniform electric field of field strength $2.7 \times 10^{5}\ \mathrm{N\,C^{-1}}$.

(c) A proton is moved in a vacuum by a uniform electric field of $2.7 \times 10^{5}\ \mathrm{N\,C^{-1}}$ from A to B, a distance of 0.0078 m. (Fig 10.15.)
(i) How much work is done by the field on the proton?
(ii) What is the gain in the kinetic energy of the proton?
(iii) Calculate the difference in potential between A and B.
State whether A or B is at the higher potential.

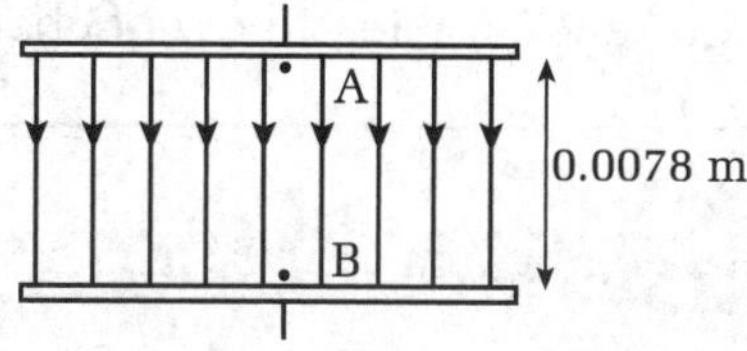

Fig 10.15

(d) In an electron microscope, an electron lens has two cylinders which are at potentials of +500 V and −100 V respectively. An electron beam passes at high speed into the lens from the left. A cross-section of the two cylinders is shown full scale in Fig 10.16, together with dotted lines showing points of the same potential at different places within the cylinders. Use the diagram, where necessary measuring distances on it with a ruler, to
(i) find the potential difference between X and Y,
(ii) find the loss in kinetic energy of an electron moving in a vacuum between X and Y,
(iii) find the approximate value of the electric field strength at Z,
(iv) sketch a graph showing how the potential varies along the axis of the lens,
(v) sketch, on the same x-axis drawn in (iv), a graph showing how the speed of the electron varies as it passes from X to Y.

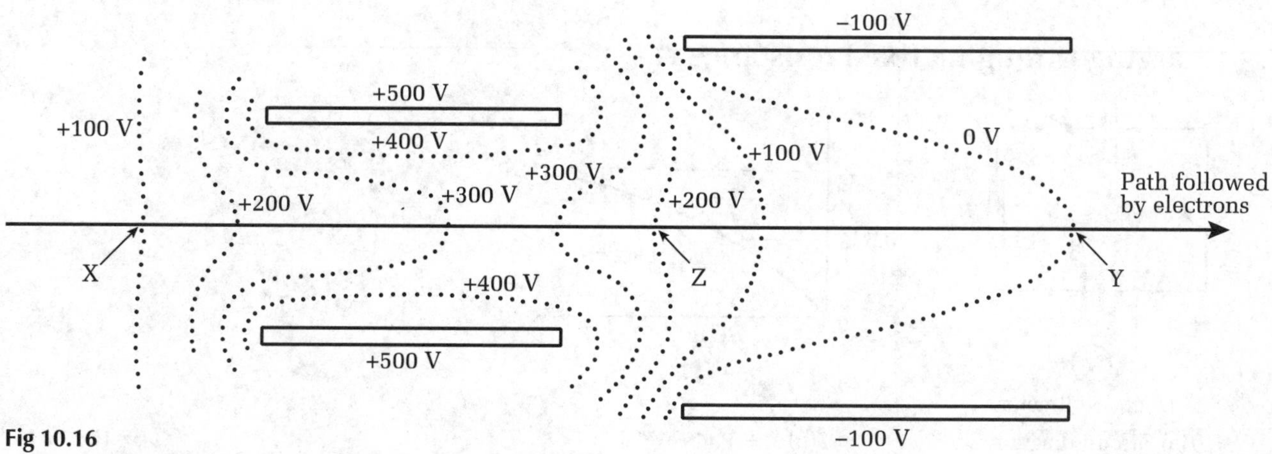

Fig 10.16

(UCLES June '93)

11 CAPACITOR CALCULATIONS

What you need to know now

- ❑ Capacitance $C = \dfrac{Q}{V}$ and energy stored $= \frac{1}{2}CV^2$.
- ❑ The capacitor combination rules.
- ❑ The equation $V = V_0 \, e^{-t/RC}$ for capacitor discharge through a fixed resistor.
- ❑ Current I = rate of flow of charge $\dfrac{dQ}{dt}$.

What you need to know next

Charging and discharging a capacitor

1. Charging at constant current *I*

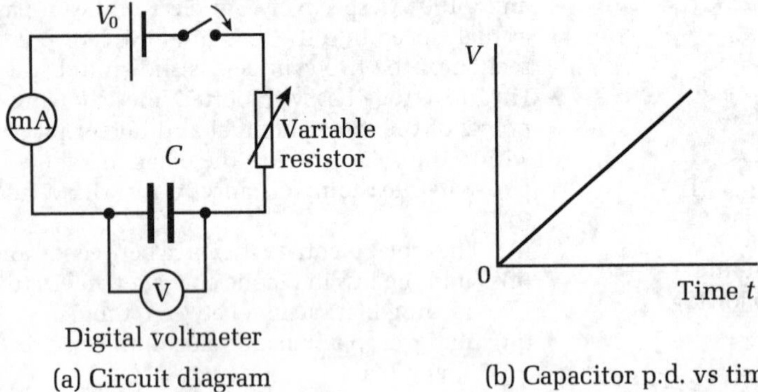

Fig 11.1 Charging at constant current

This is achieved by using a variable resistor to reduce the circuit resistance as the capacitor charges up. The capacitor p.d. after time t, $V = Q/C = It/C$ since $Q = It$.

2. Charging through a fixed resistance *R*

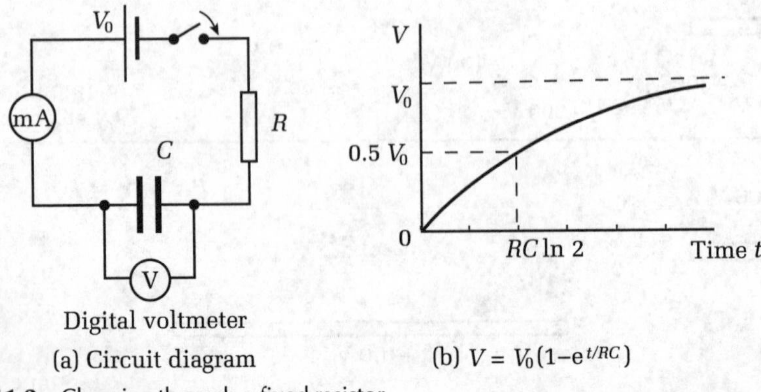

Fig 11.2 Charging through a fixed resistor

The current becomes smaller and smaller as the capacitor charges up. At any instant, the p.d. across the resistance R, $V_R = (V_0 - V_c)$ where V_0 is the battery p.d. and V_c is the capacitor p.d. Hence the current $I = (V_0 - V_c)/R$. Since $I = \frac{dQ}{dt}$ and $V_c = Q/C$, then $\frac{dQ}{dt} = \frac{(CV_0 - Q)}{CR}$.

Rearranging this equation and integrating gives

$$\int \frac{dQ}{(CV_0 - Q)} = \int \frac{dt}{CR}$$

Hence $\ln(CV_0 - Q) = -\frac{t}{CR} + \text{constant of integration } k$.

Since $Q = 0$ at $t = 0$, then $k = \ln(CV_0)$. Hence $\ln\left(\frac{CV_0 - Q}{CV_0}\right) = -\frac{t}{CR}$.

Prove for yourself that this gives $Q = CV_0(1 - e^{-t/CR})$ when rearranged. Also, use $I = \frac{dQ}{dt}$ to show that $I = \frac{V_0}{R} e^{-t/CR}$.

3. Discharging through a fixed resistor

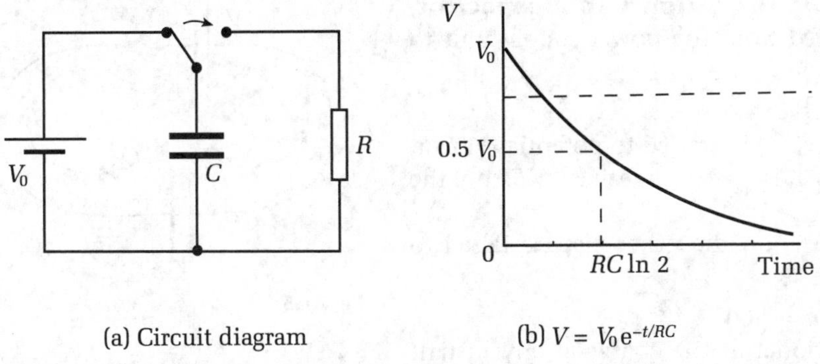

(a) Circuit diagram (b) $V = V_0 e^{-t/RC}$

Fig 11.3 Discharging through a fixed resistor

At time t after the discharge commences, the discharge current $I = V_R/R = -V_C/R$ since the resistor p.d. V_R and the capacitor p.d. V_C are equal and opposite (i.e. $V_R + V_C = 0$). Hence $\frac{dQ}{dt} = -\frac{Q}{CR}$. Rearranging and integrating this equation gives

$$\int \frac{dQ}{Q} = -\int \frac{dt}{CR}$$

Hence $\ln Q = -\frac{t}{CR} + \text{constant of integration } k$.

Since $Q = CV_0$ at $t = 0$, $k = \ln(CV_0)$. Hence $\ln \frac{Q}{CV_0} = -\frac{t}{CR}$. Prove for yourself that this gives $Q = CV_0 e^{-t/CR}$ when rearranged and that $I = -\frac{V_0}{R} e^{-t/CR}$.

4. Discharging to a second capacitor

Suppose a capacitor of capacitance C_1 is charged to a p.d. V_1 then isolated. Also, a second capacitor of capacitance C_2 is charged to p.d. V_2 then isolated. If the capacitors are now connected together, their total capacitance $C = C_1 + C_2$ since they are connected in parallel.

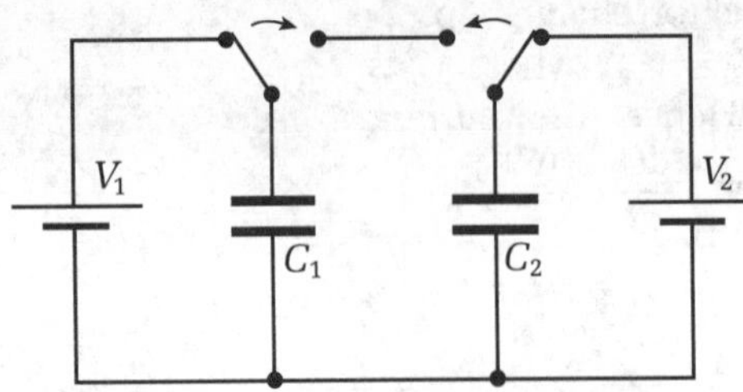

Fig 11.4 Sharing charge

- If the two positive plates are joined and the two negative plates are joined separately, the total charge stored $Q = C_1V_1 + C_2V_2$. Hence the final p.d. $V = \frac{Q}{C} = \frac{C_1V_1 + C_2V_2}{C_1 + C_2}$.
- If the positive plate of each capacitor is joined to the negative plate of the other capacitor, the total charge stored $Q = C_1V_1 - C_2V_2$. Hence the final p.d. $V = \frac{Q}{C} = \frac{C_1V_1 - C_2V_2}{C_1 + C_2}$.

Energy changes in a parallel plate capacitor

1. **As a result of connecting a d.c. power supply to a capacitor,** as in Fig 11.5, charge Q is transferred from the power supply unit to the capacitor.
   - The work done by the battery $= QV$.
     - If neither plate is earthed, charge $+Q$ is raised to potential $V/2$ on the +plate and charge $-Q$ is raised to potential $-V/2$ on the other plate.
     - If one plate is earthed, charge Q on the other plate is raised to potential V.
   - The energy stored in the capacitor $= \frac{1}{2}QV$.
     Because the plate p.d. is proportional to the charge at any instant during the charging process, when the charge on the plates is q, the work done δW to increase the potential from v to $v + \delta v$ is $q\,\delta v$. Since $q = Cv$, then $\delta W = Cv\,\delta v$. Hence the total work done to store charge Q on the plates,
     $$W = \int_{v=0}^{v=V} Cv\,\mathrm{d}v = \tfrac{1}{2}CV^2 = \tfrac{1}{2}QV$$
   - The energy dissipated due to resistance in the charging process $= \frac{1}{2}QV$.
     This is the difference between the work done by the battery (i.e. energy supplied by the battery) and the energy stored in the capacitor. Even if no resistors are present in the circuit, the resistance of the connecting wires and the internal resistance of the battery will cause dissipation of energy. No matter what the circuit resistance is, the energy dissipated is always 50% of the energy supplied by the battery.

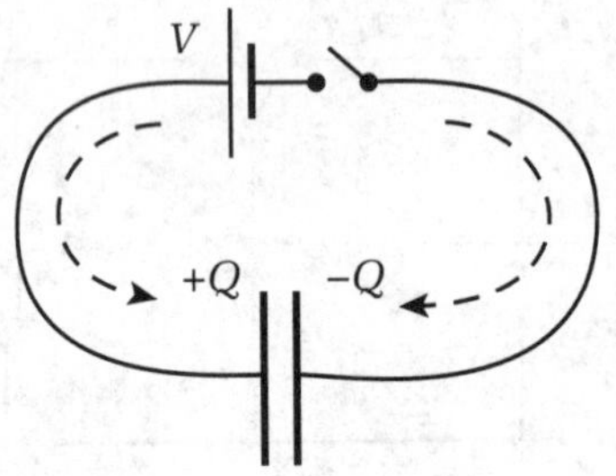

Fig 11.5

NOTE: Energy dissipated in time δt, $\delta E = I^2R\,\delta t = \frac{V^2}{R}\mathrm{e}^{-2t/RC}\,\delta t$.

Hence the total energy dissipated
$$E = \int_{t=0}^{t=\infty} \frac{V^2}{R}\mathrm{e}^{-2t/RC}\,\mathrm{d}t$$
$$= -\frac{RCV^2}{2R}\left[\mathrm{e}^{-2t/RC}\right]_{t=0}^{t=\infty}$$
$$= \tfrac{1}{2}CV^2 = \tfrac{1}{2}QV.$$

2. **As a result of moving the plates together with the d.c. power supply *still connected*,** the energy stored in the capacitor is increased. This happens because the capacitance is increased by moving the plates closer. Since the plate p.d. is unchanged as the d.c. power supply is still connected, the charge on the plates increases and the energy stored increases. If the new capacitance is C', the charge stored increases from $Q = CV$ to $Q' = C'V$ and the energy stored increases from $\frac{1}{2}QV$ to $\frac{1}{2}Q'V$.

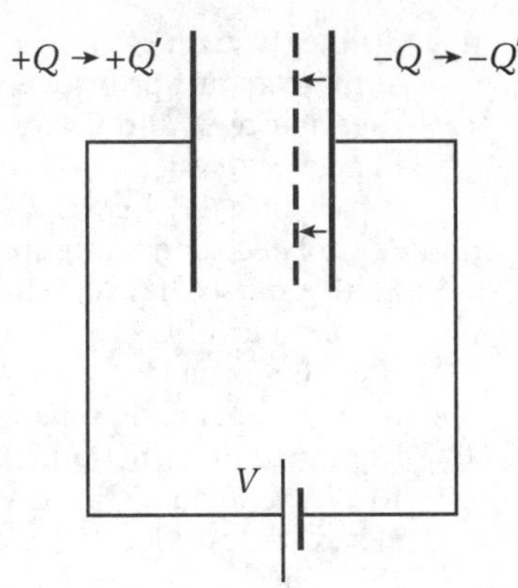

Fig 11.6 Moving the plates at fixed potential

3. **If the plates are moved together *after disconnecting* the battery,** the energy stored decreases. This happens because the charge is now constant because the plates are isolated. Moving the plates together increases the capacitance and hence the plate p.d. decreases from $V = Q/C$ to $V' = Q/C'$. The energy stored decreases from $\frac{1}{2}Q^2/C$ to $\frac{1}{2}Q^2/C'$.

   For plate separation x, the energy stored $E = \frac{1}{2}\frac{Q^2 x}{A\varepsilon_0\varepsilon_r}$ since $C = A\varepsilon_0\varepsilon_r/x$.

   Hence the magnitude of the force of attraction F between the plates $= \frac{dE}{dx} = \frac{1}{2}\frac{Q^2}{A\varepsilon_0\varepsilon_r}$.

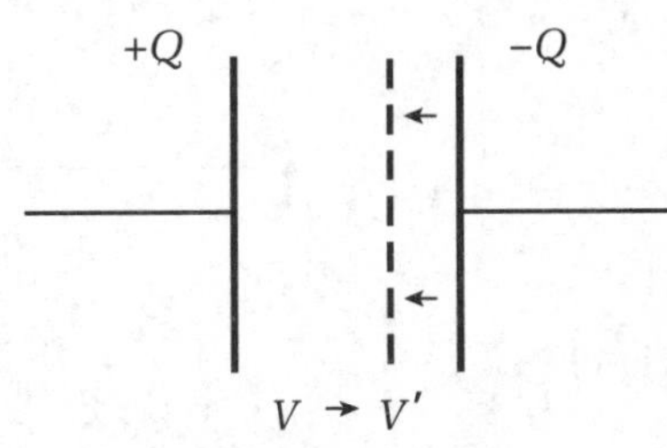

Fig 11.7 Moving the plates closer at fixed charge

4. **With a dielectric medium between the plates,** the capacitance is greater than it would be without the dielectric medium present.
   - ❏ If the plate p.d. V is constant (the battery remains connected), introducing the dielectric increases the energy stored from $\frac{1}{2}C_0V^2$ to $\frac{1}{2}CV^2$ where C is the capacitance with dielectric filling the space between the plates and C_0 is the capacitance without any dielectric present. Note that the relative permittivity of the dielectric $\varepsilon_r = \frac{C}{C_0}$ since $C = A\varepsilon_0\varepsilon_r/x$ and $C_0 = A\varepsilon_0/x$.
   - ❏ If the battery is disconnected so the plate charge Q is constant, introducing the dielectric decreases the energy stored from $\frac{1}{2}Q^2/C_0$ to $\frac{1}{2}Q^2/C$.

Questions

1. (a) Define *capacitance*.

   (b) A capacitor of capacitance 10 μF is fully charged from a 20 V d.c. supply.
   (i) Calculate the charge stored by the capacitor.
   (ii) Calculate the energy delivered by the 20 V supply.
   (iii) Calculate the energy stored by the capacitor.
   (iv) Account for the difference between the answers for (ii) and (iii).

   (c) The 10 μF capacitor in part (b) was charged from the supply through a resistor of resistance 2.0 kΩ.
   (i) Calculate the time constant for this circuit.
   (ii) When the capacitor was charged from zero charge, how long did it take for V, the potential difference across the capacitor, to reach 99% of its final value?
   (You may use the equation $V = V_0(1 - \exp(-t/CR))$ if you wish.)

   (UCLES June '92)

2. (a) Two capacitors of capacitance C_1 and C_2 respectively are connected in series. Derive an expression for the capacitance of a single equivalent capacitor.

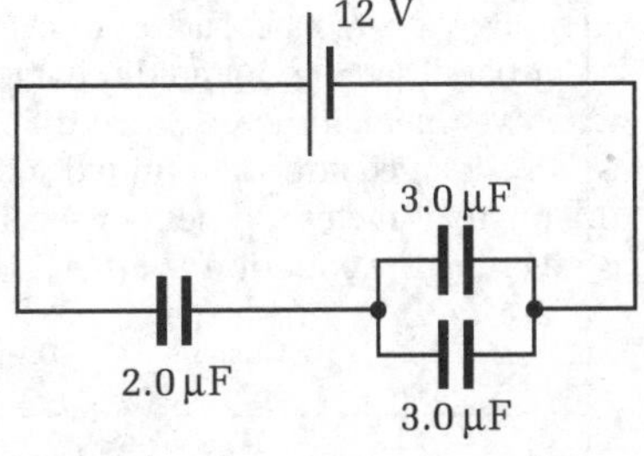

Fig 11.8

   (b) For the circuit shown, calculate
   (i) the capacitance of this combination of capacitors,
   (ii) the total energy stored in the capacitors,
   (iii) the p.d. across the 2.0 μF capacitor.

   (NEAB June '92)

3. (i) Define the term *capacitance*.
Show from first principles that two capacitors of capacitance C_1 and C_2 are, when connected in parallel, equivalent to a single capacitor of capacitance C, where $C = C_1 + C_2$.

(ii) An isolated conducting sphere of radius a near the Earth's surface has capacitance $4\pi\varepsilon_0 a$ where ε_0 is the permittivity of free space. (The Earth is effectively the other plate.)
A small conducting sphere of radius 1.00 cm is supported by a fine insulating thread and charged to a high potential, V, relative to Earth with an electrostatic device. Calculate the capacitance of this sphere.

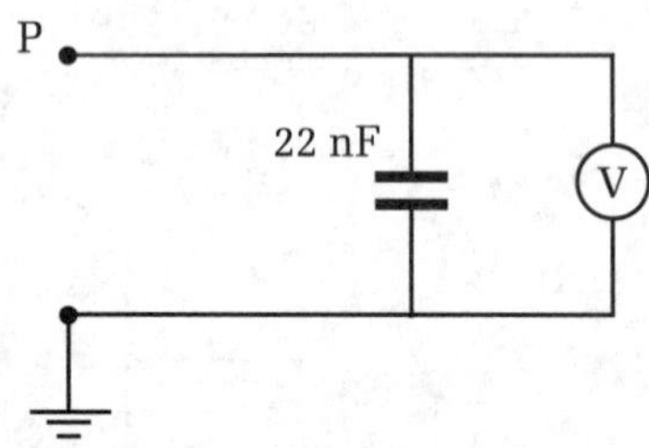

Fig 11.9

A 22 nF capacitor is connected in parallel with a high resistance voltmeter as shown in Fig 11.9. The voltmeter reads zero. The small conducting sphere, already charged, is brought into contact with the point P. Show that

$$\frac{\text{charge left on sphere}}{\text{charge transferred to capacitor}} = \frac{\text{capacitance of sphere}}{22 \times 10^{-9}\,\text{F}}$$

The voltmeter now reads 1.5 V. Calculate
(1) the charge transferred to the 22 nF capacitor, and
(2) the initial potential, V, of the small conducting sphere.
(Permittivity of free space, $\varepsilon_0 = 8.85 \times 10^{-12}\,\text{F m}^{-1}$.)

(ULEAC January '92)

4. (a) The diagram shows a circuit in which a vibrating reed switch (in the shaded rectangle) is used to alternately charge a capacitor of capacitance C to a potential difference V and discharge it through a sensitive microammeter. Show that if the capacitor is fully charged and then fully discharged through the microammeter n times per second, the current I is given by the equation $I = nCV$.

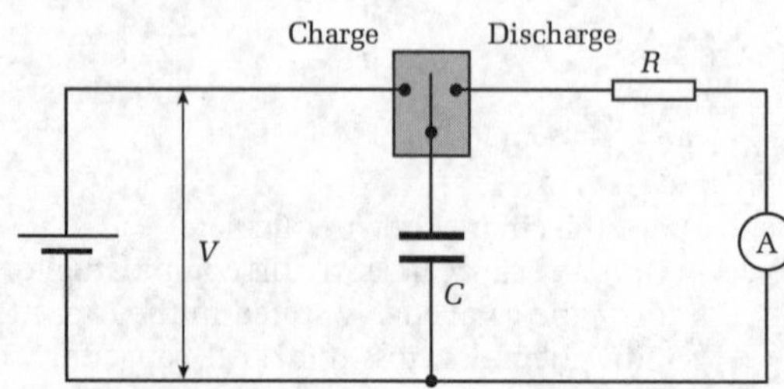

Fig 11.10

(b) (i) The arrangement described in (a) can be used to investigate the factors which determine the capacitance of a parallel plate capacitor made from two flat conducting sheets separated by an air gap. Describe an experiment to show how the capacitance depends on the distance between the plates. Show how you would use your results to demonstrate the relationship and state the result you would expect to obtain.

(ii) In this experiment a resistor, R, is connected in series with the microammeter to protect it as shown in the diagram. Explain the factors which would influence the choice of the value of R.

(c) A student is invited to make a capacitor from aluminium cooking foil and polythene film. The student has two pieces of aluminium foil, each 300 mm wide and 3.0 m long, and a plentiful supply of polythene film, 350 mm wide and of thickness 100 μm.

(i) If the relative permittivity of polythene is 2.5, calculate the maximum capacitance of the **flat** capacitor which could be made from this arrangement, stating any assumption(s) you make.

(ii) The insulation of polythene breaks down when the electric field strength in the polythene is $1.5 \times 10^6\,\text{V m}^{-1}$. Use this information to calculate the maximum p.d. to which this capacitor could be charged.

(iii) The student wishes to roll up the capacitor to make it more compact. Explain how the design should be modified so that this can be done and state how this would affect the capacitance.

Permittivity of free space $= 8.85 \times 10^{-12}\,\text{F m}^{-1}$.

(NEAB June '95)

5. (a) Show that the energy stored in a capacitor of capacitance C with a potential difference V between its plates is $\frac{1}{2}CV^2$.

(b) Apply this result to an ideal parallel plate capacitor to show that the energy stored per unit volume of free space in an electric field E is $\frac{1}{2}\varepsilon_0 E^2$, ε_0 being the permittivity of free space.

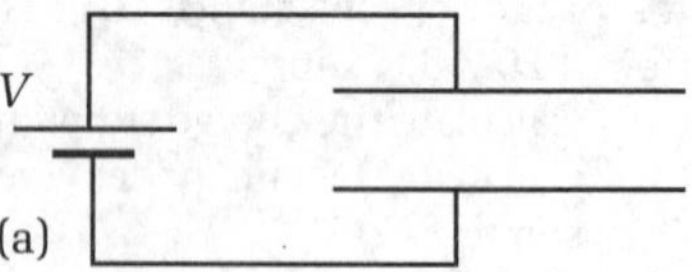

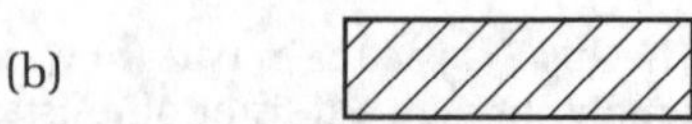

Fig 11.11

(c) In the Fig 11.11, (a) represents a parallel plate capacitor, vacuum spaced, of initial capacitance C_0. A potential difference V is maintained between the plates from a battery. (b) represents a slab of dielectric of relative permittivity ε_r, initially well outside the capacitor but which would just fill the space inside it.

Keeping the battery connected, the dielectric enters the capacitor, filling it. Discuss fully whether the dielectric needs to be *pushed* into the capacitor or whether it is *drawn* into the capacitor.

(d) A 10 μF capacitor is charged to a potential difference of 100 V and isolated. A second 10 μF capacitor is charged to 200 V and isolated. The capacitors are then connected *either*

(i) positive plate to positive plate, negative plate to negative plate

or

(ii) positive plate to negative plate, negative plate to positive plate.

Calculate the loss of stored energy in each case.

(O & C June '94)

6. (a) Define *capacitance*, and use your definition to derive the formula for the capacitance of two capacitors connected in series.

(b) Show that the energy stored by a capacitor of capacitance C, charged to a potential difference V is

$$\tfrac{1}{2}CV^2$$

(c) A capacitor of capacitance C_1 is connected to a battery of e.m.f. V, so that the energy stored is $E_1 = \tfrac{1}{2}C_1V^2$. The battery is then removed and replaced with an initially uncharged capacitor of capacitance C_2, and the total energy stored by the system of two capacitors is E_2. Derive an expression for the ratio E_2/E_1.

(d) A capacitor consisting of two large parallel plates, each of area A and of separation x, has a capacitance C given by

$$C = \frac{\varepsilon_0 A}{x}$$

The separation x of the plates in such a capacitor is increased by a small amount δx, keeping the charge constant. By considering the corresponding change in the total energy stored by the capacitor, show that the force F exerted by one plate on the other is given by

$$F = \frac{\varepsilon_0 AV^2}{2x^2}$$

where V is the potential difference across the capacitor for a plate separation x. In what direction does the force act?

(UCLES June '94, Special Paper)

12 USING KIRCHHOFF'S LAWS

What you need to know now

- ❏ The definitions of the coulomb, the volt and the ohm.
- ❏ The equations $Q = It$, $V = \frac{W}{Q}$, $R = \frac{V}{I}$ and $P = IV$.
- ❏ Ohm's law and the I–V characteristic for a resistor, a diode and a filament lamp.
- ❏ The resistor combination rules and the meaning of e.m.f. and internal resistance.
- ❏ The definition and measurement of resistivity.

What you need to know next

Conservation principles and Kirchhoff's laws

1. **Kirchhoff's first law** states that the total current entering a junction is equal to the total current leaving.

   This is a result of the conservation of charge. In any given period of time, the total charge entering a junction must be equal to the total charge leaving the junction because the junction does not retain charge. Charge is always conserved and therefore it enters and leaves the junction at the same rate. Using a convention for current directions (e.g. currents out are +, currents in are −), Kirchhoff's first law may be written as $\sum I = 0$ where $\sum$ is the summation symbol.

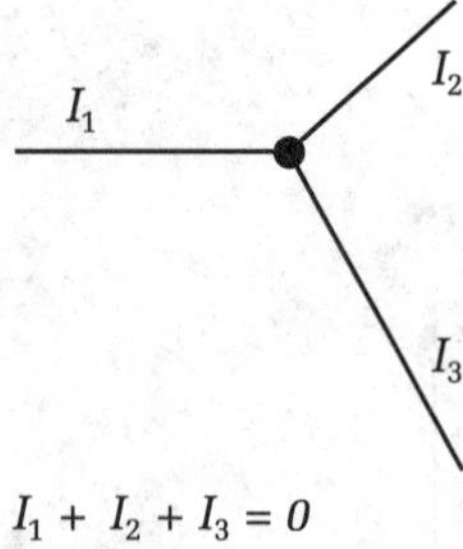

Fig 12.1 Kirchhoff's first law

2. **Kirchhoff's second law** states that the sum of the e.m.f.s round a closed loop is equal to the sum of the p.d.s round the loop.

   This is a result of conservation of energy. The e.m.f. of a cell is defined as the electrical energy generated per unit charge by the cell. The p.d. across a component in a circuit is defined as the electrical energy delivered per unit charge. An e.m.f. is a source of electrical energy whereas a p.d. is a sink of electrical energy. Kirchhoff's second law essentially states that the total electrical energy generated per unit charge by all the sources of e.m.f. in a closed loop is equal to the total electrical energy delivered per unit charge to all the components in the loop.

   Kirchhoff's second law may be written as $\sum \mathcal{E} = \sum IR$ for a closed circuit loop, where $\mathcal{E}$ represents e.m.f. and IR represents p.d. As with Kirchhoff's first law, a direction convention is essential to take account of current directions and cell polarities.

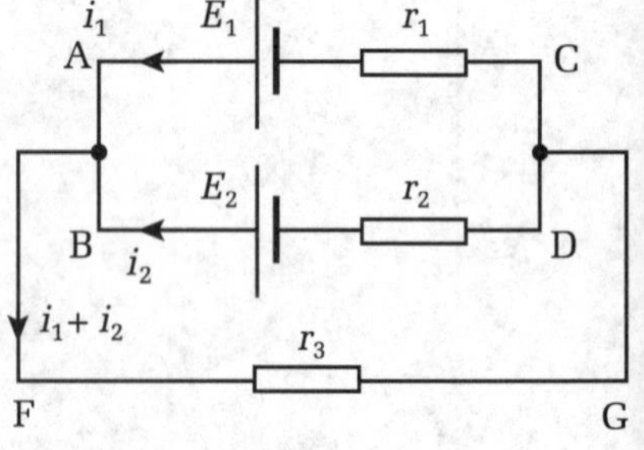

AFGCA $E_1 = i_1 r_1 + (i_1 + i_2) r_3$

BFGDB $E_2 = i_2 r_2 + (i_1 + i_2) r_3$

ABDCA $E_1 - E_2 = i_1 r_1 - i_2 r_2$

Fig 12.2 Kirchhoff's second law

Case study 1

A battery X of e.m.f. 6.0 V and internal resistance 2.0 Ω is connected in parallel with a second battery Y of e.m.f. 3.0 V and internal resistance 0.5 Ω by joining the terminals of the same polarity together. A 10.0 Ω resistor R is then connected between the terminals, as in Fig 12.3. Calculate

(a) the current through resistor R, and
(b) the % of the power generated delivered to resistor R. Account for the difference between the power generated and the power supplied to resistor R.

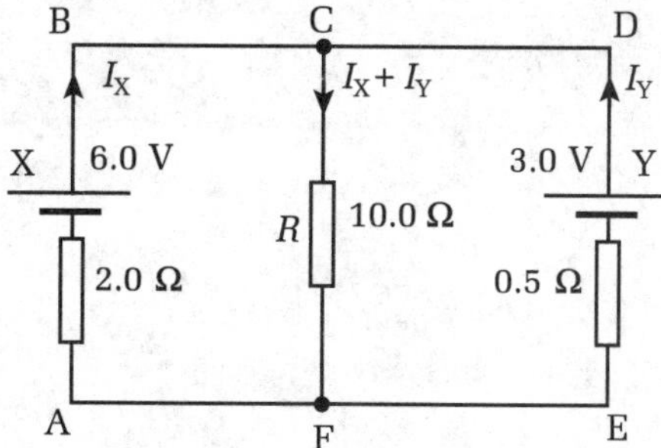

Fig 12.3

Solution

(a) Let the current through X be I_X and the current through Y be I_Y as in Fig 12.3.

❑ Using Kirchhoff's first law, the current through R is $I_X + I_Y$.

❑ Using Kirchhoff's second law gives an equation for each loop:

1. Loop ABCF; $6 = 2I_X + 10(I_X + I_Y)$ since $\sum \mathcal{E} = 6\,V$ and $\sum IR = 2I_X$ across the 2 Ω resistor + $10(I_X + I_Y)$ across the 10 Ω resistor.
2. Loop ABCDEF; $6 - 3 = 2I_X - 0.5I_Y$ since Y's polarity and the current through Y are in the opposite direction to the loop direction ABCDEF.
3. Loop DCFE; $3 = 0.5I_Y + 10(I_X + I_Y)$.

Note that adding equations 2 and 3 gives equation 1. It is only necessary to consider two equations to solve for I_X and I_Y since there are only two unknown currents. Prove for yourself that $I_X = 1.27\,A$ and $I_Y = -0.92\,A$. Note that the significance of the – sign for I_Y is that the current through Y is from C to D, not D to C as originally assumed.

(b) The power generated by cell X = $I_X \mathcal{E}_X$ where $\mathcal{E}_X$ is the e.m.f. of cell X. Hence the power generated by X is $1.27 \times 6 = 7.62\,W$. Cell Y does not generate power since the current passes through it in reverse. The power supplied to resistor R is $(I_X + I_Y)^2 R = (1.27 - 0.92)^2 \times 10 = 1.22\,W$. Hence the % of the power generated supplied to $R = \frac{1.22}{7.62} \times 100 = 16.0\%$.

Prove for yourself that the difference between the power generated by X and the power supplied to R (= 7.62 – 1.22 = 6.40 W) is accounted for by the power dissipated in the internal resistances r_X and r_Y $(= I_X{}^2 r_X + I_Y{}^2 r_Y)$ and power delivered to cell Y $(= I_Y \mathcal{E}_Y)$ causing chemical changes in Y.

Case study 2

Fig 12.4 shows a network of equal resistors, each of resistance R, forming a cube such that each resistor is joined to two other resistors at each end. A cell of e.m.f. E and negligible internal resistance is connected between two vertices diagonally opposite each other. Derive an expression for the equivalent resistance of the network.

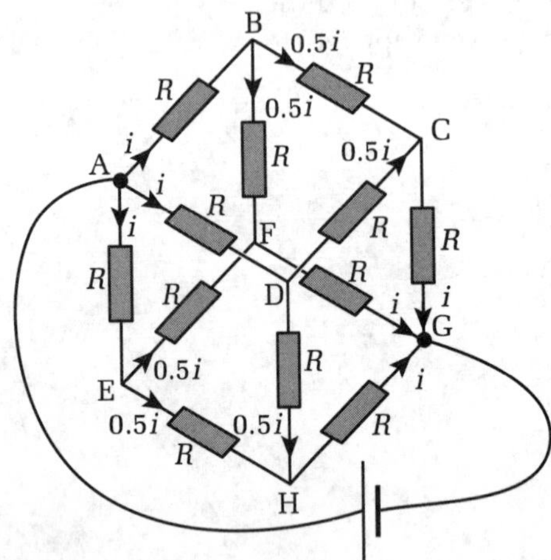

Fig 12.4 A resistor cube

Solution

Assume at the outset that each of the 12 resistors carries a different current. Before applying Kirchoff's laws, the symmetric nature of the network may be used to reduce the number of unknown currents.

1. The axis of symmetry is from A to G, hence AB, AD and AE are equivalent and therefore carry equal currents. Label this current as i on the diagram, i.e. $I_{AB} = I_{AD} = I_{AE} = i$.
2. Similarly, GC, GF and GH are equivalent and therefore also each carry current i, i.e. $I_{GC} = I_{GF} = I_{GH} = i$.
3. The current along AB splits equally at B because C and F are equivalent. Hence $I_{BF} = I_{BC} = 0.5i$.
4. Similar considerations give $0.5i$ for the current in DC, DH, EF and EH.

Kirchoff's second law may now be applied to just one loop to determine i; consider the loop consisting of the cell and the path ABCG through the network,

the sum of the e.m.f.s $= E$

the sum of the p.d.s $= V_{AB} + V_{BC} + V_{CG} = iR + 0.5iR + iR = 2.5iR$.

Hence $2.5iR = E$, which gives $i = \dfrac{E}{2.5R}$.

The total current entering the network $= 3i = \dfrac{3E}{2.5R}$.

The total resistance $= \dfrac{E}{3E/2.5R} = \dfrac{2.5}{3}R = 0.833R$.

Note: Prove that $R_{AC} = 0.7R$ and $R_{AB} = 0.583R$.

Ring main and spur circuits

A ring main circuit supplies current to an appliance from the two possible directions between the appliance and the mains supply to the ring main. Consider the ring main circuit in Fig 12.5 which shows an appliance P drawing 12.0 A from the ring main. Suppose P is quarter way round the ring main from where the mains supply S is connected.

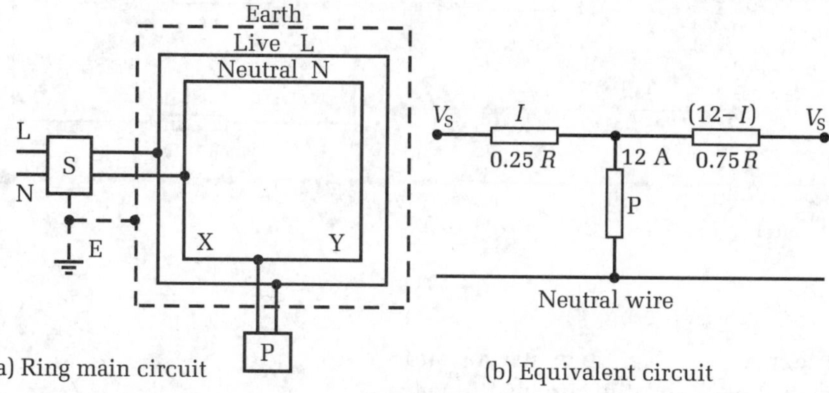

Fig 12.5 Using the ring main

Suppose current I reaches P through the shorter section SXP of the ring main. Hence the current reaching P through the section SYP is $12.0 - I$. If the resistance of the ring main is R, the resistance of section SXP is $0.25R$ and the resistance of section SYP is $0.75R$.

Applying Kirchoff's second law to each section in turn therefore gives

$$V_S = 0.25RI + V_P \qquad \text{for section SXP}$$

and $$V_S = 0.75R(12 - I) + V_P \qquad \text{for section SYP}$$

where V_S is the mains supply voltage and V_P is the appliance voltage.

Hence $0.25RI = 0.75R(12 - I)$ which gives $I = 9.0$ A. In other words, P is supplied with 9.0 A through section SXP and 3.0 A through section SYP. More significantly, $V_P = V_S - 2.25R$. The loss of voltage due to the ring main is therefore $2.25R$. Show for yourself that this loss would be $3R$ if all the current for P was supplied through section SXP. By supplying the appliance through both parts of the ring main, the voltage loss due to the ring main is reduced in comparison with supplying the appliance through a 'spur' connected to the mains supply voltage at one end only.

Diode circuits

A silicon diode will not conduct in the forward direction unless its p.d. exceeds 0.6 V approximately. Fig 12.6 shows the I–V characteristic of a typical silicon diode. In most situations in a d.c. circuit, the resistance in the reverse direction may be assumed to be infinite (i.e. negligible current passes through). In the forward direction, the diode resistance may be assumed to be negligible if the applied p.d. exceeds 0.6 V. If not, the diode barely conducts and its resistance may be assumed to be infinite in low resistance circuits.

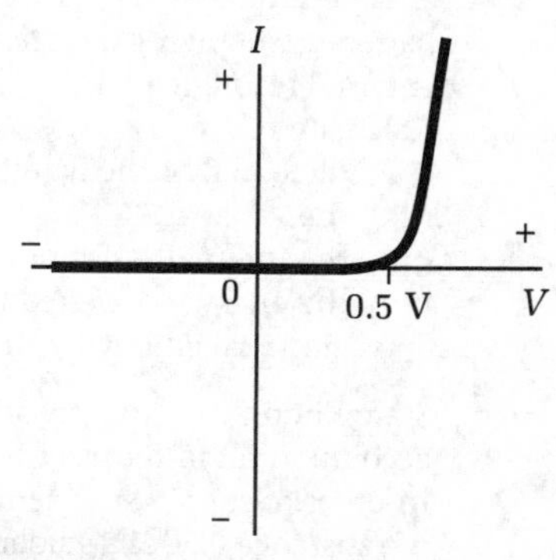

Fig 12.6 *IV* curve for a diode

Worked example

The circuit in Fig 12.7 includes a silicon diode D with I–V characteristics as in Fig 12.6 in series with a 2.0 Ω resistor P. The diode and resistor P are in parallel with a second 2.0 Ω resistor Q. A cell of e.m.f. 1.5 V and internal resistance 0.5 Ω is connected across the combination. Determine the current through each resistor and the cell current. 5 marks

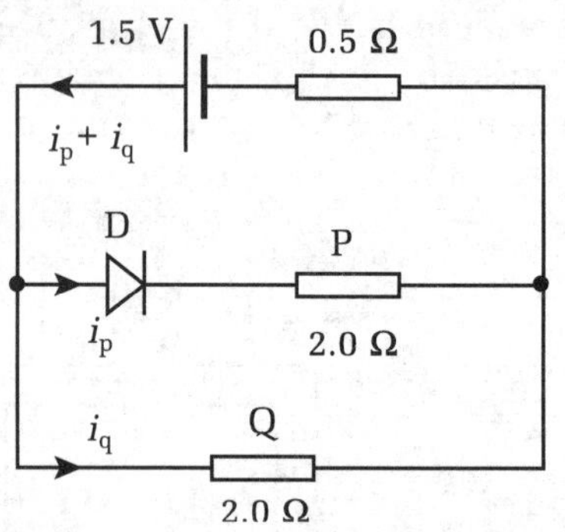

Fig 12.7

Solution

The diode conducts because the cell e.m.f. is greater than its 'forward voltage' of 0.6 V. Let the current through P be i_p and the current through Q be i_q. The current through the cell is therefore $i_p + i_q$. ✓

- Applying Kirchhoff's second law to the outer loop gives $1.5 = 2.0i_q + 0.5\,(i_p + i_q)$

  i.e. $1.5 = 0.5i_p + 2.5i_q$ (Equation 1) ✓

- Applying Kirchhoff's second law to the top loop gives $1.5 = V_D + 2.0i_p + 0.5\,(i_p + i_q)$ where the forward voltage across the diode, $V_D = 0.6$ V. Hence $1.5 = 0.6 + 2.5i_p + 0.5i_q$

  i.e. $0.9 = 2.5i_p + 0.5i_q$ (Equation 2) ✓

  Prove for yourself that the solution to this pair of simultaneous equations is $i_p = 0.25$ A and $i_q = 0.55$ A. ✓✓

  Hence the cell current is 0.80 A.

Questions

1. (a) Define the *electromotive force* of, and explain the meaning of the *internal resistance* of a d.c. supply.
A high resistance voltmeter reads 1.5 V when attached to the terminals of a dry battery. When the battery is supplying a current of 0.30 A through an external resistance R the voltmeter reads 1.2 V.
Calculate
(i) the e.m.f. of the battery,
(ii) the value of R,
(iii) the internal resistance of the battery,
(iv) the energy converted from chemical to electrical energy by the battery in 2.0 seconds.

(b) State Kirchhoff's first law and explain how it is accounted for in terms of a conservation law.
In order to supply sufficient current to light a lamp of resistance 0.50 Ω a student uses two dry batteries, each with e.m.f. 1.5 V and internal resistance 1.0 Ω.
They are connected in parallel as shown in Fig 12.8.
Calculate the power dissipated by the lamp.

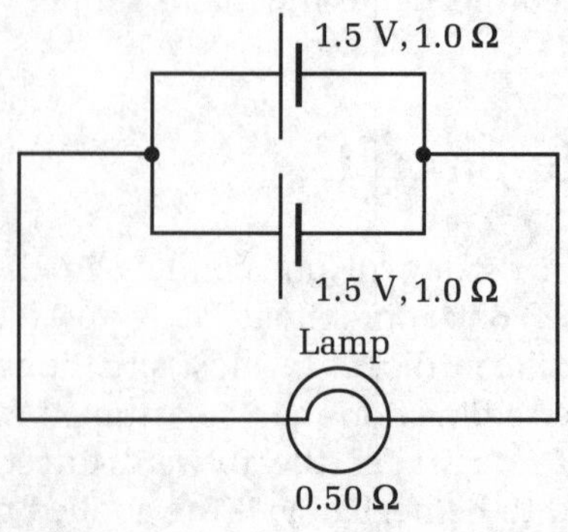

Fig 12.8

(O & C June '94)

2.

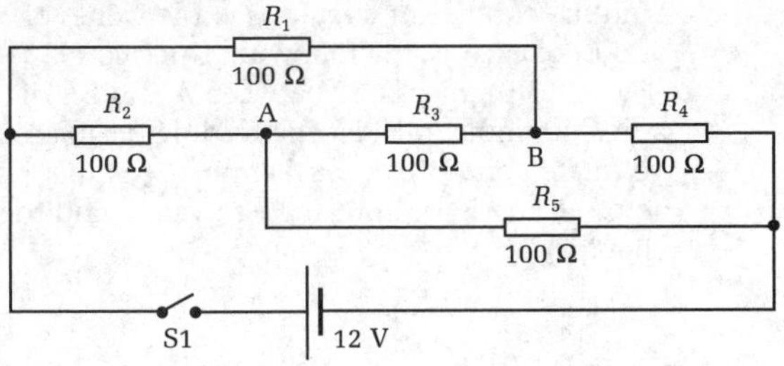

Fig 12.9

Five resistors having the same resistance, 100 Ω, are connected as shown in the circuit above. A battery of e.m.f. 12 V and negligible internal resistance is connected across the circuit via a switch S1.

(a) Switch S1 is closed.
  (i) By considering the arrangement of resistors, determine the potential difference between the points A and B.
  (ii) Determine the current flowing through each of the resistors and the current through the battery.

(b) Switch S1 is opened and R_4 is replaced by an uncharged capacitor of capacitance 100 μF. Determine the maximum charge on the capacitor several minutes after switch S1 is again closed.

(NEAB June '93, Special Paper)

3. (a) A laboratory ammeter of resistance 100 Ω with a linear scale and a true linear response has been incorrectly calibrated so that it reads 69.0 mA when a true current of 60.0 mA is passing through it. Devise a circuit using only resistors to make the ammeter read correctly whilst still presenting a resistance of 100 Ω to an external circuit. Give a circuit diagram of your design together with full details of the components.

(b) The ammeter with its correcting circuit is connected in series with a cell (e.m.f. 6 V, internal resistance 3 Ω) and a lamp (operating current 60 mA at a p.d. of 6 V) in an attempt to check the operating current of the lamp.

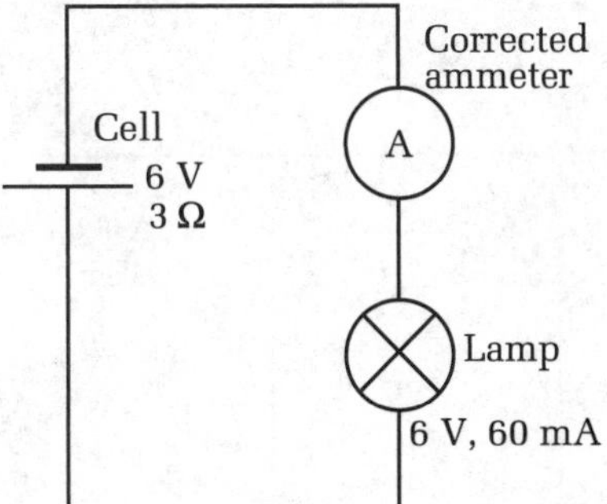

Fig 12.10

Explain with physical reasoning whether this circuit will successfully measure the current through the fully-lit lamp.

(NEAB June '94, Special Paper)

4. (a) Distinguish between the emf of a cell and the potential difference across a resistor.

(b) State Kirchhoff's laws.

(c)

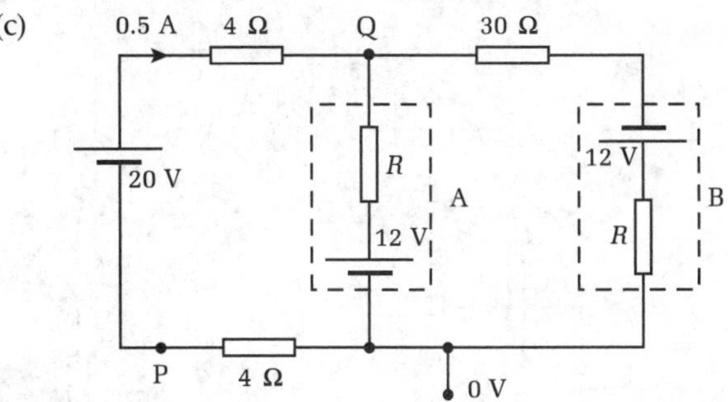

Fig 12.11

Two identical rechargeable cells A and B, of emf 12 V and internal resistance R are connected to a 20 V d.c. power supply as shown in the diagram above.
  (i) Prove that $R = 40\,\Omega$ and calculate the currents through each of the cells A and B.
  (ii) Determine the potentials at points P and Q.
  (iii) Describe and quantify the energy transfer processes operating in each of the cells A and B.

(WJEC June '94, Special Paper)

5. (a) Derive the standard formula for the equivalent resistance of two resistors connected in parallel.

(b)

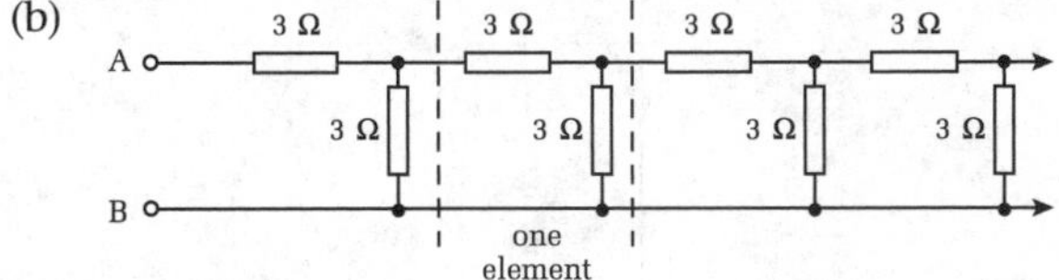

Fig 12.12

A transmission line can be represented by a chain of resistors. Such a chain has elements which consist of two 3 ohm resistors. These elements are connected to form the chain as shown in the diagram. Calculate the resistance between the points A and B of such a chain which consists of
  (i) 2 elements only (i.e. 4 resistors),
  (ii) 3 elements only (i.e. 6 resistors).

(c) By calculating the resistance of an infinitely long chain, show that adding more elements to a chain which is already 3 elements long produces negligible change in resistance.

(NEAB June '88, Special Paper)

6. (a) Explain why an ideal ammeter has zero resistance, and an ideal voltmeter infinite resistance. To what extent, and by what methods, are these ideals achieved in practice?

(b) You may assume the result (called Thévenin's theorem) that any combination of batteries and resistors can be replaced, in its effect on any circuit, by a simple *equivalent circuit* which consists of a single battery with a series resistance as shown in Fig 12.13(a).

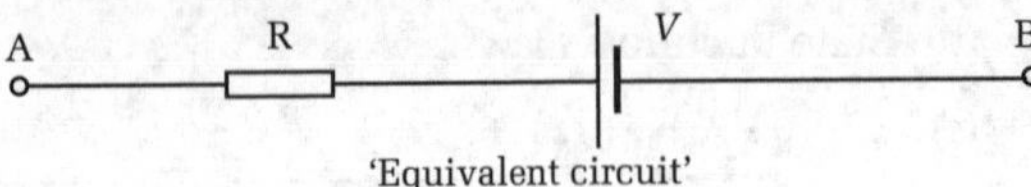

Fig 12.13(a)

Find the equivalent circuits (i.e. the values of V and R) of each of the following three combinations (Fig 12.13(b), measured between A and B. [Hint: As a first attempt, consider the reading on (i) an ideal voltmeter, and (ii) an ideal ammeter connected across A and B for both the equivalent and the real circuits.]

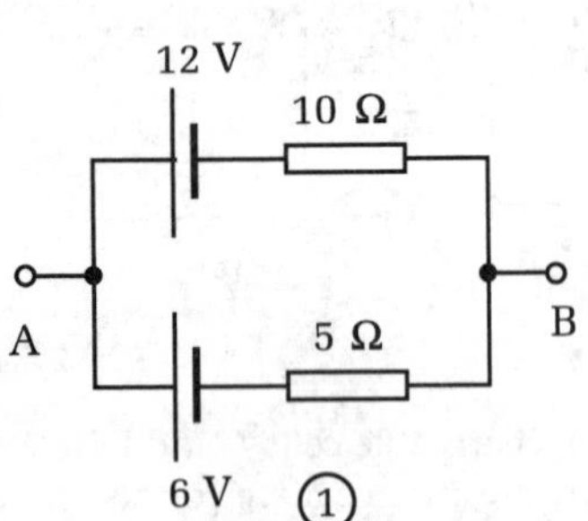

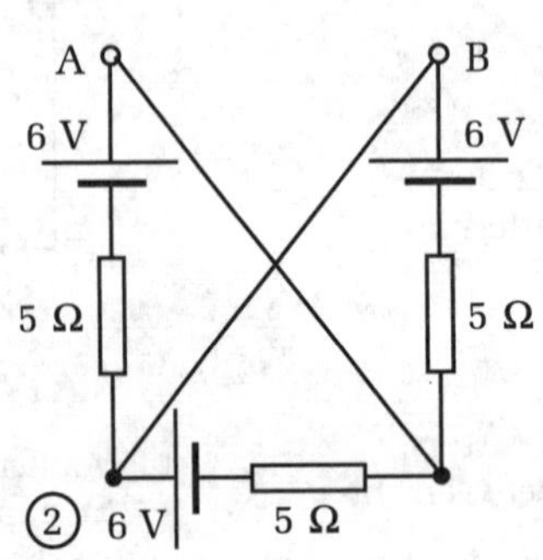

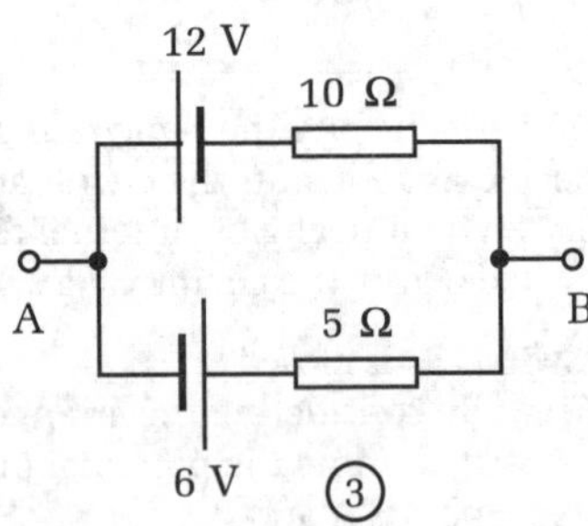

Fig 12.13(b)

(O & C June '93, Special Paper)

13 ELECTROMAGNETISM

What you need to know now

- ❑ The definition and unit of magnetic field strength (i.e. magnetic flux density) and magnetic flux.
- ❑ The meaning and use of the force equations $F = BIl \sin\theta$ and $F = Bqv \sin\theta$.
- ❑ Induced e.m.f. = rate of change of magnetic flux.
- ❑ The definition and unit of self inductance and of mutual inductance.

What you need to know next

Magnetic field formulae

The magnetic field inside a long solenoid carrying a steady current is uniform along most of its length. Measurements show that the magnetic field strength B is proportional to the number of turns per metre, n, of the coil and the current I. Hence $B = \mu_0 nI$ where the constant of proportionality, μ_0, is the permeability of free space.

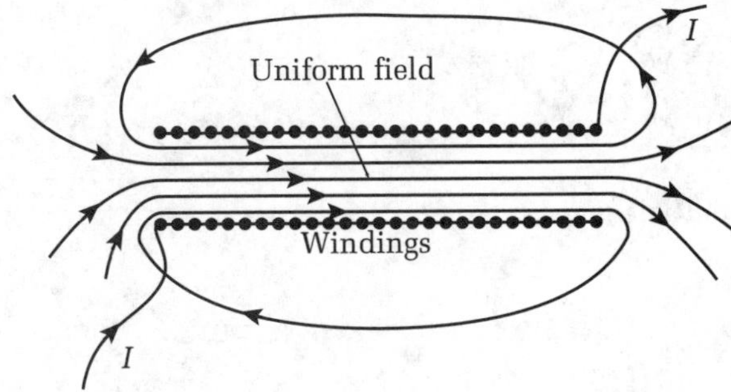

Fig 13.1 In a solenoid

This formula was originally derived from the experimental discovery that the force between two 'circuit elements' at separation r is proportional to $1/r^2$. Further investigations showed that for two parallel circuit elements of length δl_1 and δl_2 carrying currents I_1 and I_2 respectively,

the force due to electromagnetic interaction

$$\delta F = k\frac{I_1\,\delta l_1 \times I_2\,\delta l_2}{r^2}\sin\alpha$$

where r is the separation, α is the angle between either element and the line between them and k is a constant. As shown below, setting $k = \frac{\mu_0}{4\pi}$, gives the formula $B = \mu_0 nI$ for a long solenoid. Hence the magnetic field strength due to element X at the position of the other,

$$\delta B = \frac{\delta F}{I_y\,\delta l_y} = \frac{\mu_0}{4\pi}\frac{I_x\,\delta l_x}{r^2}\sin\alpha$$

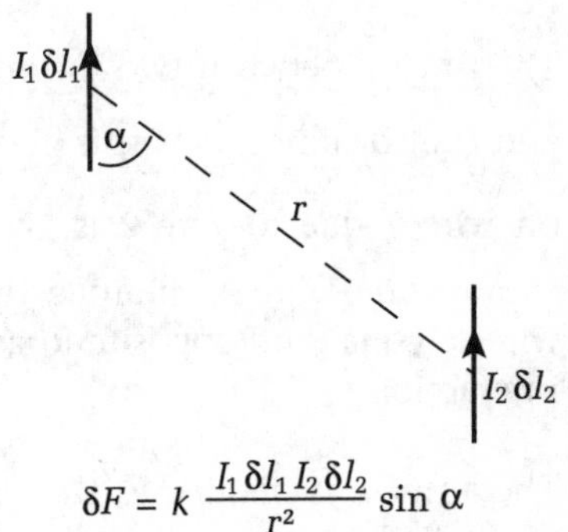

Fig 13.2 Biot Savat's law

1. At distance d from the centre of an infinitely long straight wire carrying current I, the contribution to the total magnetic field strength B from an element of length δs, $\delta B = \frac{\mu_0}{4\pi}\frac{I}{r^2}\sin\alpha\,\delta s$.

$$\text{Hence}\quad B = \int_{s=-\infty}^{s=\infty}\frac{\mu_0}{4\pi}\frac{I}{r^2}\sin\alpha\,\mathrm{d}s = \frac{\mu_0}{2\pi}I\int_{s=0}^{s=\infty}\frac{\sin\alpha}{r^2}\,\mathrm{d}s$$

$$= \frac{\mu_0}{2\pi}\int_{s=0}^{s=\infty}\frac{d}{(d^2+s^2)^{3/2}}\,\mathrm{d}s.$$

The integral can be solved by substituting $s = d\tan\theta$ and integrating from $\theta = 0$ to $\pi/2$ to give $\frac{1}{d}$ as the result. Hence $B = \frac{\mu_0 I}{2\pi d}$.

Magnetic field formulae can be derived for certain other circuit configurations using the integration technique described above.

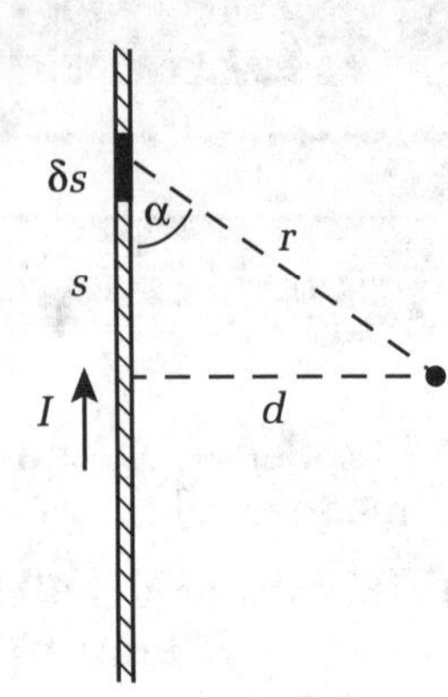

Fig 13.3 Magnetic field strength B near a long straight wire

2. The above formula may be written as $Bl = \mu_0 I$ where $l = 2\pi d$. In other words, for a loop of length l along which B is constant, the product Bl is equal to $\mu_0 \times$ the total current through the loop. This rule, known as Ampere's rule, may be applied to a toroidal solenoid since the field along its axis is constant. The loop is along its axis and the total current through this loop is NI, where N is the number of turns of the solenoid. Hence $B = \mu_0 nI$, where $n = \frac{N}{l}$.

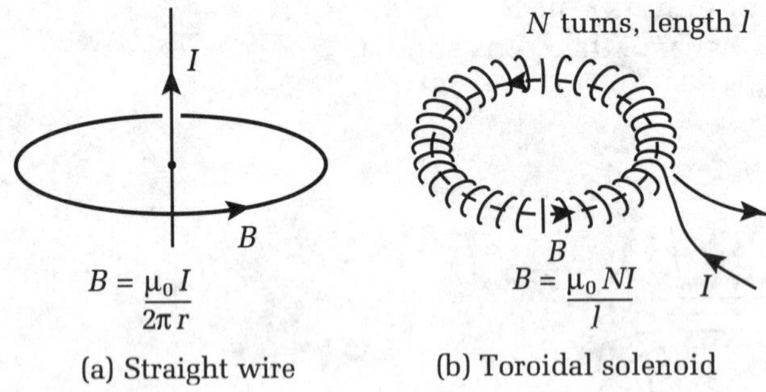

Fig 13.4 Using Ampere's rule

The definition of the ampere

The force F between two infinitely long straight wires carrying currents I_1 and I_2 at distance d apart is given by $F = \frac{\mu_0}{2\pi}\frac{I_1 I_2}{d}$. This is because the force on wire 1 due to wire 2 is given by $F = BI_1 l_1$ and $B_1 = \frac{\mu_0}{2\pi}\frac{I_2}{d}$. The same expression for F is obtained by considering the force on wire 2 due to wire 1. Equal and opposite forces act on the two wires due to their mutual interaction.

The ampere is defined as that current in two infinitely long parallel wires of negligible cross section in a vacuum, placed exactly 1 m apart, which causes a force on each wire of exactly 2×10^{-7} N per metre length of wire. This definition therefore requires the value of μ_0 to be exactly $4\pi\times10^{-7}\,\mathrm{N\,m\,A^{-2}}$ so that $I_1 = I_2 = 1$ A and $d = 1$ m gives a force of $2\times10^{-7}\,\mathrm{N\,m^{-1}}$ on each wire as required.

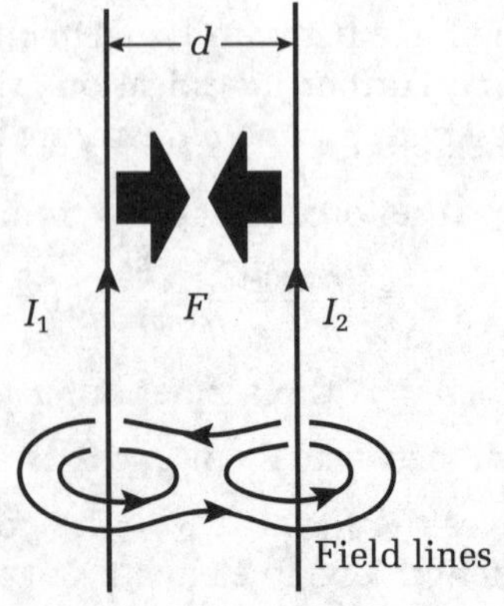

Fig 13.5 Definition of the ampere

The cause of induced e.m.f.s

A point charge q moving at speed v perpendicular to the lines of a magnetic field of strength B experiences a force Bqv at right angles to both its direction and the direction of the field. In a conductor cutting across the lines of a magnetic field, conduction electrons are being made to move across the field lines. The magnetic field forces the conduction electrons to move along the conductor, as shown in Fig 13.6, thus creating an induced e.m.f. $\mathcal{E}$.

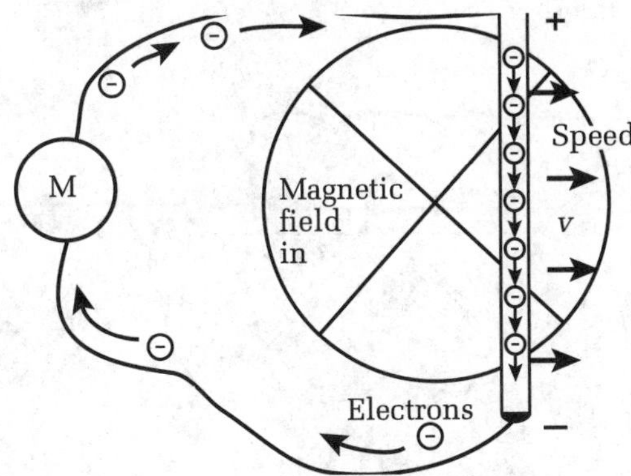

Fig 13.6 Induced current

If the conductor is part of a complete circuit, a current I therefore passes round the circuit. Hence a reaction force BIl acts on the conductor, equal and opposite to the applied force. The work done per second by the applied force is therefore Fv or $BIlv$. Since this is the origin of the electrical power $I\mathcal{E}$ generated, it therefore follows that the induced e.m.f. $\mathcal{E} = Blv$. Because lv is the area A swept out per second by the conductor, Faraday's law of electromagnetic induction follows,

the induced e.m.f. $\mathcal{E}$ = the rate of change of magnetic flux ϕ through the circuit

where the magnetic flux ϕ is defined as BA.

More generally, Faraday's law is written $\mathcal{E} = -\dfrac{d\Phi}{dt}$ where Φ is the total magnetic flux through a circuit. The $-$ sign is necessary because the induced current is always in a direction opposing its cause. The equation $\mathcal{E} = Blv$ only applies where a conductor is moving across the lines of a magnetic field whereas Faraday's law applies to any situations where magnetic flux changes occur. For example, in a transformer, there is no movement of the windings and the induced secondary e.m.f. is due to the changing primary current.

Case study 1 The a.c. generator

Consider the coil rotating at constant frequency f. When the coil is at angle θ to the normal to the magnetic field lines, the total magnetic flux Φ passing through the coil is $BAN\cos\theta$. Using Faraday's law therefore gives the induced e.m.f.,

$$\mathcal{E} = -\frac{d\Phi}{dt} = -\frac{d}{dt}(BAN\cos\theta) = BAN\frac{d\theta}{dt}\sin\theta$$

Since $\theta = \omega t$ where $\omega = 2\pi f$, then $\mathcal{E} = BAN\omega\sin\omega t$.

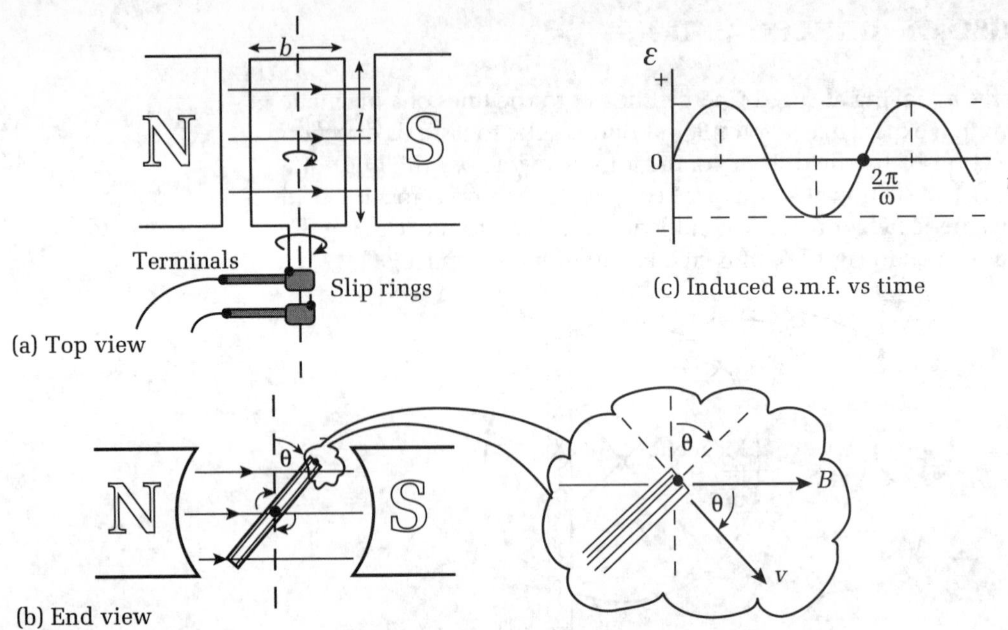

Fig 13.7 The a.c. generator

The same equation may be derived by considering the motion of the two sides of the coil through the magnetic field. At the instant shown in Fig 13.7, each side is moving at angle θ to the field. Hence the induced e.m.f. in each side is $NBlv \sin\theta$. Each side moves in a circle of radius $b/2$ at speed v where $v = \omega b/2$. Hence the induced e.m.f. due to both sides

$$\mathcal{E} = 2NBlv \sin\theta = \frac{2NBl\omega b}{2} \sin\theta = BAN\omega \sin\omega t$$

The torque on the coil due to the field $= Fb\sin\theta = BI\,lN\,b\sin\theta$ since the magnetic field exerts a force $F = BI\,lN$ on each side of the coil and the lines of action of these two forces are a distance $b\sin\theta$ apart.

To maintain steady rotation, the applied torque must be equal and opposite to the torque due to the field. The work done per second or power P to maintain the motion is given by

$$P = \text{torque} \times \text{angular speed } \omega = BI\,lN\,b\sin\theta\,\omega = \mathcal{E}I$$

since $v = \omega b/2$ and $\mathcal{E} = 2NBlv\sin\theta$.

Thus the work done per second by the applied force is equal to the electrical power generated.

Case study 2 The transformer

Consider a transformer with N_p turns on the primary coil and N_s turns on the secondary coil. Let ϕ represent the flux per turn in the core. Hence the total flux in the primary coil is $N_p\phi$ and $N_s\phi$ in the secondary coil. Using Faraday's law therefore gives

$$\text{e.m.f. induced in the secondary,} \quad \mathcal{E}_s = \frac{d}{dt}(N_s\phi) = N_s\frac{d\phi}{dt}$$

$$\text{and} \quad \text{e.m.f. applied to the primary,} \quad \mathcal{E}_p = \frac{d}{dt}(N_p\phi) = N_p\frac{d\phi}{dt}.$$

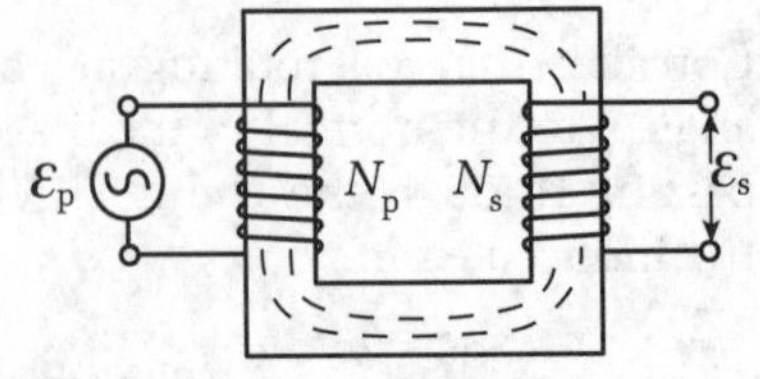

Fig 13.8 A model transformer

Hence $\dfrac{\mathcal{E}_s}{\mathcal{E}_p} = \dfrac{N_s}{N_p}$.

The two case studies illustrate the application of Faraday's law, where the flux change is in one case due to motion of the conductor and in the other case due to changing current. Some further applications are shown in Fig 13.9.

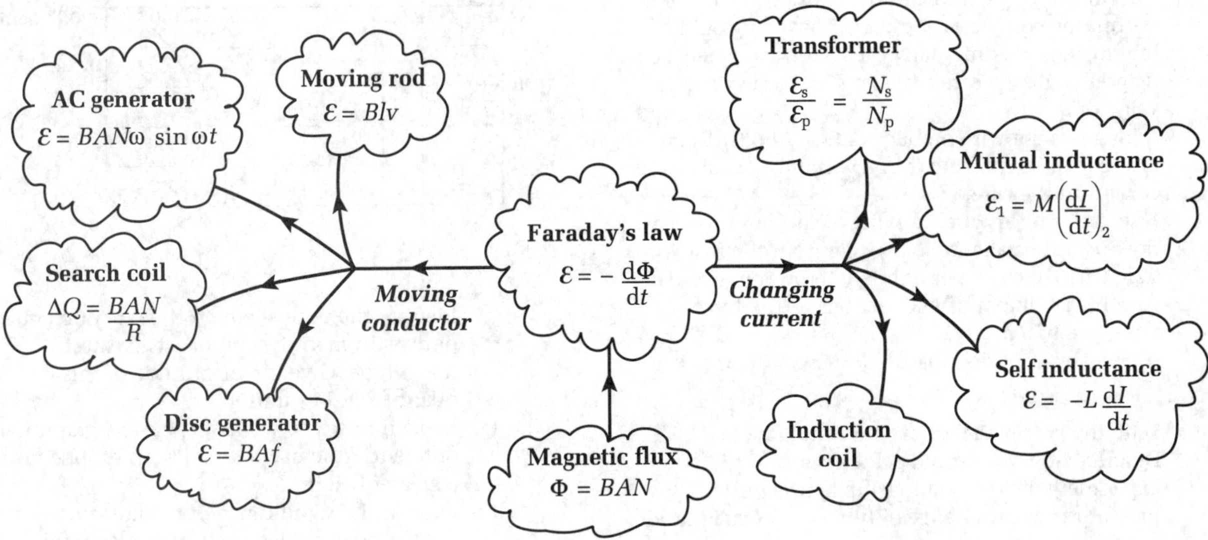

Fig 13.9 Using Faraday's law

Questions

1. (a) Provide a suitable sketch to indicate the direction of a magnetic field due to a current I flowing in a long straight wire.

(b) Describe how you would *use* a magnetic fluxmeter (search coil) to *verify* that the magnetic field intensity B at a point P in the vicinity of a long straight thin wire carrying a current I is proportional to I and inversely proportional to the distance r of P from the wire.

(c) The magnetic field B due to a long thin straight wire is given by the expression

$$B = \frac{\mu_0 I}{2\pi r}$$

What is μ_0 called?

(d) Write down the equation for the force experienced by a straight wire of length l carrying a current I if the wire is
(i) normal to a magnetic field B,
(ii) parallel to a magnetic field B.

(e) A small single turn rectangular coil of height 5 mm and width 2 mm carrying a current of 1 A is placed at a distance of 200 mm from a long vertical straight wire carrying a current of 10 A, as shown in Fig 13.10.

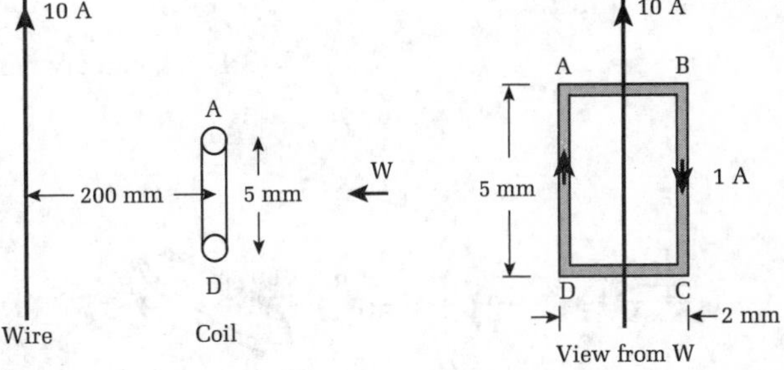

Fig 13.10

(i) *Estimate* the magnitude and determine the direction of the forces on **each** section of the coil.

(ii) Calculate the net effect of the long wire on the coil.

$[\mu_0 = 4\pi \times 10^{-7}\,\mathrm{H\,m^{-1}}]$

(WJEC June '92)

2. *Answer part (a) and* ***either*** *part (b)* ***or*** *part (c).*

(a) The word 'field' is used in physics in connection with electrostatics and gravitation. For each of these explain what is meant by *field* and *field strength*.

An electrostatic field may be produced by a small charge and a gravitational field by a small mass. Explain clearly

(i) *two* ways in which these fields behave similarly, and

(ii) *two* ways in which these fields behave differently.

EITHER

(b) The magnetic flux density, B, near a long straight current-carrying conductor depends on the distance, r, from the conductor. Describe how you would investigate experimentally the relationship between B and r. State the other factors which affect the value of B.
A long straight wire produces a field of $6.0\,\mu T$ at a distance of 30 cm from it in a vacuum. Calculate the current in the wire.
A second similar wire, carrying a current of 8.0 A, is now placed parallel to and 10 cm from the first wire. Calculate the force per unit length on the wire. The currents are in opposite directions. Is the force attractive or repulsive?
(Permeability of free space, $\mu_0 = 4\pi \times 10^{-7}\,H\,m^{-1}$.)

OR

(c) State the laws of electromagnetic induction. Describe how you would demonstrate experimentally the relationship between the magnitude of the change of flux and the magnitude of the induced e.m.f.
A long magnet is removed from the centre of a coil of 20 turns. The speed of the magnet is controlled to maintain an induced e.m.f. of $60\,\mu V$ across the coil. Removing the magnet in this way takes two minutes. Calculate the change of flux through the coil.
Explain, with the aid of a diagram, how you would determine the polarity of the magnet from this experiment.

(ULEAC January '93)

3. (a)

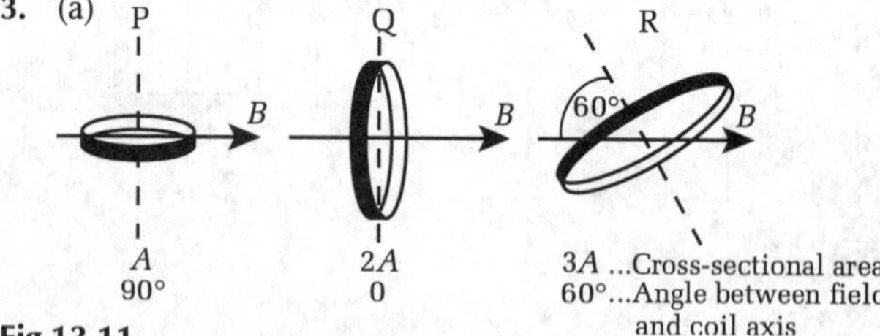

Fig 13.11

P, Q and R in Fig 13.11 are circular coils each with the same number of turns placed in a magnetic field of flux density B. The area of each coil is as shown. In which case is the flux passing through the coil (i) least, (ii) greatest?
Explain your answers.

(b) A coil is connected to a datalogger, which is a device which records voltages at regular time intervals. The coil is positioned with its axis vertical and a bar magnet is held above the coil with its axis lined up with that of the coil. It is dropped so that it falls through the coil and the datalogger, triggered by the approaching magnet, records the induced e.m.f. The results are shown in the graph below.

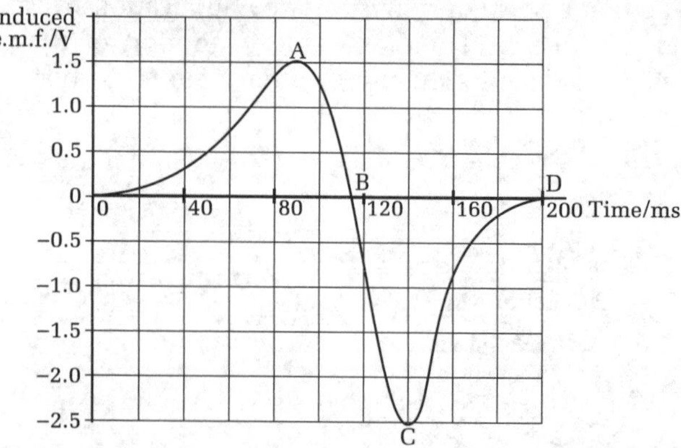

Fig 13.12

(i) Identify the time at which the rate of change of flux through the coil has its greatest magnitude. Give the magnitude of this quantity and its unit.

(ii) Explain how you would expect the graph to be different if the magnet had been dropped from a greater height.

(iii) Explain the significance of the area under the curve. Discuss whether or not you would expect the positive and negative areas to be equal.

(c) The coil in (b) has a resistance of $20\,\Omega$. If it had been short-circuited when the magnet was dropped instead of being connected to the datalogger, calculate

(i) the current which would have flowed corresponding to point A on the graph,

(ii) the power being dissipated at A due to this current and hence make an estimate of the energy dissipated in the solenoid in the time represented by OB.

(NEAB June '92)

4.

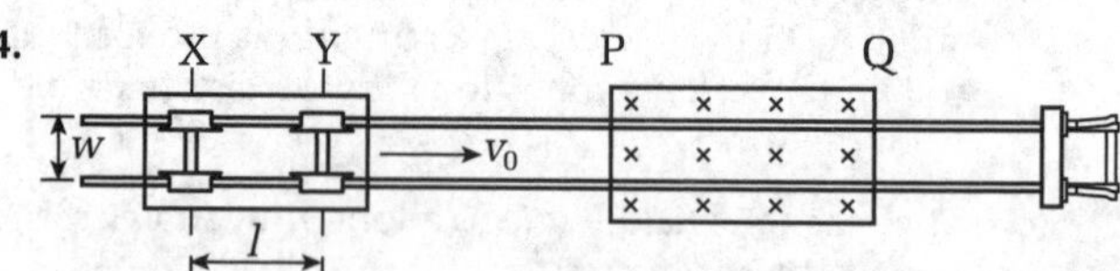

Fig 13.13

A physicist designs an electromagnetic braking system for a truck on a siding in his model railway as illustrated. The truck has mass $M = 0.15$ kg and axle spacing $l = 0.10$ m. It is projected at velocity v_0 into the siding, which is on a level track with rail spacing $w = 0.050$ m. Mechanical friction is negligible.
The truck runs into a limited region of vertical magnetic field $B = 0.7$ T over the length $L = 0.15$ m between points P and Q. The field is negligible outside this region. The truck has metal wheels and axles. Around a loop consisting of the two axles, X and Y, and two lengths l of track, the circuit resistance R is equal to $0.020\,\Omega$.

For an initial velocity $v_0 = 30\,\mathrm{mm\,s^{-1}}$, the braking system works well, with the truck XY coming to rest straddling the magnetic field entry point P.

(a) Explain how the braking occurs. Show that the truck velocity v varies in time as $v = v_0\,e^{-\lambda t}$ and that the constant $\lambda = 0.41\,\mathrm{s^{-1}}$.

(b) Show that the truck comes to rest when $PX = 73\,\mathrm{mm}$.

The initial velocity is now increased to $50\,\mathrm{mm\,s^{-1}}$.

(c) Describe the motion, giving a qualitative sketch of v against time. Where does the rest position (if any) now occur?

(d) Repeat part (c) with $v_0 = 100\,\mathrm{mm\,s^{-1}}$.

(e) Briefly discuss some disadvantages of this braking system.

(O & C June '91, Special Paper)

5. A transformer consists of a long solenoid with n primary turns per unit length and m secondary turns per unit length; both the primary and secondary coils may be considered to have negligible resistance.

(a) Show that $M^2 = L_p \times L_s$ where L_p and L_s are the self inductances of the primary and secondary, and M is the mutual inductance of the coils.

(b) The primary is connected to an alternating voltage of amplitude V. By considering the equations which describe how the voltages in the secondary and primary circuits depend on the rates of change of current, show that the secondary circuit behaves as though it were connected in series with a source of alternating voltage of amplitude

$$\left(\frac{mV}{n}\right)$$

State any assumptions you make.

(c) A load resistor of resistance R is connected across the secondary coil. Calculate the effective resistance of the primary circuit, stating any assumptions you make.

(d) You are asked to design a power supply for an electrical heater which can deliver 25 W of power. It is to be supplied with current from the mains (240 V r.m.s., 50 Hz) via a step-down transformer. The resistance and inductance of the heater are 0.5 Ω and 2 mH respectively.
Calculate the turns ratio of the transformer.

(NEAB June '91, Special Paper)

6. This question is about the production of large magnetic fields over large volumes.
Suppose that it is required to produce a magnetic field of strength 10 T over a cylindrical region 2 m long by 0.2 m in diameter, using a conventional solenoid (see Fig 13.14).

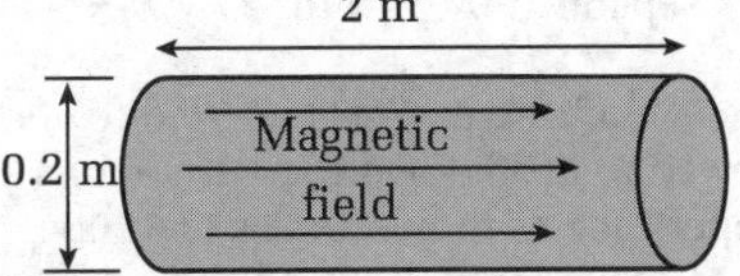

Fig 13.14

A solenoid is designed in which the windings occupy a hollow cylinder having an inner radius of 0.1 m and an outer radius of 0.2 m. Copper wire having a *rectangular* cross-sectional area of $10\,\mathrm{mm^2}$ is used.

(a) Show, by considering the geometry of the situation, that the number of turns per metre length of the solenoid is 10^4.

(b) Now show that the required current in each turn is close to 800 A.

(c) Again use the geometry of the situation to show that the total length of wire is about 19 km.

(d) Now find the total resistance of the windings and show that the power dissipated is about 20 MW.

(e) Collect the calculations (a) to (d) together in algebraic form to demonstrate that the power dissipated is independent of the area of cross-section of the wire.

(f) Comment upon the practicality of producing the desired magnetic field in this fashion.

(g) A modern technique is to use a superconducting magnet. This is essentially a solenoid wound with wire whose material can be made superconducting, i.e. having zero resistivity, by holding it at a suitably low temperature. No power is dissipated while the magnet is in operation but energy has to be supplied in order to establish the magnetic field in the first place.
Approximately how much energy is stored in a solenoid of the same dimensions as above but with a magnetic field of 100 T assuming that the field occupies a volume having an effective radius of 0.15 m? (A magnetic field of strength B stores energy with a density of $B^2/2\mu_0\,\mathrm{J\,m^{-3}}$.)

(h) With such high fields the mechanical stability of the solenoid has to be considered since any windings except the outer layer lie in a magnetic field.
What would be the total radial force exerted by the field on one of the inner turns, which has a radius of 0.1 m, for
(i) the 'conventional' solenoid with $B = 10\,\mathrm{T}$ and
(ii) the superconducting solenoid with $B = 100\,\mathrm{T}$?

(i) By considering the work done when such a loop of wire has its radius increased by a small quantity δr, show that the longitudinal force in the wire is equal to the radial force divided by 2π. Hence find the stress in the wire and comment upon your result, using the data below, from the point of view of the mechanical construction of the solenoid.
Data: Resistivity of copper $= 1.7 \times 10^{-8}\,\Omega\,\mathrm{m}$; tensile strength of copper = 150 MPa; tensile strength of superconducting material is a few 100 MPa.

(O & C Nuffield June '93, Special Paper)

7. (a) Describe and briefly explain one practical example of electromagnetic induction, other than the transformer.

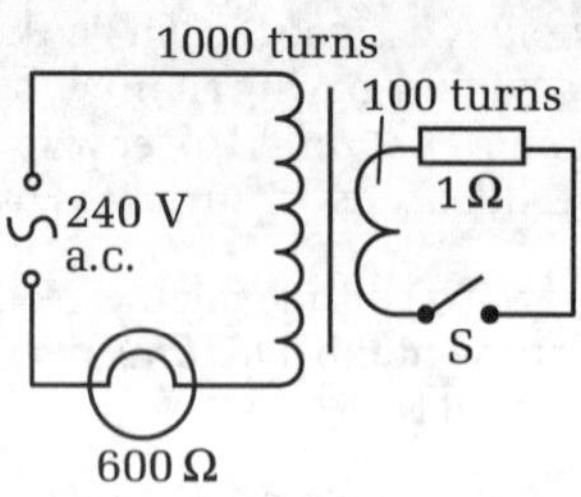

Fig 13.15

(b) Fig 13.15 shows the primary winding of a transformer connected to a 240 V r.m.s. a.c. supply through a light-bulb which may be assumed to have a constant resistance of 600 Ω. The secondary winding is connected to a 1 Ω resistor by a switch S, which is initially closed. The primary winding has 1000 turns and the secondary has 100 turns. The transformer may be assumed to be ideal, and the effects of the self-inductances of the windings can be ignored.

(i) Write down the relationship between
  (1) V_p (the voltage across the primary winding) and V_s (the voltage across the secondary winding),
  (2) I_p (the current in the primary winding) and I_s (the current in the secondary winding),
  (3) I_s and V_s when the switch S is closed.

(ii) Use these relationships to deduce the relationship between I_p and V_p, and hence calculate the power dissipated in the bulb when the switch S is closed.

(iii) What happens to the brightness of the bulb when the switch S is opened?

(c) Fig 13.16 shows a square loop of wire of side s and cross-sectional area A falling at speed v through a region containing a magnetic field of flux density B. The field is normal to the plane of the loop, and the lower arm of the loop is outside the region of the magnetic field.

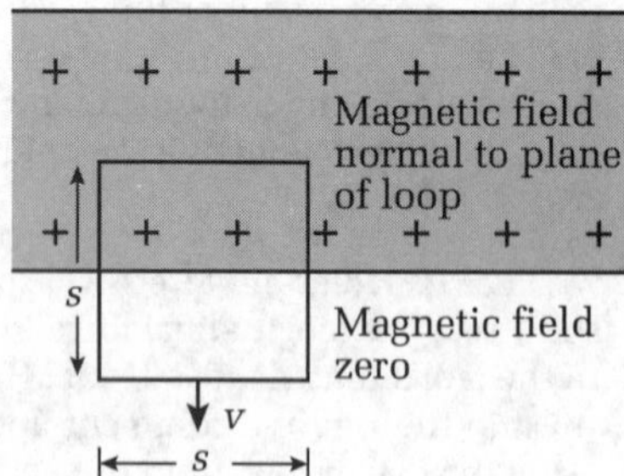

Fig 13.16

(i) Show that the current in the loop is $\dfrac{BvA}{4\rho}$, where ρ is the resistivity of the wire.

(ii) Hence deduce an expression for the force acting on the loop due to electromagnetic induction. State the direction in which the force acts, giving your reason.

(iii) For a certain value of v, this force balances the weight of the loop so that the loop falls with a steady speed. Calculate this steady value of v for a loop made of aluminium (resistivity $2.65 \times 10^{-8}\,\Omega\,m$, density $2.71 \times 10^3\,kg\,m^{-3}$) falling out of a field of flux density 2.00 T.

(UCLES June '94, Special Paper, Q6.)

8. (a) (i) State the principal laws of magnetic induction attributed to Faraday and Lenz.

(ii) Describe a laboratory demonstration of Lenz's law.

(b) Fig 13.17 shows an arrangement involving circular ring magnets with poles on their flat faces. The lower magnet is fixed to the smooth glass tube and the upper magnet is held in suspension by magnetic repulsion.

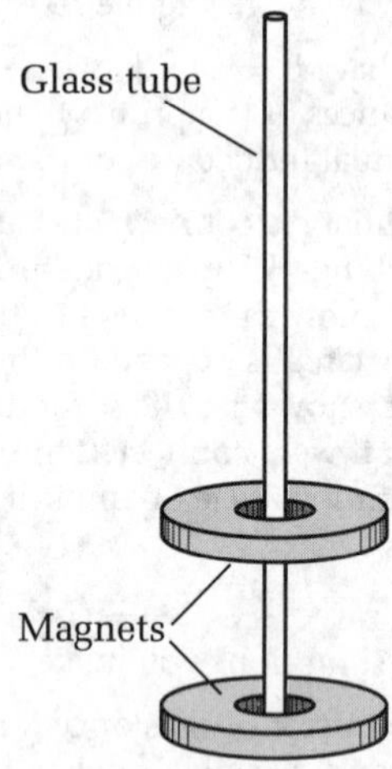

Fig 13.17

When the upper magnet is depressed slightly and released it is found to oscillate vertically. Careful timing shows that 5 oscillations occur in 1.7 s and 10 oscillations in 3.4 s. The upper magnet eventually settles with its lower face 30 mm above the upper face of the lower magnet. The mass of each magnet is 50 g.

(i) The oscillations are suspected to be a simple harmonic motion. What aspect of the data confirms this suspicion?

(ii) What is the magnitude of the force separating the magnets when they are at rest?

(iii) Assuming that the oscillations are s.h.m., find the magnitude of the repulsive force between the magnets when their nearer faces are separated by 35 mm.

(c) One of the ring magnets referred to above is now allowed to drop down the outside of a smooth copper tube as shown in Fig 13.18(a).
The ring magnet falls at a constant speed and takes 20 s to travel 0.80 m.

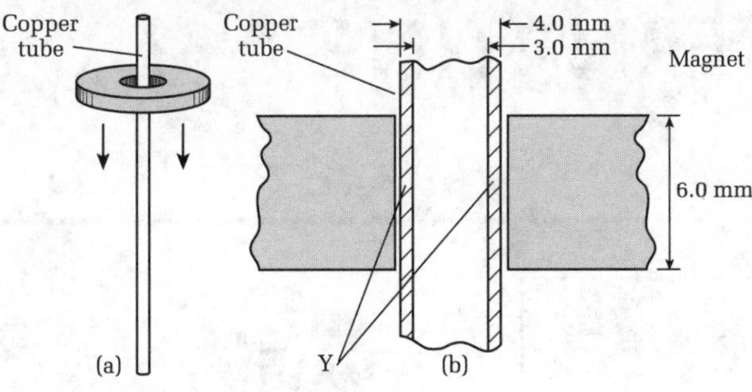

Fig 13.18

(i) At what rate does the ring magnet lose gravitational potential energy during its fall?

(ii) Explain, using electromagnetic principles, why the ring does not fall more swiftly.

(iii) The copper tube (see Figure 13.18(b)) has an external diameter of 4.0 mm and an internal diameter of 3.0 mm. The resistivity of copper is $1.5 \times 10^{-8}\ \Omega\,\text{m}$. The magnet has a vertical thickness of 6.0 mm.
What electrical resistance does the tube offer to an electric current flowing uniformly around the horizontal ring Y of tubing enclosed by the magnet?

(iv) Suppose the falling ring generated such a current only. What would be the magnitude of this current?

(UODLE June '94, Special Paper)

14 MORE ABOUT ALTERNATING CURRENT

What you need to know now

- A sinusoidal current can be represented by the equation $I = I_0 \sin \omega t$.
- The r.m.s. value of a sinusoidal current $I_{rms} = \dfrac{I_0}{\sqrt{2}}$.
- For a capacitor, its reactance $= 1/\omega C$ and the current is $\frac{1}{4}$ cycle ahead of the p.d.
- For an inductor, its reactance $= \omega L$ and the current is $\frac{1}{4}$ cycle behind the p.d.
- For a series LCR circuit, its impedance $= (R^2 + (\omega L - 1/\omega C)^2)^{1/2}$.
- At resonance, $\omega L = 1/\omega C$.

What you need to know next

Phasors

An alternating current which varies sinusoidally with time according to the equation $I = I_0 \sin \omega t$ may be represented either by a graph of current vs time or by a phasor diagram, as in Fig 14.1. The phasor length represents the peak current I_0 and it rotates at frequency f about the origin. Hence its projection onto the y-axis represents the current I at time t, assuming it rotates anticlockwise and passes through the $+x$-axis at time $t = 0$. At time t, the phasor is therefore at angle ωt to the $+x$-axis, where $\omega = 2\pi f$. Hence $I_0 \sin \omega t$ is the projection of the phasor onto the y-axis.

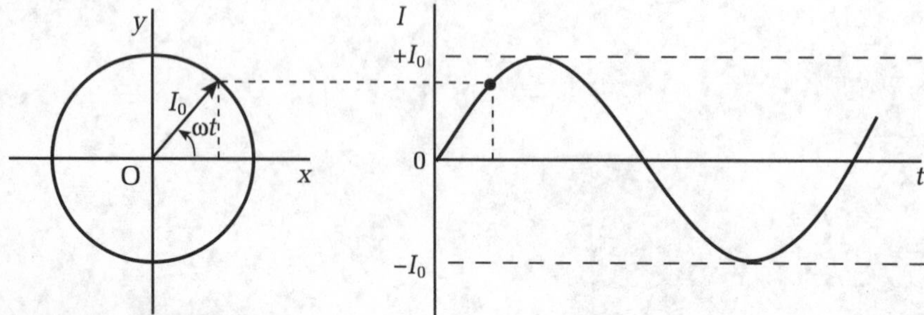

Fig 14.1 Phasor representation

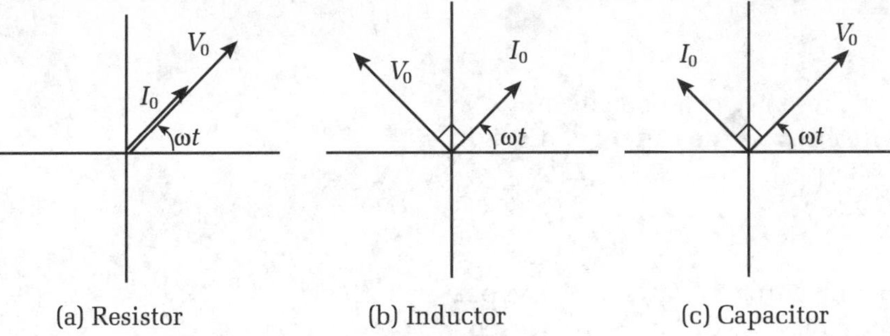

(a) Resistor (b) Inductor (c) Capacitor

Fig 14.2 Phase relationships

1. **For a resistor R in an a.c. circuit**, the potential difference $V_R = IR$ hence the phasors for p.d. and current are in phase.
2. **For an inductor L in an a.c. circuit**, the potential difference $V_L = L\frac{dI}{dt} = L\frac{d}{dt}(I_0 \sin \omega t)$. Since $\frac{d}{dt}(\sin \omega t) = \omega \cos \omega t$, then $V_L = V_0 \cos \omega t$ where $V_0 = \omega L I_0$. Hence the phasor for p.d. V_L is 90° ahead of I_0 and the reactance $X_L = V_0/I_0 = \omega L$.
3. **For a capacitor C in an a.c. circuit**, the capacitor charge at any instant, $Q = CV_C$, where V_C is the capacitor p.d. Hence the current $I = \frac{dQ}{dt} = C\frac{dV_C}{dt} = \omega C V_0 \cos \omega t$ if $V_C = V_0 \sin \omega t$. Thus the phasor for the capacitor current I is 90° ahead of V_0 and the reactance $X_0 = V_0/I_0 = 1/\omega C$.
4. **For a series LCR circuit**, the current phasor I_0 is the same for each component because they are in series. Hence the peak supply p.d. $V_S = (V_R{}^2 + (V_L - V_C)^2)^{1/2}$ where $V_R = I_0 R$, $V_L = \omega L I_0$ and $V_C = I_0/\omega C$. Thus the phase angle ϕ between the current phasor and the supply p.d. phasor is given by the equation $\tan \phi = (V_L - V_C)/V_R = (\omega L - 1/\omega C)/R$. See Fig 14.5.

NOTE: To prove $\frac{d}{dt}(r \sin \omega t) = \omega r \cos \omega t$, consider a phasor of length r at time t and at time $t + \delta t$ later, as shown in Fig 14.3. The y-coordinate of the tip of the phasor is given by $y = r \sin \omega t$. The tip moves a distance $\delta s = \omega r\, \delta t$ along the circle in time δt. Considering the triangle formed by δy and δx, its third side is δs provided δt is small. Since angle θ in this triangle is equal to ωt, then $\delta y = \delta s \cos \omega t$. Hence $\delta y = \omega r\, \delta t \cos \omega t$ thus $\frac{dy}{dt} = \frac{\delta y}{\delta t}_{\delta t \to 0} = \omega r \cos \omega t$.

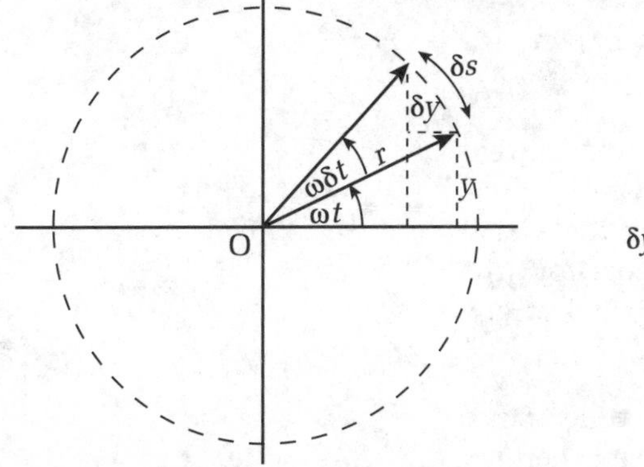

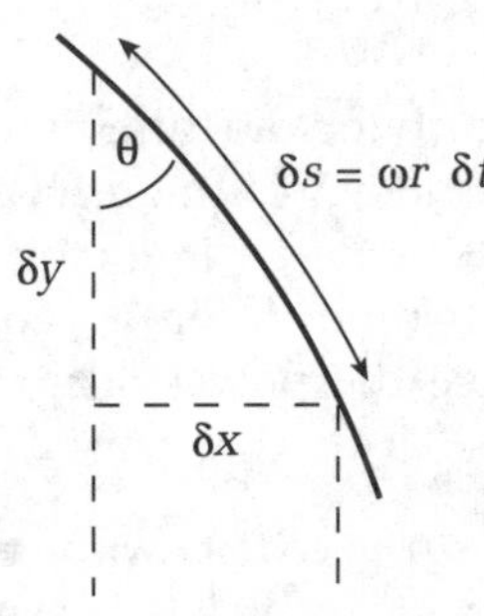

Fig 14.3 Using triangles

Power in a.c. circuits

Power is dissipated in an a.c. circuit in the resistive components only. No power is dissipated in reactive components because the current and p.d. in a reactive component are $\frac{1}{4}$ cycle out of phase.

1. For a resistance R carrying an alternating current $I = I_0 \sin \omega t$, the p.d. $V = I_0 R \sin \omega t$, hence the power dissipated at any instant $P = IV = I^2R = I_0{}^2 R \sin^2 \omega t$.

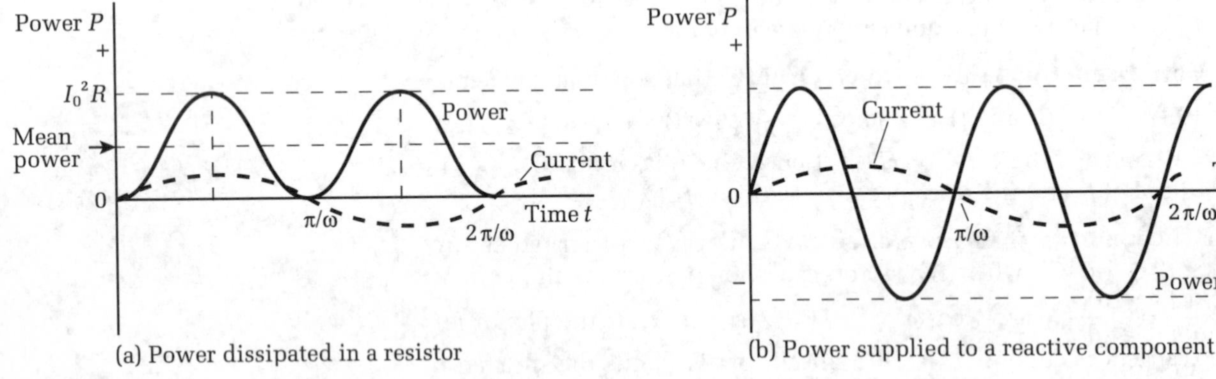

Fig 14.4

Fig 14.4(a) shows the variation of $\sin^2 \omega t$ with time. Since $\sin^2 \omega t = (1 - \cos 2\omega t)/2$ and the mean value of $\cos 2\omega t$ is 0, then the mean value of $\sin^2 \omega t$ is $\frac{1}{2}$. Hence the mean power $P = \dfrac{I_0{}^2R}{2}$.

NOTE: In mathematical terms, the mean power over one complete cycle

$$= I_0{}^2R \int_{t=0}^{t=T} \sin^2 \omega t \, dt/T$$

$$= \frac{I_0{}^2R}{2T} \int_{t=0}^{t=T} (1 - \cos 2\omega t) dt$$

$$= \frac{I_0{}^2R}{2}$$

The r.m.s. current is defined as that value of direct current which gives the same power in a given resistor as the alternating current. Hence $I_{rms}{}^2R = \dfrac{I_0{}^2R}{2}$ which gives $I_{rms} = I_0/\sqrt{2}$.

2. For a capacitor or a pure inductor carrying an alternating current $I = I_0 \sin \omega t$, the p.d. $V = \pm I_0 X \cos \omega t$ where X is the reactance. The + sign applies to the inductor since V leads I for an inductor; the – sign applies to the capacitor since V is behind I for a capacitor (the mnemonic *CIVIL* is useful here!). Hence the power dissipated at any instant, $P = IV = I_0{}^2 X \sin \omega t \cos \omega t$.

   Fig 14.4(b) shows the variation of $\sin \omega t \cos \omega t$ with time. Since $\sin 2\omega t = 2 \sin \omega t \cos \omega t$ and the mean value of $\sin 2\omega t$ is zero, then the mean power over one full cycle is zero.

NOTE: In mathematical terms, the mean power over one complete cycle

$$= I_0{}^2R\int_{t=0}^{t=T} \sin \omega t \cos \omega t \, \mathrm{d}t/T$$

$$= \frac{I_0{}^2R}{2T}\int_{t=0}^{t=T} \sin 2\omega t \, \mathrm{d}t = 0$$

3. In general for a circuit in which the current and p.d. are out of phase by angle ϕ, the power supplied at any instant $P = I_0V_0 \sin \omega t \sin(\omega t + \phi)$. Since $\sin(\omega t + \phi) = \sin \omega t \cos \phi - \cos \omega t \sin \phi$, the mean power supplied over one full cycle

$$= \int_{t=0}^{t=T} I_0V_0 \sin \omega t \sin(\omega t + \phi) \, \mathrm{d}t/T$$

$$= \frac{I_0V_0}{T}\cos\phi \int_{t=0}^{t=T} \sin^2 \omega t \, \mathrm{d}t - \frac{I_0V_0}{T}\sin\phi\int_{t=0}^{t=T} \sin \omega t \cos \omega t \, \mathrm{d}t$$

$$= \tfrac{1}{2}I_0V_0\cos\phi$$

where $\cos\phi$ is referred to as the **power factor** for the circuit.

Phasors and resonance

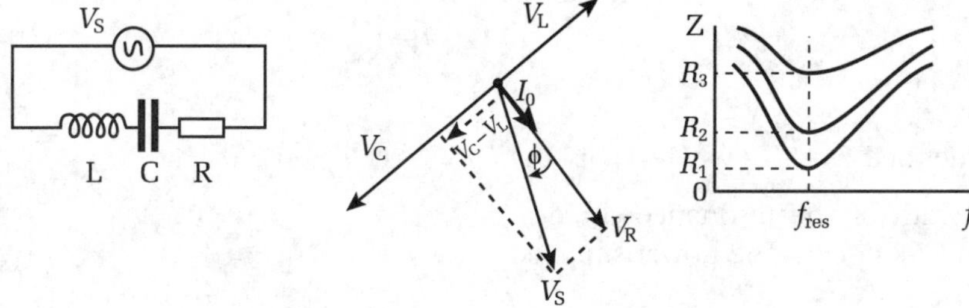

(a) Series LCR circuit (b) Series LCR phasor diagram (c) Impedance vs frequency

Fig 14.5 The series LCR circuit

1. The series LCR circuit

The phasor diagram for a series LCR circuit is shown in Fig 14.5. The current phasor I_0 acts as the reference for the other phasors since the current in each component is the same because the components are in series. The supply p.d. $V_S = (V_R{}^2 + (V_L - V_C)^2)^{1/2}$ since V_L and V_C are respectively $\frac{1}{4}$ cycle ahead and behind V_R which is in phase I_0. Substituting $V_R = I_0R$, $V_C = I_0/\omega C$ and $V_L = I_0\omega L$ into the above equation therefore gives the equation for the circuit impedance Z,

$$Z = \frac{V_S}{I_0} = (R^2 + (\omega L - 1/\omega C)^2)^{1/2}$$

Fig 14.5(c) shows the variation of impedance with frequency for different resistances. The impedance $Z = R$ since $V_L = V_C$ at resonance. Hence $\omega_r L = 1/\omega_r C$ where ω_r is the value of ω at resonance. Hence the resonant frequency $f_{res} = \omega_r/2\pi = \dfrac{1}{2\pi\sqrt{LC}}$.

2. The parallel LC circuit

The phasor diagram for this circuit is shown in Fig 14.6. This assumes negligible resistance in the coil and the capacitor. The supply p.d. V_S is the same across the coil and the capacitor; hence the current through the coil $I_L\,(= V_S/\omega L)$ is 180° out of phase with the capacitor current $I_C\,(= \omega CV_S)$. At resonance, the coil current is exactly equal and opposite to the capacitor current; hence the condition for resonance is the same as for the series circuit, i.e. $\omega_r L = 1/\omega_r C$. Essentially the capacitor repeatedly charges and discharges and recharges with opposite polarity through the coil. In a tuning circuit, the capacitor value is altered until the resonant frequency of the LC circuit is equal to the carrier frequency of the radio or television signal to be detected.

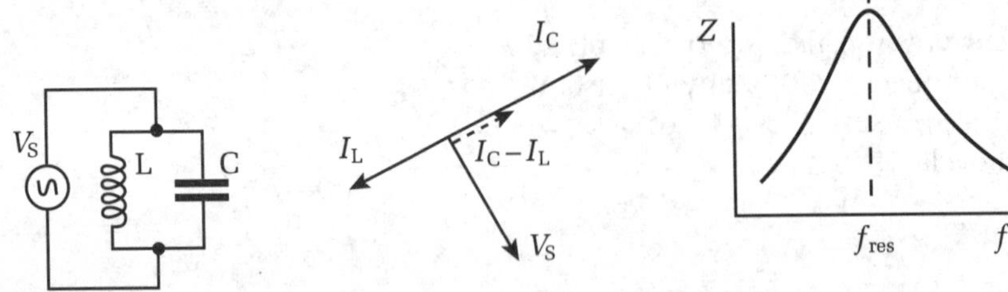

(a) Parallel LCR circuit (b) Phasor diagram (c) Impedance vs frequency
Fig 14.6

The variation of impedance with frequency for a parallel LC circuit is shown in Fig 14.6. In practice, resistance limits the impedance at resonance. The lower the circuit resistance, the sharper the peak of the impedance curve.

3. Q factor

The Q factor of a resonant circuit is defined as $\frac{f_{res}}{\Delta f_{res}}$ where f_{res} is the resonant frequency and Δf_{res} is the width of the resonance curve at half the resonant power. For the series LCR circuit, the power supplied is $V_S{}^2/2Z \cos\phi$ since $I_0 = V_S/Z$.

- The power supplied at resonance is $V_S{}^2/2R$ because $Z = R$ and $\phi = 0$ at resonance.
- At half the resonant power, $\cos\phi = Z/2R = V_S/2V_R$. However $V_R = V_S \cos\phi$; hence $\cos^2\phi = 0.5$ at 'half-resonant' power. Prove for yourself that this condition corresponds to $Z = R\sqrt{2}$ and $f = f_{res} \pm \frac{R}{4\pi L}$. Hence show that the Q-factor is $\frac{L\omega_{res}}{R}$. Thus the lower the resistance, the sharper the resonance.

Questions

1. Distinguish between the terms *resistance* and *impedance*.

A 300 Hz, 10 V r.m.s. a.c. supply of negligible impedance is connected across a coil of inductance 0.1 H and resistance 250 Ω.

(i) Calculate the r.m.s. current drawn from the supply.
(ii) Calculate the phase difference between the current and the applied voltage.
(iii) What component must be connected in series with the coil and what must its value be to reduce the phase difference between current and voltage to zero? Calculate the current drawn from the supply when this is connected.
(iv) Without calculation, describe how the amplitude of the current in the final circuit in (iii) would vary when the frequency of the supply is raised from 100 Hz to 500 Hz, the voltage amplitude remaining constant.

(O & C June '91)

2. (a) (i) Draw a sketch showing the magnetic field of a solenoid conducting a steady (d.c.) current. Show in your diagram how the direction of the magnetic flux is related to the direction of the current.

(ii) State an SI unit for magnetic flux.

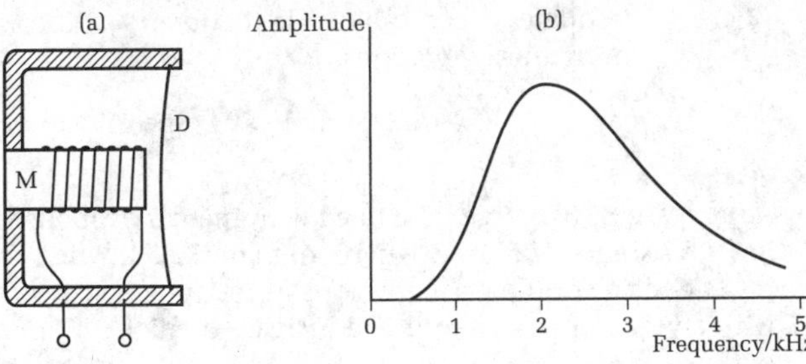

Fig 14.7

The headset for a portable stereo system has two earphones of the type shown in Fig 14.7(a).
Each earphone contains a permanent magnet M that attracts a flexible iron diaphragm D. Alternating current in the solenoid, wound around M, produces variations in magnetic flux density. These variations cause vibrations of D and the production of sound waves.

(b) When the headset is in use, small electric currents flow in the diaphragms. Explain the origin of these currents.

(c) Fig 14.7(b) shows the frequency response of an earphone. It shows how the amplitude of the sound waves produced by each earphone varies for similar currents of different frequency.
Suggest briefly why the graph has this shape.

(d) The manufacturers provide the following data about the earphones.

EACH EARPHONE	resistance:	1.2 Ω
	impedance at 2000 Hz:	4.0 Ω

For a power input of 0.15 W to each earphone when the input signal is sinusoidal at 2000 Hz, calculate
(i) the r.m.s. current
(ii) the applied peak voltage
(iii) the reactance.

(e) State, with reasoning, whether or not the impedance of each earphone at a frequency of 4000 Hz would be twice that at 2000 Hz.

(f) Draw a circuit diagram for a full-wave mains transformer and rectifier unit that will provide a suitable 6 V supply voltage for the stereo system. Identify the principal components and state their functions. Label (+) the positive output terminal.

(AEB November '92)

3. (a) (i) Explain why alternating voltages and currents are usually expressed in terms of r.m.s. values rather than peak values.
(ii) Describe a practical situation in which it is necessary to distinguish between r.m.s. and peak values.

(b) (i) Draw a careful graph showing the waveform of two complete cycles of the output from an a.c. mains supply (240 V r.m.s., 50 Hz). Show on your axes significant time and voltage values.
(ii) Calculate the instantaneous value of the mains voltage 2.5 ms after the beginning of a cycle.

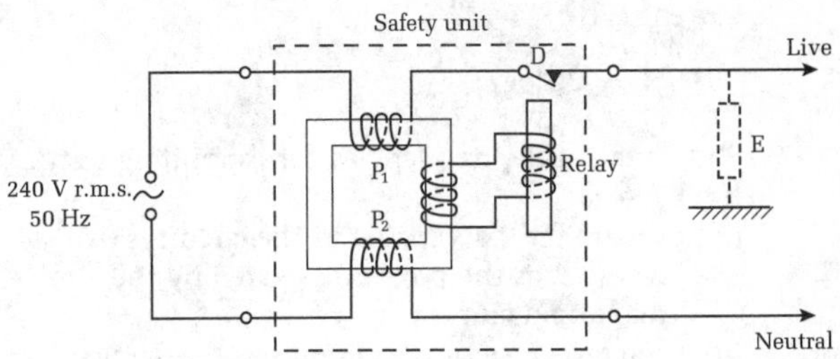

Fig 14.8

(c) Fig 14.8 shows a safety unit that disconnects the mains supply when either live or neutral leads are accidentally earthed.
In this unit 'outgoing' and 'return' currents pass through similar primary coils P_1 and P_2 in a transformer. In normal (safe) operation these currents are equal and zero magnetic flux is generated. However, if there is a current leakage (for example through E) so that the currents in P_1 and P_2 differ, the relay is energized and the live lead is disconnected at D.
The manufacturer's specifications for the unit are:

minimum short-circuit current for operation	30 mA r.m.s.
reactance of each primary coil at 50 Hz	50 mΩ.

(i) Explain, in terms of electromagnetic principles, how the unit works when a fault occurs.
(ii) What is meant by the term *reactance* in the manufacturer's specification?
(iii) Calculate the self inductance of one of the primary coils.
(iv) Calculate the range of resistances between the live wire and earth that will activate the unit.

(UODLE June '92)

4. (a) The following components are connected to an a.c. source which produces a sinusoidal voltage V of constant amplitude but variable frequency.
(i) A capacitor.
(ii) An inductor.
Draw sketch graphs showing how the current I in the circuit varies with frequency f in each case.

(b) The capacitor and inductor are now connected in series with a resistor as shown in Fig 14.9(a). The current I varies with frequency f as shown in Fig 14.9(b).

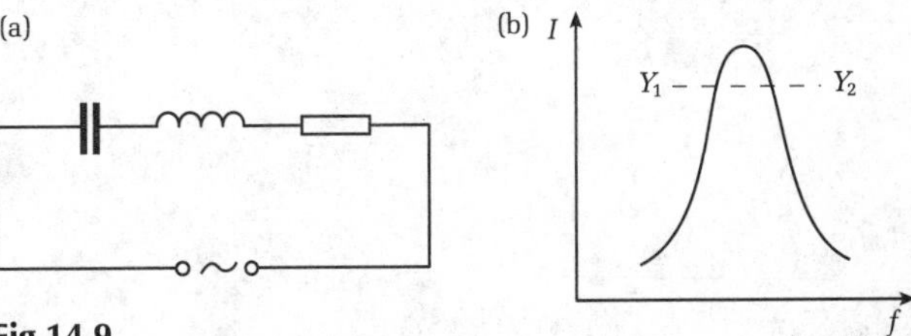

Fig 14.9

The width of a curve such as that in Fig 14.9(b) is conventionally determined at the level Y_1–Y_2, where the current I has a value related to the maximum current I_0 by

$$-3 = 20\log_{10}\left(\frac{I}{I_0}\right)$$

Show that, at the frequencies corresponding to the level Y_1–Y_2:

(i) the power P dissipated in the circuit is $0.5P_0$, where P_0 is the power dissipated by the maximum current I_0;

(ii) the reactance of the circuit has the same magnitude as its resistance;

(iii) there is a phase difference of 45° between I and the source voltage V.

(c) Fig 14.10(a) shows an ultrasonic transducer, such as that used to produce ultrasound in security systems.

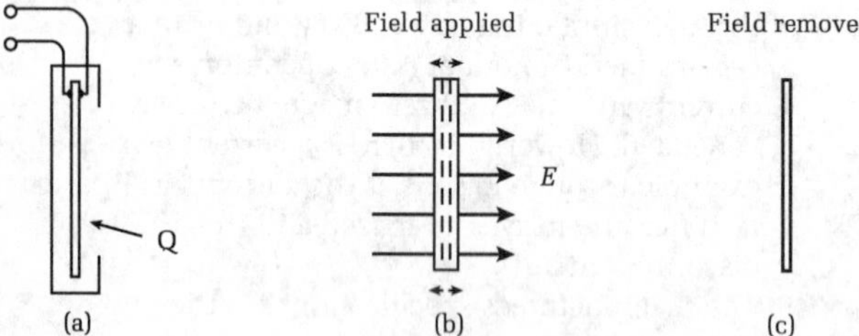

Fig 14.10

The transducer consists of a thin disc of quartz Q with metallized faces. When a uniform electric field E is applied horizontally to Q, the quartz molecules align themselves with the field and the disc expands horizontally (Fig 14.10(b)). When the field is removed Q returns to its normal size (Fig 14.10(c)). The application of an alternating electric field of suitable frequency can hence set up standing longitudinal waves between the vertical faces of Q, provided Q is one-half a wavelength wide.

The transducer also behaves electrically as an LCR combination in which $LC \gg R$.

(i) The frequency of the mechanical vibrations produced is twice that of the alternating electric field. Explain why.

(ii) The speed of compression waves in quartz is $5760\,\text{m}\,\text{s}^{-1}$. Calculate the thickness of Q if ultrasound of frequency 10.00 MHz is to be produced.

(iii) The metallized faces of Q are each of area $2.0\,\text{cm}^2$. The metal provides electrical contacts. Calculate the capacitance of Q, viewed as a parallel-plate capacitor. (The permittivity of quartz is $4.0 \times 10^{-11}\,\text{F}\,\text{m}^{-1}$.)

(iv) Use your result from (iii) to calculate the self inductance of Q. Assume that the quartz 'resonates' electrically at the frequency of the mechanical vibrations.

(AEB Summer '94, Special Paper)

5. A fluorescent discharge tube filled with mercury vapour has a resistance of $5.0\,\text{M}\Omega$ when unlit and $22.5\,\Omega$ when lit. The inside of the glass envelope of the tube is coated with a white powder in order to increase the light output.

The tube, together with a series inductor coil of inductance 0.54 H and resistance $7.5\,\Omega$ form a lighting unit. A starter establishes an initial discharge which is then sustained by the current through the tube when the unit is connected to the mains 240 V, 50 Hz supply.

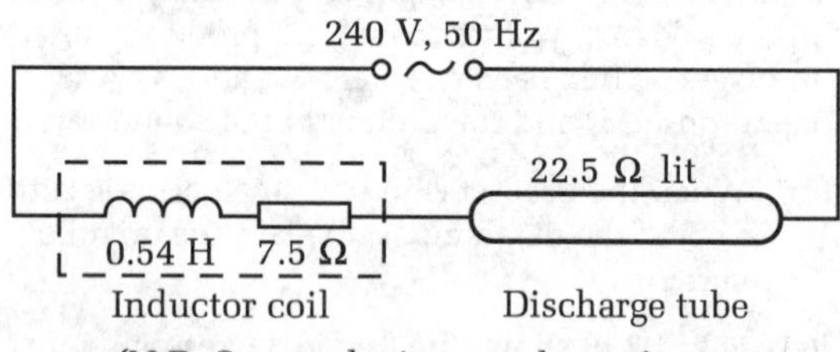

Fig 14.11

(a) (i) Describe the way in which the powder coating increases the visible output of the tube.

(ii) Why is a starter needed to establish an initial discharge?

(iii) Why is it necessary to have an inductor or resistor in series with the tube when lit?

(b) (i) Calculate the power dissipated in the lighting unit once a stable discharge has been established.

(ii) Determine the fraction of the power dissipated in the lighting unit which is in the form of light. You may assume 20% of the electrical power dissipated in the discharge tube results in light output.

(iii) The inductor may be replaced with a resistor so that the current through the lamp is unchanged. Calculate the value of such a resistor.
What fraction of the total power dissipated would now be in the form of light?

(c) State two disadvantages for the use of fluorescent lighting in the home.

(NEAB June '93, Special Paper)

15 OSCILLATING SYSTEMS

What you need to know now

- ❑ The definitions of displacement, amplitude, time period, frequency and angular frequency.
- ❑ The defining equation for simple harmonic motion
$$\frac{d^2s}{dt^2} = -\omega^2 s$$
- ❑ Graphical representations of the sinusoidal waveforms $s = r\sin\omega t$ and $s = r\cos\omega t$.
- ❑ Speed $v = \omega(r^2 - s^2)^{1/2}$ for a body oscillating with s.h.m.
- ❑ The time period formulae $T = 2\pi\sqrt{\frac{l}{g}}$ and $T = 2\pi\sqrt{\frac{m}{k}}$ for a simple pendulum and a mass on a spring.

What you need to know next

Simple harmonic motion proofs

In any oscillating system, the forces on the system try to restore it to equilibrium. If the system is moving away from equilibrium at some instant, then the restoring forces reduce its speed, stop it momentarily and pull it back towards equilibrium. Because of inertia, the system overshoots the equilibrium position and the restoring forces once again try to restore it back to equilibrium.

To prove a point mass m in a system is capable of oscillating, it is only necessary to show that the resultant force F is proportional to the displacement s from equilibrium and is directed towards equilibrium. This may be written as an equation of the force $F = -ks$, where k is a constant and the – sign signifies 'acting towards equilibrium'.

Hence the acceleration of the point mass, $\frac{d^2s}{dt^2} = -\frac{ks}{m} = -\omega^2 s$ where $\omega^2 = k/m$.

Case study 1 A mass *m* suspended on a spring

Assuming the spring obeys Hooke's law, the restoring force F on the mass when it is at displacement s from equilibrium is equal and opposite to the change of tension from equilibrium.

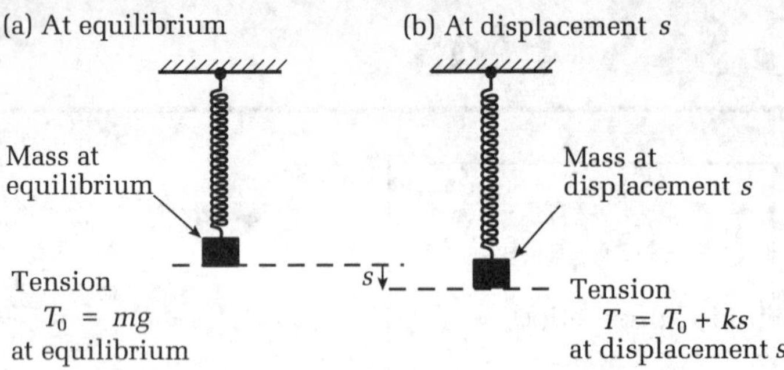

Fig 15.1 Spring oscillations

Hence $F = -ks$ where k is the spring constant and therefore the acceleration $\frac{d^2s}{dt^2} = -\frac{k}{m}s$.

NOTE: The tension lies in the range from $T_{max} = T_0 + kr$ to $T_{min} = T_0 - kr$ where r is the amplitude and T_0 is the equilibrium tension ($= mg$).

Case study 2 The simple pendulum

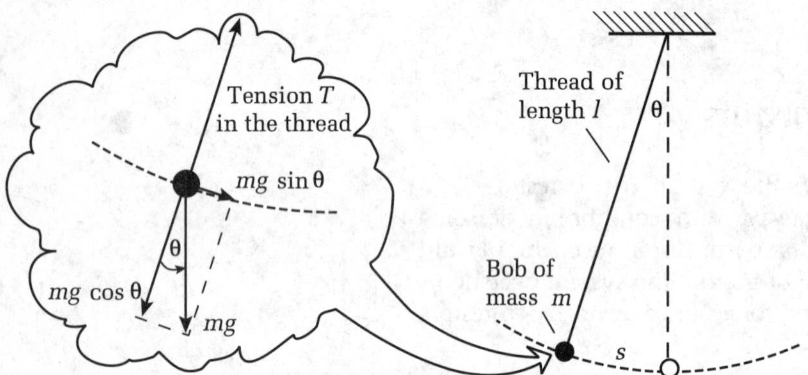

Fig 15.2 Oscillations of a simple pendulum

The restoring force F on the pendulum bob is $mg\sin\theta$ when the string is at angle θ to the vertical and the bob is at displacement s..

Provided $\theta \leqslant 10^\circ$ approximately, $\sin\theta = \frac{s}{l}$; hence $F = -\frac{mgs}{l}$.

Therefore the acceleration $\frac{d^2s}{dt^2} = \frac{F}{m} = -\frac{g}{l}s = -\omega^2 s$ where $\omega^2 = g/l$.

NOTE: The maximum tension T_{max} is when the mass passes through equilibrium. $T_{max} = mg + \frac{mv^2}{l}$.

Case study 3

A loaded test tube floating vertically in water

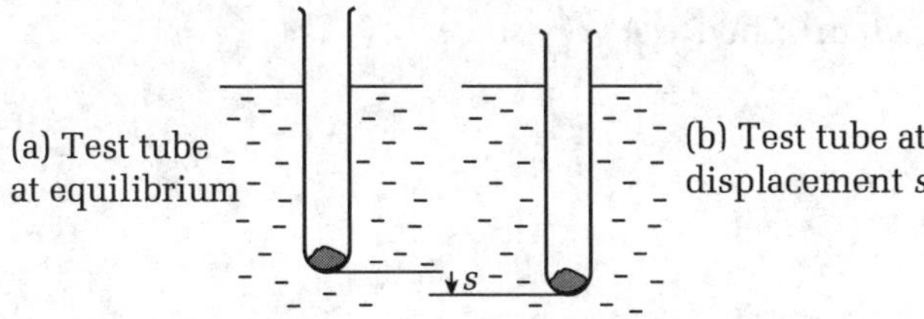

Fig 15.3 Oscillations of a test tube

At equilibrium, the tube floats because the upthrust due to the water is equal to its weight. At displacement s from equilibrium, the change of the volume of water displaced is As where A is the cross-sectional area of the tube. Hence the change of upthrust is $As\rho g$ where ρ is the density of water. Thus the restoring force F on the tube $= -As\rho g$.

Therefore the acceleration $\dfrac{d^2s}{dt^2} = \dfrac{F}{m} = -\dfrac{A\rho g}{m}s = -\omega^2 s$ where $\omega^2 = \dfrac{A\rho g}{m} = \dfrac{g}{l_0}$, m is the mass of the test tube and l_0 is the equilibrium depth of the test tube (assuming its cross-sectional area is uniform).

The general solution of the s.h.m. equation

You can prove for yourself by differentiation that the general solution of the s.h.m. equation $\dfrac{d^2s}{dt^2} = -\omega^2 s$ is $s = A\sin\omega t + B\cos\omega t$ where A and B are constants determined by the initial conditions. Also, prove that velocity $v = \dfrac{ds}{dt} = \omega A\cos\omega t - \omega B\sin\omega t$.

Consider a simple pendulum

1. **released from rest at initial displacement *r***

   $\left(\text{i.e. } s = r \text{ and } \dfrac{ds}{dt} = 0 \text{ at } t = 0\right)$

   The velocity equation gives $0 = \omega A\cos 0 - \omega B\sin 0$; hence $A = 0$.

   The displacement equation gives $r = A\sin 0 + B\cos 0$; hence $B = r$ since $A = 0$.

   Therefore the displacement at time t, $s = r\cos\omega t$.

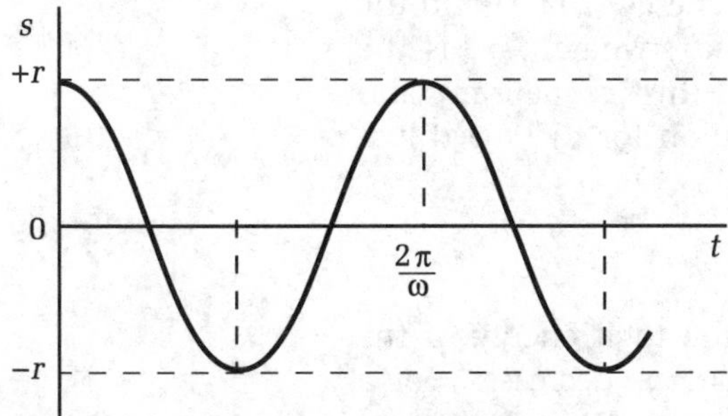

Fig 15.4 $s = r\cos\omega t$

2. **given an initial velocity u at $s = 0$** $\left(\text{i.e. } s = 0 \text{ and } \frac{ds}{dt} = u \text{ at } t = 0\right)$

The displacement equation gives $0 = A\sin 0 + B\cos 0$; hence $B = 0$.

The velocity equation gives $u = \omega A\cos 0 - \omega B\sin 0$; hence $A = \frac{u}{\omega}$ since $B = 0$.

Therefore the displacement at time t, $s = \frac{u}{\omega}\sin \omega t$.

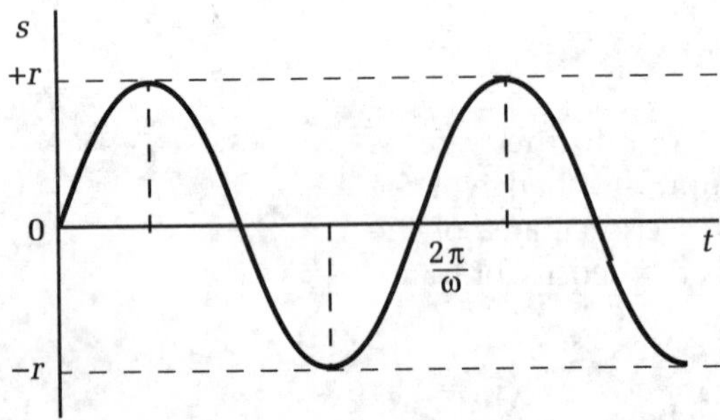

Fig 15.5 $s = r \sin \omega t$

Energy in an oscillating system

- In a freely oscillating system, frictional forces are entirely absent and the system oscillates with a constant amplitude as the system's kinetic energy is changed into potential energy and back repeatedly. The total energy of the system is constant, equal to the maximum potential energy or the maximum kinetic energy.

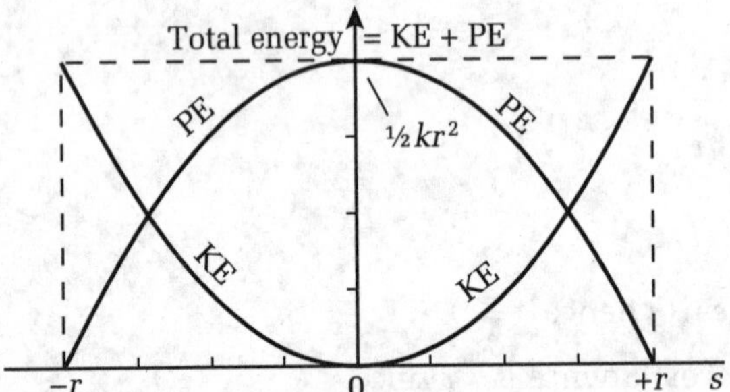

Fig 15.6 Free oscillations

Since the total energy is the sum of the kinetic energy $(\frac{1}{2}mv^2)$ and the potential energy $(\frac{1}{2}ks^2)$, then $\frac{1}{2}mv^2 + \frac{1}{2}ks^2 = \frac{1}{2}kr^2$, where $\frac{1}{2}kr^2$ is the maximum potential energy. Rearranging this equation and using $\omega^2 = k/m$ then gives the following equation for the speed v at displacement s,

$$v^2 = \omega^2 (r^2 - s^2)$$

- In a damped system, frictional forces reduce the total energy of the oscillating system and the amplitude of oscillations decreases. For a damping force which is proportional to the speed, the equation of motion may be written,

$$m\frac{d^2s}{dt^2}+\lambda\frac{ds}{dt}+\omega^2 s = 0$$

where λ is the damping constant.

This equation is the same form as the equation for the discharge of a capacitor C through an inductor L in series with a resistor R,

$$L\frac{d^2Q}{dt^2}+R\frac{dQ}{dt}+\frac{Q}{C} = 0$$

where Q is the capacitor charge at any instant.

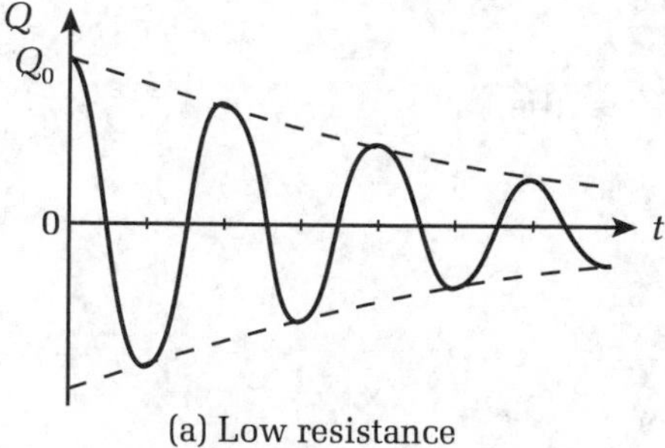

(a) Low resistance

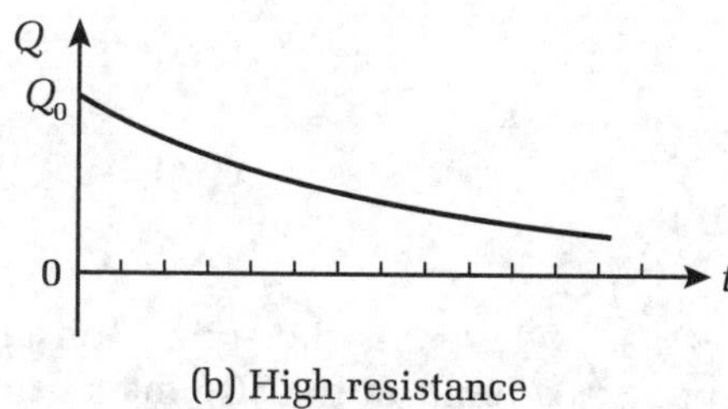

(b) High resistance

Fig 15.7 Damped oscillations

Fig 15.7 shows how charge Q varies with time for different ranges of R. The same curves if relabelled would represent the variation of displacement s with time for different amounts of damping.

Resonance

Resonance occurs when a periodic force is applied to an oscillating system if the frequency of the force (i.e. the applied frequency) is equal to the natural frequency of the oscillating system. At resonance, the applied force is in phase with the velocity just as in a series LCR circuit the applied voltage is in phase with the current at resonance. The amplitude builds up to a maximum value as the applied force supplies energy to the system. At maximum amplitude, the damping force removes energy at the same rate as it is supplied by the applied force. Hence the amplitude remains constant as long as the applied force continues to act. Again, comparison of mechanical and electrical resonance gives similar equations.

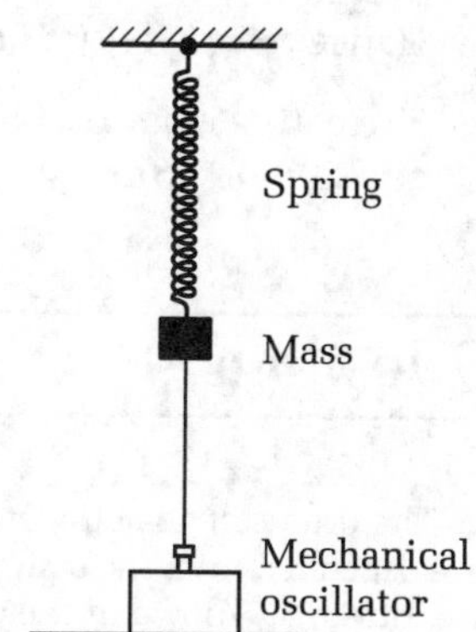

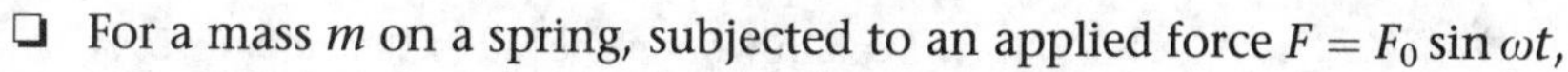

- For a mass m on a spring, subjected to an applied force $F = F_0 \sin \omega t$,

$$m\frac{d^2s}{dt^2}+\lambda\frac{ds}{dt}+\omega^2 s = F_0 \sin \omega t$$

- For a series LCR circuit in which the applied voltage $V = V_0 \sin \omega t$

$$L\frac{d^2Q}{dt^2}+R\frac{dQ}{dt}+\frac{Q}{LC} = V_0 \sin \omega t$$

Comparison of these two equations shows that inductance and inertial mass play a similar role. Likewise, resistance and the damping constant λ both correspond to energy dissipation and the capacitor acts as the electrical equivalent of a spring.

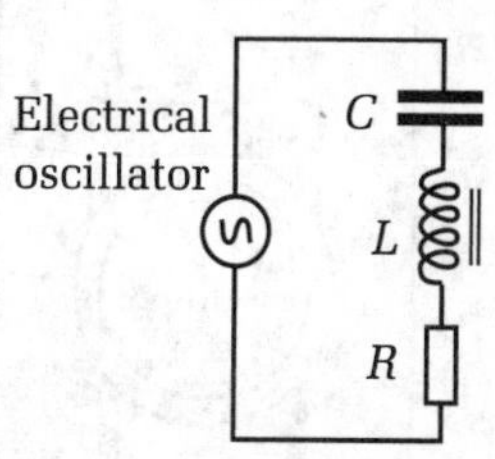

Fig 15.8 Electrical and mechanical analogies

Worked example

A 50 g mass hanger is suspended by a short thread from the lower end of a light spring which hangs vertically from a fixed point. The spring extends by a distance of 25 mm as a result of the mass hanger being on it. A further mass m is then placed on the hanger. When the combined mass on the spring is displaced downwards and released, it oscillates freely with a time period of 0.74 s. Calculate

(a) the mass m, **4 marks**

(b) the maximum initial downwards displacement of the mass and hanger if the thread is not to become slack after release. **4 marks**

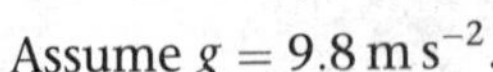

Assume $g = 9.8\,\text{m s}^{-2}$.

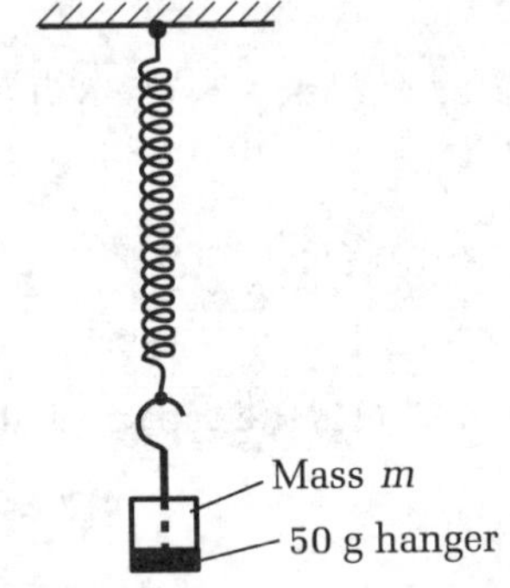

Fig 15.9

Solution

(a) At equilibrium $0.050g = ke$ where k is the spring constant and e is the extension of the spring as a result of the 50 g mass being hung on it. Hence $k = 0.050g/0.025 = 2g$ since $e = 0.025$ m. ✓

With a mass $M = m + 0.050$ kg on the spring, its time period $T = 2\pi\sqrt{\dfrac{M}{k}} = 2\pi\sqrt{\dfrac{M}{2g}}$. ✓

Hence $M = 2gT^2/4\pi^2 = 2 \times 9.8 \times 0.74^2/4\pi^2 = 0.272$ kg. ✓

Hence $m = 0.222$ kg. ✓

(b) The thread will become slack at maximum upward displacement r if the acceleration $\omega^2 r = g$ ✓ where $\omega = 2\pi/T = 8.5\,\text{rad s}^{-1}$. ✓

Hence $r = g/\omega^2 = 0.136$ m. ✓

Since the mass oscillates freely, its initial displacement is therefore equal to 0.136 m. ✓

Questions

1. The drums of an automatic washing machine are suspended from the casing by springs, at the top and bottom, as shown in the diagram. The inner drum rotates within the outer drum at variable speeds according to the washing programme.

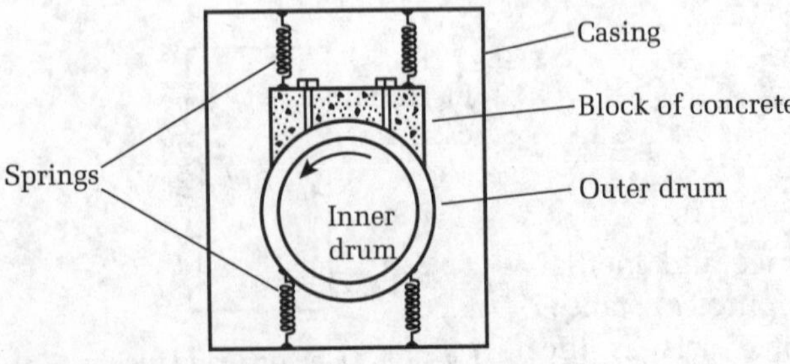

Fig 15.10

The total mass of the drums is 25 kg. A block of concrete of mass 25 kg is added to the outer drum. The natural period of oscillation of the system is 2 s.

(a) (i) Explain what is meant by the *natural period of oscillation*.

(ii) Calculate the effective spring constant of the mass–spring system which gives the natural period of 2 s.

(b) When the washing machine enters the spin part of its programme, it starts from rest building up rotational speed gradually. As the speed increases the system is observed to oscillate with increasing amplitude which reaches a maximum value of 3 cm before decreasing again at higher speeds.

(i) Why does the system oscillate when the inner drum is rotated?

(ii) What will be the speed of the drum in revolutions per minute when the maximum amplitude of oscillation is observed?

(iii) Sketch a graph showing how the amplitude varies with frequency of rotation of the inner drum. Label the axes of the graph giving the axes suitable scales.

(iv) State and explain one effect on the oscillations of running the machine without the block of concrete fixed to the drum.

(AEB June '91)

2. A student suspends a mass of 0.1 kg from a string which is known to obey Hooke's law. The resulting extension of the string is 10.0 cm.

(a) What do you understand by the statement that the string is 'known to obey Hooke's law'?

(b) Use the information given in part (a) to calculate the spring constant (stiffness) of the string.

(c) The mass is now pulled down a further 1.0 cm from its equilibrium position and then released. Calculate the frequency of oscillation of the mass on the string.

(d) (i) State the maximum distance through which the mass can be displaced from the equilibrium position, before the resulting motion is no longer simple harmonic. (For this purpose you may assume that Hooke's law continues to apply to the string however much it is stretched.)

(ii) Explain why the motion is not simple harmonic beyond the limit you have stated in (d)(i).

(iii) Sketch a displacement–time graph for this oscillator as it vibrates with an amplitude greater than that needed to ensure simple harmonic motion. (Detailed calculations relating to the non-simple harmonic part of the motion are **not** required.)

(UCLES March '92)

3. One model of the hydrogen chloride molecule describes it as a positively charged hydrogen atom linked by a springy bond to a negatively charged chlorine atom. This model is shown in Fig 15.11.

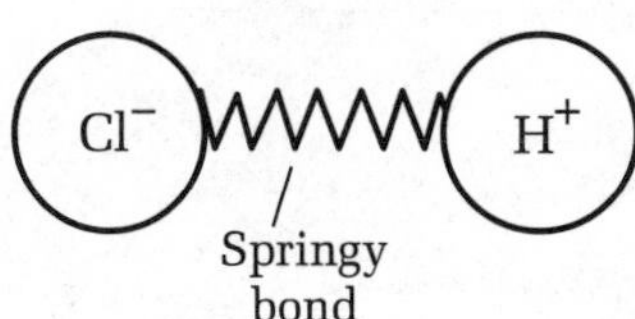

Fig 15.11

The bond in this model involves at least two forces, one attractive and one repulsive. What provides the attractive force between the atoms? Explain why a repulsive force must be present.

The mass of the chlorine atom is in fact much larger than that of the hydrogen atom; so the chlorine atom can be considered to be fixed while the hydrogen atom oscillates. If these oscillations are simple harmonic, explain what can be said about the net force on the hydrogen atom.

The frequency of oscillation of the hydrogen atom is 8.8×10^{13} Hz. The mass of a hydrogen atom is 1.67×10^{-27} kg. Calculate the force per unit extension, k, of the bond.

Part of the electromagnetic spectrum which has the same frequency as this oscillation is strongly absorbed by hydrogen chloride. Explain

(i) what part of the electromagnetic spectrum this would be,

(ii) why this absorption occurs, and

(iii) why you might expect *sodium* chloride to exhibit this behaviour at a different frequency.

(ULEAC January '92)

4. A group of students is asked to investigate the characteristics of identical moving-coil loudspeakers with a view to their possible use as mechanical vibrator units.

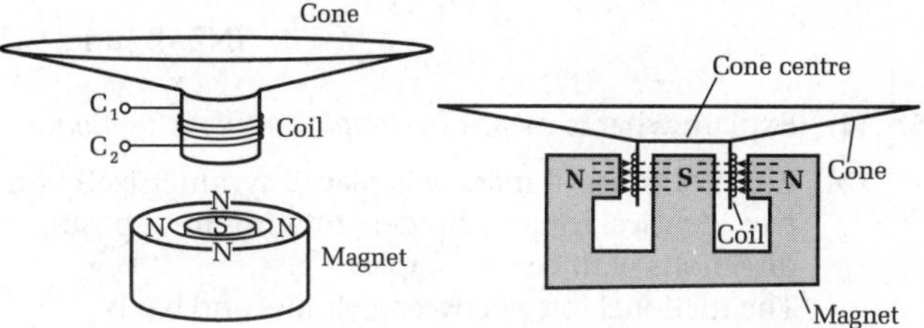

Fig 15.12

The cone is fixed at its outer rim and supports the coil between the magnet poles as shown in Fig 15.12. The cone and coil together act as a mass–spring system. The students discover that the vertical displacement of the cone is directly proportional to the load placed on the flat centre of the cone.

The coil consists of 50 turns of fine wire and has a mean diameter of 2.0 cm. A load of 0.2 kg placed on the centre of the cone displaces it by 2.5 mm. The d.c. current required to restore the loaded cone to its original position is 1.2 A.

(a) (i) State whether this restoring current flows through the coil from C_1 to C_2 or from C_2 to C_1; justify your answer.

(ii) Show that the flux density in the air gap between the poles is 0.53 T.

(iii) Show that the stiffness of the system is $0.80\,\text{kN}\,\text{m}^{-1}$.

(b) The students check the value for the stiffness of the system by connecting the coil to the input terminals of an oscilloscope. The input sensitivity of the oscilloscope is set to $0.20\,\text{V}\,\text{cm}^{-1}$ and the timebase set to $50\,\text{ms}\,\text{cm}^{-1}$.

When the loaded cone is raised to its unloaded position and released, a trace is obtained which shows the oscillations dying away to a negligible amplitude in 0.5 seconds.

(i) Show that if the value of stiffness is $0.80\,\text{kN}\,\text{m}^{-1}$, the natural frequency of vibration of the system is 10 Hz.
(ii) Explain why an oscillatory trace is obtained on the oscilloscope.
(iii) Estimate the initial amplitude of the trace.
(iv) Sketch the trace seen on the oscilloscope, indicating important values.

(c) When the experiment is repeated with no load on the cone, the natural frequency of oscillation increases to 100 Hz.
One of the unloaded speakers is connected to a signal generator (oscillator) with a constant voltage output, and the frequency of the generator output is gradually increased from 1 Hz to 1 kHz. The amplitude of oscillation of the cone is found to decrease initially and then to increase rapidly before dropping away again.
(i) Explain why the natural frequency of oscillation increases.
(ii) Explain why the amplitude decreases as the frequency is raised from 1 Hz.
(iii) State the frequency at which the amplitude will be a maximum.
(iv) Explain why such a maximum occurs and discuss the importance of this phenomenon for using the speaker as a mechanical vibrator.

(NEAB June '91)

5. (a) Explain what is meant by *simple harmonic motion.*
(b) A uniform bar of mass m is placed symmetrically on two identical rough cylinders rotating in opposite directions with centres l apart.
The frictional force between cylinder and bar is related to the reaction force at the point of contact by:

(frictional force) $=$ $k \times$ (reaction force)

where k is a constant.

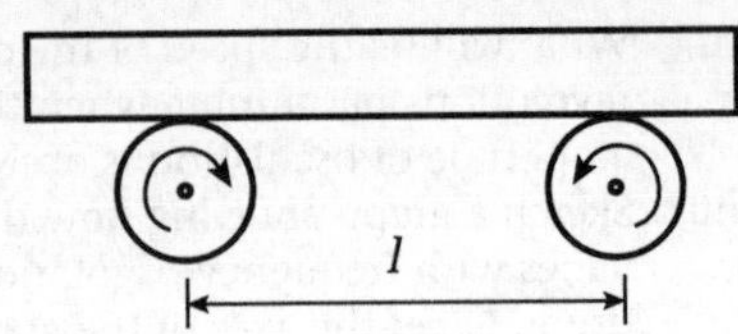

Fig 15.13

(i) The bar is given a small horizontal displacement from its equilibrium position. Show that the subsequent motion is simple harmonic. State your assumptions clearly.
(ii) Show that the natural frequency f of the oscillation is given by

$$f = \frac{1}{2\pi}\sqrt{\frac{2kg}{l}}$$

(NEAB June '93, Special Paper)

6. (a) A short cylinder is placed with its axis vertical on a horizontal surface which can be set in simple harmonic motion in its own plane with an amplitude of 5 cm. If the frequency of the oscillations is gradually increased, at what frequency would the cylinder slip if the frictional force has a value equal to 40% of the cylinder's weight (i.e. the coefficient of limiting friction is 0.40)?
You may ignore any tendency for the cylinder to topple over.
(b) If the cylinder has a height equal to twice its diameter, what is the minimum value of the ratio frictional force to weight of cylinder if the cylinder is to start to tip over before slipping?

(NEAB June '95, Special Paper)

16 THE MATHEMATICS OF WAVEFORMS

What you need to know now

- ❏ The meaning of the terms displacement, amplitude, wavelength, frequency and phase difference as applied to waveforms.
- ❏ Descriptive explanations of reflection, refraction, diffraction, interference and the formation of stationary waves.
- ❏ The equations for double slit interference and the diffraction grating.
- ❏ The differences between progressive waves and stationary waves in terms of the motion of particles in the wave-carrying medium.

What you need to know next

Progressive waves

1. The equation for a progressive wave

Consider snapshots of a progressive wave on a string of two successive instants, as in Fig 16.1.

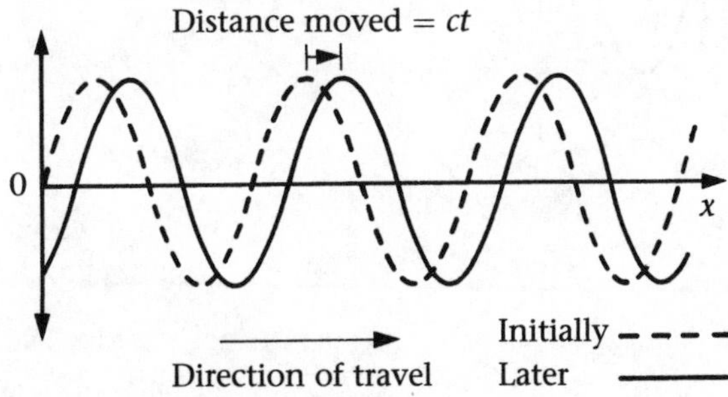

Fig 16.1 Superimposed snapshots

- ❏ Initially, the wave displacement is zero at O. The initial displacement at any point P, y, varies with distance OP according to the equation $y = a\sin\frac{(2\pi x)}{\lambda}$ where $x = OP$ and a is the wave amplitude. Displacement zeros occur at points where $x = m\lambda/2$ where m is an integer, corresponding to $2\pi x/\lambda = m\pi$.

  Displacement maxima or minima occur at points where $x = (m + 0.5)\,\lambda/2$, corresponding to $2\pi x/\lambda = (m + 0.5)\,\pi$.

- At time t later, the wave has moved a distance ct to the right, where c is the wave speed. Hence the equation for this wave snapshot is $y = a\sin\dfrac{2\pi(x-ct)}{\lambda}$ since distance ct must be subtracted from x to give the distance from any point to O′, the moving 'origin' of the wave. Note that if the wave had been moving to the left, the distance ct would need to be added. Hence the equation for a progressive wave moving leftwards (i.e. in the $-x$ direction) has $(x+ct)$ instead of $(x-ct)$,

i.e. $y = a\sin\dfrac{2\pi(x-ct)}{\lambda}$ for a wave travelling in the $+x$ direction

and $y = a\sin\dfrac{2\pi(x+ct)}{\lambda}$ for a wave travelling in the $-x$ direction.

Each particle on a string carrying a wave oscillates in simple harmonic motion as the wave travels along the string.

1. The frequency of vibration, $f = c/\lambda$ for all points on the string. One full cycle of vibration occurs in time T where $\dfrac{2\pi cT}{\lambda} = 2\pi$. Hence the frequency of vibration $f = 1/T = c/\lambda$. The equation for y may therefore be written $y = a\sin 2\pi\left(\dfrac{x}{\lambda} - ft\right)$.

2. The amplitude of vibration, a, is the same for all points along the string since the maximum value of the sine function is 1.

3. The phase difference ϕ between any two points at distance Δx apart is given by $\phi = \dfrac{2\pi\,\Delta x}{\lambda}$. The phasor diagram in Fig 16.2 may be used to represent the variation of displacement with time at any point. The phase between two points is represented on a phasor diagram as the angle between the two corresponding phasors.

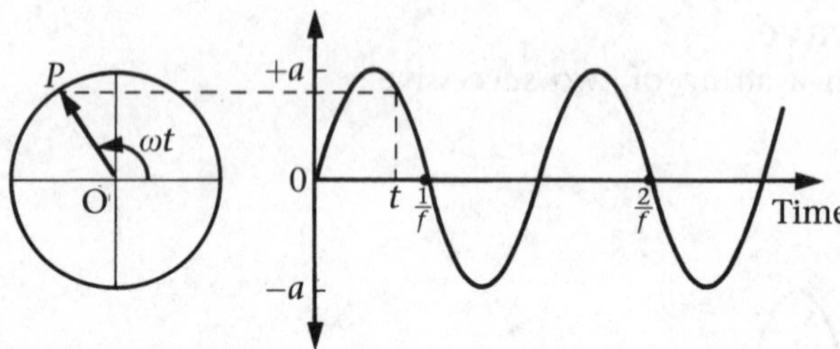

Fig 16.2 Phasor representation

Wave speed factors

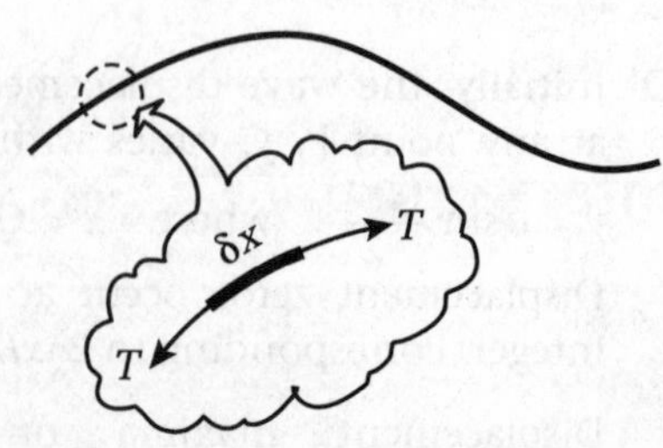

Fig 16.3 Waves on a string

The equation for a progressive wave is a solution of the differential equation $\dfrac{d^2y}{dx^2} = \dfrac{1}{c^2}\dfrac{d^2y}{dt^2}$ which describes the motion of any particle of the string. An element of length δx experiences tension T at either end. For small displacements the y-component of tension at any point is $T\dfrac{dy}{dx}$ and the x-component is T.

Hence the resultant force on the element is $\frac{d}{dx}\left(T\frac{dy}{dx}\right)\delta x$ towards equilibrium

and so the y-component of acceleration $\frac{d^2y}{dt^2} = \frac{1}{m}\frac{d}{dx}\left(T\frac{dy}{dx}\right)\delta x$ $= \frac{T}{\mu}\frac{d^2y}{dx^2}$ where m is the mass of the element and μ is the mass per unit length of the string. Substituting $c^2 = \frac{T}{\mu}$ therefore gives the differential equation above. Hence the speed of waves on a string or wire $c = (T/\mu)^{1/2}$.

2. The Principle of Superposition

When waves pass through each other, the resultant displacement is equal to the sum of the individual displacements. Fig 16.4 shows a sequence of snapshots of two waves as they pass through each other. At any given instant, the resultant displacement at each position is the sum of the displacements each wave alone would give at that position.

Where two sine waves of equal amplitude pass through each other, cancellation occurs where crests from one set arrive at the same time as troughs from the other set. The resultant displacement is zero where this happens. Reinforcement occurs where the crests from one set of waves arrive at the same time as the crests from the other set. This principle is used to explain wave phenomena such as interference, the formation of stationary waves and beats. These topics are developed in more detail in the following sections.

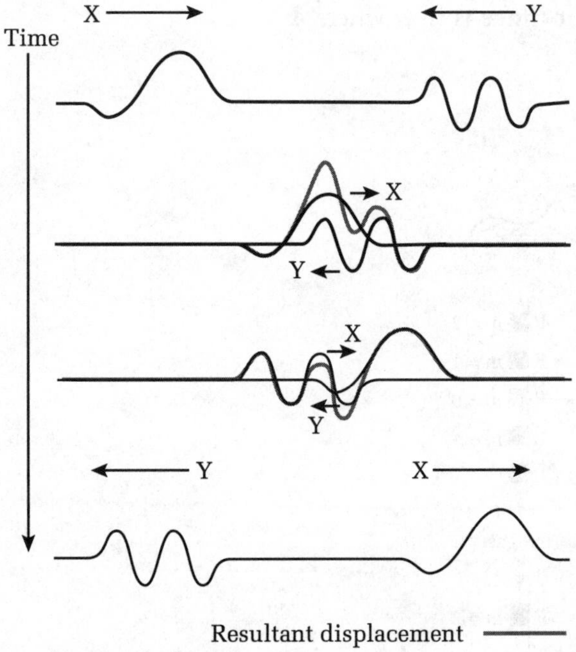

Fig 16.4 Superposition

Interference

Consider two adjacent point sources S_1 and S_2 emitting waves at the same frequency, as in Fig 16.5. If the sources are coherent (i.e. emit waves with a constant phase difference), the points of cancellation and reinforcement are fixed, so an interference pattern is formed.

- At distance x_1 from source S_1, the displacement
$$y_1 = a\sin\left(2\pi\frac{x_1}{\lambda} - 2\pi ft\right)$$
- At distance x_2 from source S_2, the displacement
$$y_2 = a\sin\left(2\pi\frac{x_2}{\lambda} - 2\pi ft + \phi\right)$$
where ϕ is the phase difference between waves emitted by S_1 and S_2.
- Using the standard formula for adding two sine functions, the resultant displacement
$$y = y_1 + y_2 = A\sin\left(2\pi\frac{x}{\lambda} - 2\pi ft + \frac{\phi}{2}\right)$$
where the resultant amplitude $A = a\cos\left(\frac{\pi}{\lambda}(x_1 - x_2) - \frac{\phi}{2}\right)$ and $x = (x_1 + x_2)/2$.

NOTE: The standard formula for adding two sine functions is $\sin A + \sin B = 2\sin(A+B)/2\ \cos(A-B)/2$.

1. Suppose the sources emit in phase. Hence $\phi = 0$. The condition for maximum resultant amplitude A is then $x_1 - x_2 = m\lambda$ where m is an integer. This condition ensures that at any point of reinforcement, waves from S_1 arrive m cycles earlier or later than waves from S_2.
2. Suppose the waves emit out of phase exactly. Hence $\phi = \pi$; so the condition for reinforcement is now $x_1 - x_2 = m\lambda + \frac{\lambda}{2}$. Because the waves are emitted exactly out of phase, this condition gives the points where they arrive exactly in phase. Each bright fringe is now where a dark fringe would have been had ϕ been zero.

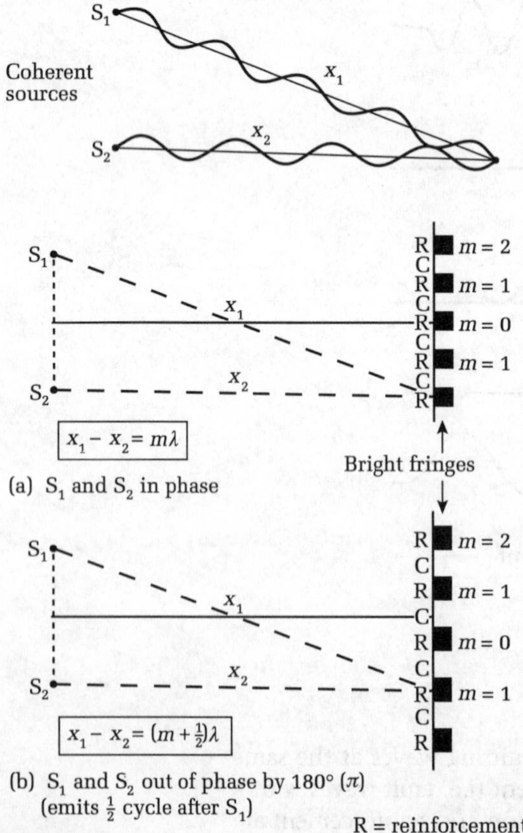

Fig 16.5 Interference

3. Suppose it is possible to change ϕ gradually from 0 to 2π. The effect would be to shift the fringes through one fringe spacing. If ϕ changes at random, the points of cancellation and reinforcement change positions at random. No interference pattern would then be observable. This is why no interference pattern is seen when light from two separate lamps overlaps. Each lamp emits photons at random so the phase difference changes at random. Interference of light is achieved by illuminating a pair of double slits with light from a single slit. This ensures the double slits emit light waves with a constant phase difference.

NOTE: In general the path difference $x_1 - x_2 = m\lambda + \dfrac{\lambda\phi}{2\pi}$ for reinforcement. Hence the change of the path difference from one bright fringe to the next is one wavelength. The position of the mth bright fringe from the centre of the screen is given by $\dfrac{\text{path difference} \times \text{slit spacing } (d)}{\text{slit–screen distance } (X)}$. Hence the distance from one bright fringe to the next is equal to $\dfrac{\lambda d}{X}$.

4. If slit S_2 is covered with a thin piece of transparent material, the phase difference is increased and the fringes are displaced. The reason is that light travels more slowly through the material than through air thus delaying waves from S_2 compared with those from S_1. Prove for yourself that the time delay Δt due to thickness z of material of refractive index n is $nz/c_0 - z/c_0$, where c_0 is the speed of light in air. Hence show that this is equivalent to the waves from S_2 travelling an extra distance through the air equal to $(n-1)z$. This is sometimes called the **optical path difference** due to the piece of material.

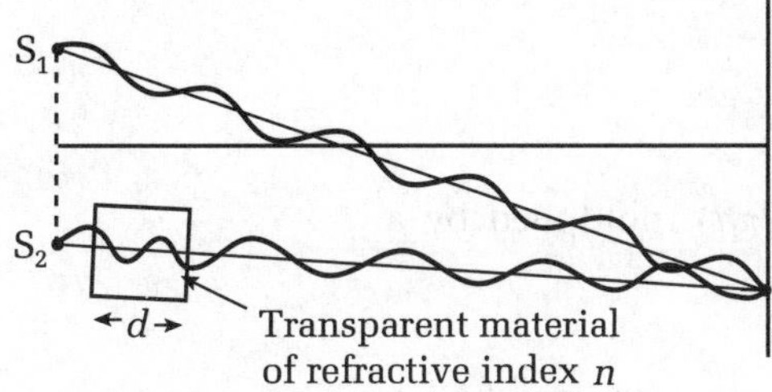

Fig 16.6 Optical path difference

Stationary waves

When two sets of waves of the same wavelength and amplitude pass through each other, a stationary wave pattern is set up. **Nodes** are fixed points where the resultant amplitude is always zero. **Antinodes** are fixed points where the resultant amplitude is always maximum. Nodes and antinodes are characteristic of a stationary wave pattern. The distance from a node to the nearest antinode is $\frac{1}{4}\lambda$.

To understand more fully how stationary waves are formed, consider the displacements y_1 and y_2 at distance x for each wave separately,

$$y_1 = a\sin\left(2\pi\frac{x}{\lambda} - 2\pi ft\right) \quad \text{and} \quad y_2 = a\sin\left(2\pi\frac{x}{\lambda} + 2\pi ft\right)$$

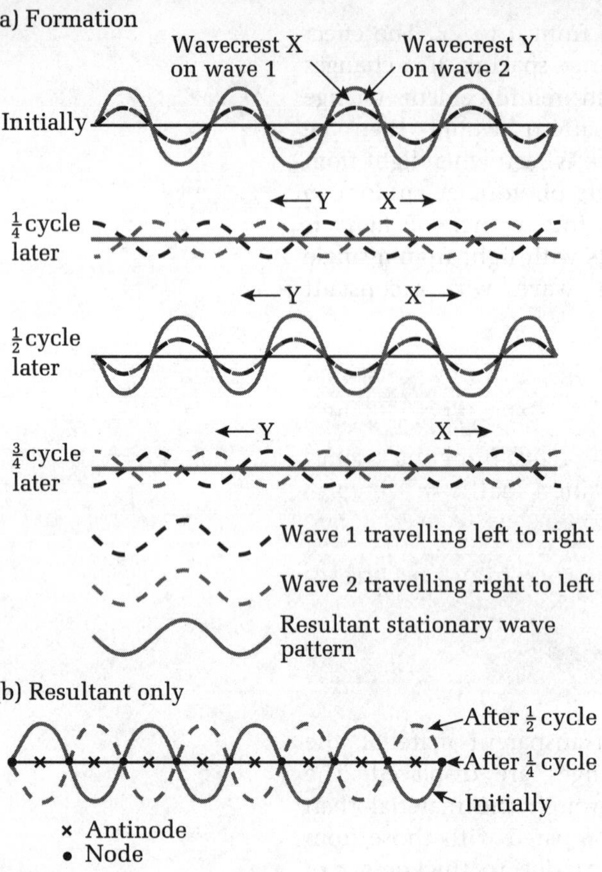

Fig 16.7 Stationary waves

Hence the total displacement $y = y_1 + y_2 = a\sin\left(2\pi\frac{x}{\lambda} - 2\pi ft\right) + a\sin\left(2\pi\frac{x}{\lambda} + 2\pi ft\right)$.

Using the standard formula for adding two sine functions together therefore gives

$$y = 2a\sin\frac{2\pi x}{\lambda}\cos 2\pi ft$$

The equation for y has a time-dependent part ($\cos 2\pi ft$) multiplied by a position-dependent part $\left(\sin\frac{2\pi x}{\lambda}\right)$.

Fig 16.7(b) shows how the stationary wave pattern changes over half a cycle.

- All the particles of the medium vibrate at frequency f with a position-dependent amplitude $2a\sin\frac{2\pi x}{\lambda}$.
- Nodes are at positions where $x = m\lambda/2$, where m is an integer, corresponding to $2\pi x/\lambda = m\pi$.
- Antinodes are at positions where $x = (m + 0.5)\lambda/2$ corresponding to $2\pi x/\lambda = (m + 0.5)\pi$.

Some different arrangements for producing stationary waves are shown in Fig 16.8. In all these examples, waves travelling away from the source pass through reflected waves travelling towards the source. In each example, the two sets of waves create a stationary wave pattern because they have the same wavelength and amplitude.

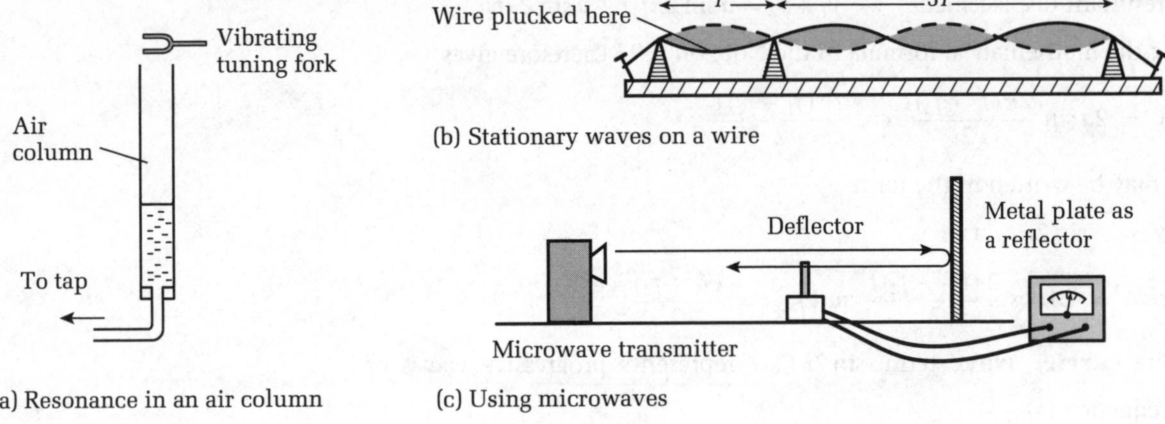

Fig 16.8 Stationary waves

Beats

Where two sets of waves of different frequencies overlap, the vibrations of the particles of the medium vary regularly in amplitude. For sound waves, the amplitude variations are detected as **beats** of sound, each beat being heard when the amplitude reaches a maximum. The beat frequency is equal to the difference in frequency between the two sets of waves producing the effect. If the time T between two successive beats corresponds to n cycles of waves of frequency f_1, reinforcement with waves of lower frequency f_2 will occur if there are $(n + 1)$ cycles of these waves in the same time. Hence $T = n/f_1 = (n + 1)/f_2$. Prove for yourself from these equations that the beat frequency $f = f_1 - f_2$.

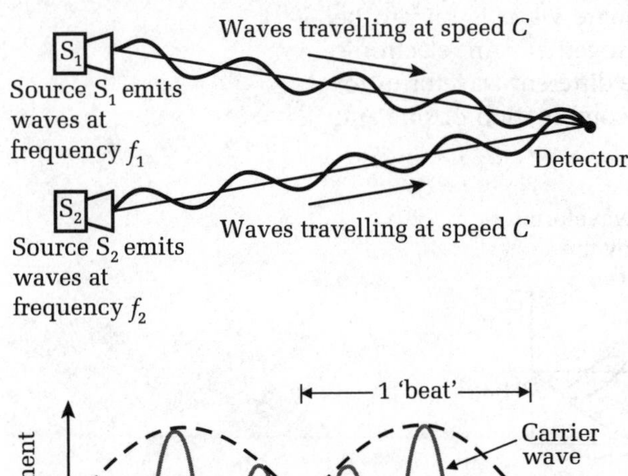

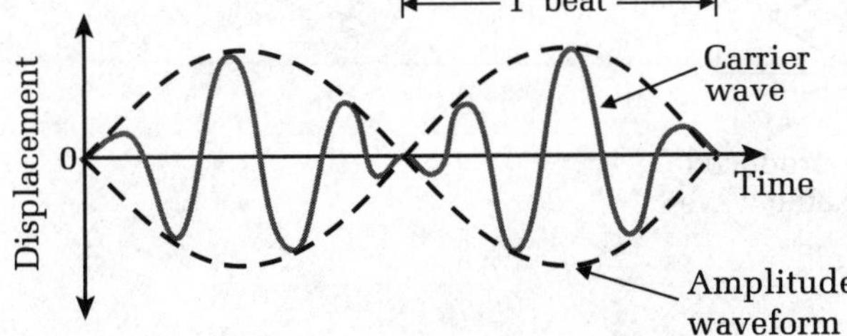

Fig 16.9 Beats

This formula can be derived by considering the two sets of waves travelling in the same direction as they pass a fixed position. Considering the position $x = 0$ for simplicity, the individual displacements are

$$y_1 = a \sin 2\pi f_1 t \quad \text{and} \quad y_2 = a \sin 2\pi f_2 t$$

The resultant displacement $y = y_1 + y_2 = a \sin 2\pi f_1 t + a \sin 2\pi f_2 t$.

Using the mathematical formula in the Note on p.97 therefore gives

$$y = 2a \sin \frac{2\pi (f_1 + f_2) t}{2} \cos \frac{2\pi (f_1 - f_2) t}{2}$$

This may be written in the form

$$y = A \sin 2\pi f_{ave} t$$

where $A = 2a \cos \dfrac{2\pi (f_1 - f_2) t}{2}$ and $f_{ave} = \dfrac{(f_1 + f_2)}{2}$.

- The **carrier wave** term, $\sin 2\pi f_{ave} t$ represents progressive waves of frequency $\dfrac{(f_1 + f_2)}{2}$.
- The **amplitude** A of the carrier wave varies sinusoidally at frequency $\dfrac{(f_1 - f_2)}{2}$. The amplitude waveform travels at the same speed as the carrier waves. For each beat, the amplitude increases from zero to maximum and back to zero each half-cycle. Hence $\dfrac{2\pi (f_1 - f_2) T}{2} = \pi$ where T is the time for 1 beat. Thus the beat frequency $= 1/T = (f_1 - f_2)$.

Waveform synthesis and analysis

Synthesis

A beat's waveform is made by adding two sine waves of different frequencies together. Any waveform can be made by adding a suitable combination together. Fig 16.10 shows how a square waveform can be made by adding sine waves together. The square wave is said to be synthesised by adding suitable sine waves together. An electronic synthesiser adds sine and cosine waves to make different waveforms for sound production. Each waveform is a unique combination of sine and cosine waves.

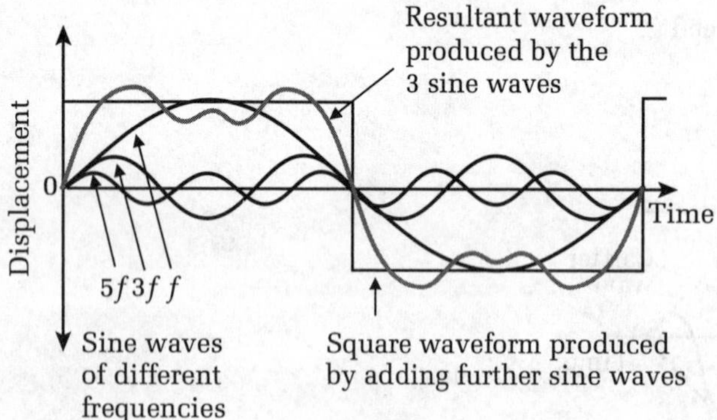

Fig 16.10 Synthesis

Analysis

Because a waveform is a unique combination of sine and cosine waves, it can be analysed to find out what the combination is. This is useful if the waveform is to be amplified or filtered. For example, an amplifier with an uneven frequency response would distort the waveform because each frequency component would be amplified differently. Another example is an electrocardiograph (ECG) machine used to filter, amplify and display 'heart beat' signals. These signals contain frequencies up to about 20 Hz. The amplifier must therefore have an even frequency response up to about 20 Hz. However, if its frequency response extends beyond about 20 Hz, then unwanted signals from muscle activity (EMG) will be amplified too.

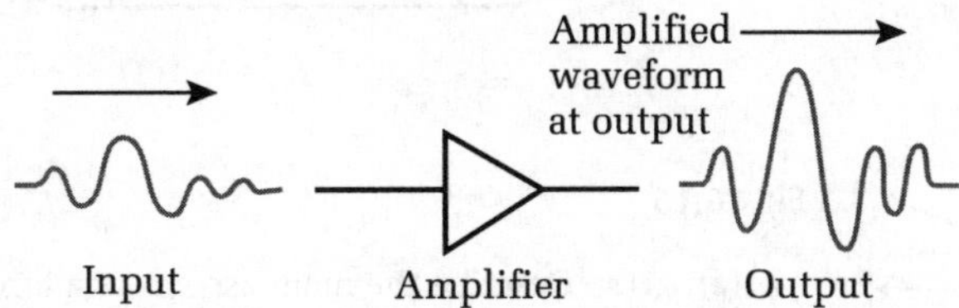

Fig 16.11 Using an amplifier

Questions

1. (a) A sound wave in air is represented by the equation

$$y = 5 \times 10^{-3} \sin(3.14 \times 10^2 t + 0.95x)$$

where y is measured in metres. Find the (i) amplitude, (ii) frequency, (iii) wavelength, and (iv) speed of the wave.

(b) A second wave of the same amplitude beats with the above wave with a beat frequency of 5 Hz. Find **one** corresponding equation for the second wave. Give a brief explanation.

(WJEC June '93)

2.

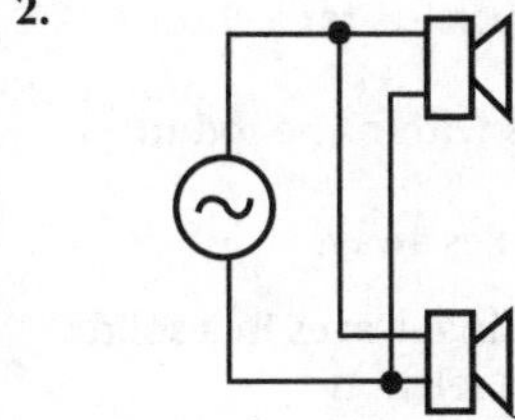

P

Fig 16.12

The variation in signal received by a detector P which is moved about in front of two microwave transmitters, A and B, emitting monochromatic coherent radiation of wavelength λ, can be explained in terms of the *phase difference* or *path difference* between the two waves. Explain the terms in italics and show that the relationship between them is

$$(\textit{phase difference}) = \frac{2\pi}{\lambda}(\textit{path difference})$$

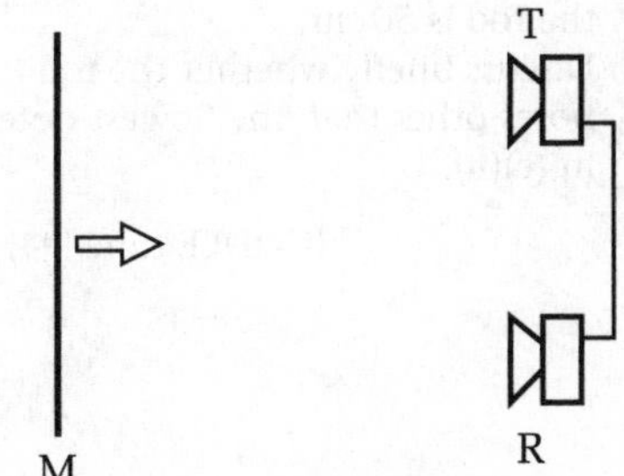

Fig 16.13

T

R

M H

Fig 16.14

Some students are asked to use the laboratory 28 mm microwave transmitter T and receiver R apparatus to design a demonstration to illustrate the principle of a radar speed measuring device. Two of their suggested solutions are shown above.

In Fig 16.13 a fraction of the transmitted signal passes directly to the receiver. This is added to the signal reflected from the movable metal sheet M.

In Fig 16.14 a movable hardboard sheet H, which is a partial reflector of microwaves, is placed in front of the metal sheet M, which is fixed in this case. There is no direct connection between the transmitter and receiver.

(a) For the detected signal intensity to change from a maximum to a minimum, how far must
  (i) the metal sheet be moved in Fig 16.13 and
  (ii) the hardboard sheet be moved in Fig 16.14?

(b) Explain qualitatively why
  (i) the detected signal strength varies in each case, and
  (ii) the minimum signal strength is unlikely to be zero.

(O & C June '92)

3. (a) (i) With reference to sound waves in air and light waves, distinguish between *longitudinal* and *transverse* waves.

(ii) Describe an experiment to demonstrate that light is a transverse wave. State what you would expect to observe, and explain these observations.

(b) A stretched cord is fixed at one end and made to oscillate at the other by a vibrator connected to a signal generator. The diagram shows **part** of the sinusoidal stationary (standing) wave which is set up. The solid line shows one extreme position of the cord, at time $t = 0$. The broken line shows the cord's position at $t = 10\,\text{ms}$, half a cycle later.

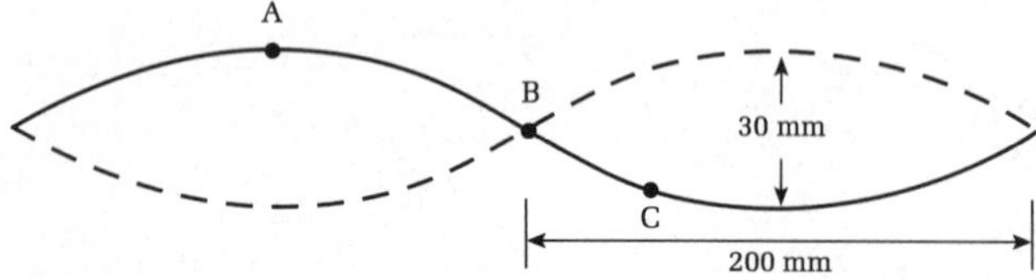

Fig 16.15

The mass of 0.80 m of cord is 0.064 kg. Other dimensions are shown on the diagram.

(i) Sketch the appearance of the cord at $t = 15\,\text{ms}$.
(ii) Describe the motion of the particle at A, calculating its frequency and amplitude.
(iii) Compare the motion of the particle at C with that of the particle at A, stating the phase difference between them.
(iv) Explain why the particle at B remains stationary.
(v) Calculate the tension in the cord.

(NEAB June '95)

4. (a) (i) The equation $y = A\sin(\omega t - kx)$ represents a sound wave travelling in the x-direction. Explain clearly what the letters y, A, ω and k represent for a sound wave.
(ii) State the connection between the above sound wave and one which has the equation $y = A\sin(\omega t + kx)$.

(b) Consider the following paragraph:

A sound wave in air is reflected by a solid wall placed at right angles to the direction of travel of the wave, so that the incident and reflected waves are *superimposed*. A system of *stationary* waves is set up and as a result there are regularly spaced displacement *nodes* and *antinodes*.

(i) Explain the meanings of the words in italics, giving diagrams where appropriate.
(ii) If the sound wave is produced by a source of frequency 500 Hz, and the distance between adjacent nodes is 34.0 cm, calculate the speed of the sound wave.
(iii) The temperature of the air increases from 20 °C to 30 °C. Calculate the new distance between adjacent nodes. Take 0 °C = 273 K.

Note: Speed of sound in a gas at absolute temperature T is proportional to $\sqrt{T}$.

(WJEC June '91)

5.

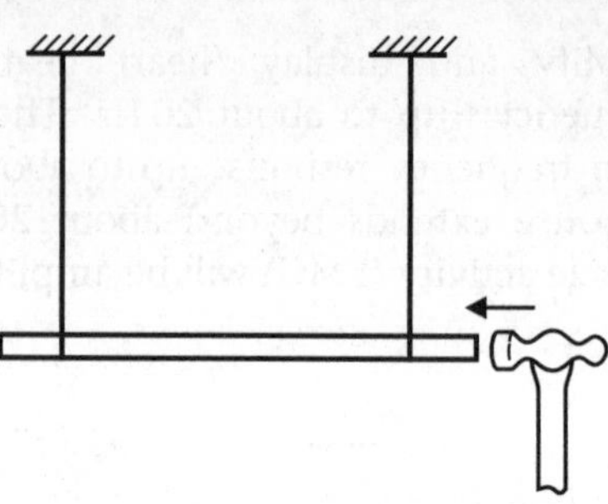

Fig 16.16

(a) (i) Describe the main aspects of a longitudinal wave.
(ii) A longitudinal wave can be described by the equation

$$y = a\sin 2\pi f(t - x/c)$$

Explain the significance of each algebraic term in this equation.
(iii) A wave passes through a medium with negligible change in amplitude. How can the wave equation in (ii) be adapted to give expressions for the velocity and the acceleration of a particle remote from the wave source? Write down these two expressions.
(iv) State the phase relation (in radians) between the displacement of the particle from its mean position and (1) its velocity, (2) its acceleration.

(b) A suspended steel rod (see Fig 16.16) is struck on its end by a small hammer. This action causes the rod to emit a musical note that persists for a short period and then dies away.
(i) Describe what happens within the rod to generate this note.
(ii) Explain why the note dies away.

(c) (i) The speed c of longitudinal waves in a solid material is given by the relation

$$c = \sqrt{\left(\frac{E}{\rho}\right)}$$

where E is the Young modulus and ρ the density of the material.
Use the method of dimensions to check the validity of this equation. State a limitation to your check.
(ii) The Young modulus of steel is 1.5×10^{11} Pa and its density $8500\,\text{kg m}^{-3}$. Determine the frequency of the lowest note that the rod in (b) could produce when struck if the length of the rod is 50 cm.
(iii) Discuss briefly whether the rod could produce notes other than the 'lowest note' mentioned in (c)(ii).

(UODLE June '94, Special Paper)

17 ELECTROMAGNETIC WAVES

What you need to know now

- ❑ The main characteristics of each part of the electromagnetic spectrum, including approximate wavelengths.
- ❑ The main similarities and differences between different parts of the electromagnetic spectrum.
- ❑ The nature of electromagnetic waves as travelling electric and magnetic fields.
- ❑ The historical development of the nature of light, including Young's double slits experiment and Einstein's photon theory used to explain photoelectricity.

What you need to know next

Photons

An atom emits light when an electron in the atom moves to a lower energy level in the atom. The light from a single electron transition is emitted as a single photon which is a 'packet' of electromagnetic waves moving in a certain direction away from the atom. The photon is created and emitted when the electron undergoes the transition. Each photon carries away energy $E = hf$, where f is the light frequency and h is the Planck constant.

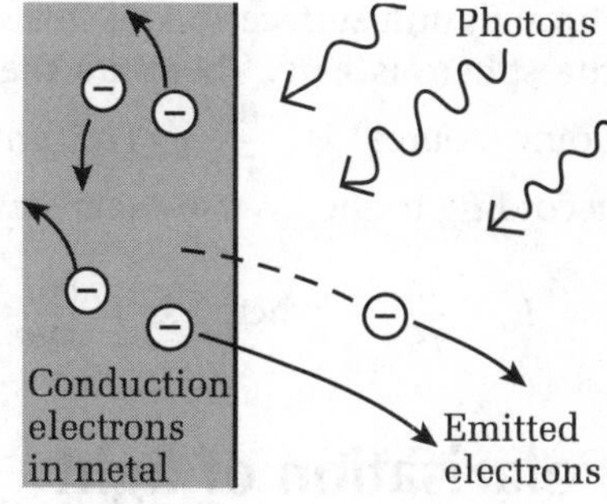

Fig 17.1 Photoelectric emission

The photon energy equation $E = hf$ was put forward by Einstein to explain the threshold frequency in photoelectric emission. When monochromatic light is incident on an uncharged model surface, electrons are emitted from the surface only if the light frequency is greater than a certain value which is characteristic of the metal. This is referred to as the 'threshold frequency' of the metal surface. Each photoelectron was a conduction electron in the metal which gained sufficient energy to leave the metal by absorbing a single photon. Hence the maximum KE of a photoelectron $= hf - \phi$, where ϕ, the work function of the metal, is the work necessary for an electron to leave the metal. Hence the threshold frequency $f_0 = \phi/h$, corresponding to an electron just escaping from the metal with zero KE.

Some further points on the nature of photoelectric emission are summarised below.

1. The wave theory of light cannot explain the threshold frequency. According to classical wave theory, electrons should be emitted by any frequency. The photon theory gives a complete explanation of photoelectricity.

2. If the frequency exceeds the threshold value, the number of photoelectrons emitted per second is increased by increasing the number of photons per second incident on the surface. This is achieved by increasing the intensity of the incident light.
3. Photoelectric emission can be stopped by making the metal plate sufficiently positive. At this 'stopping potential' V_s, all the kinetic energy of a photoelectron is used to do work against the potential. Hence the stopping potential is given by the equation $eV_s = hf - \phi$.
4. Conduction electrons in a metal move about at random, like molecules in an ideal gas. The mean kinetic energy of a conduction electron in a metal at temperature T is $\frac{3}{2}kT$, where k is the Boltzmann constant. Prove for yourself that this is negligible at room temperature in comparison with the energy of a light photon.

Intensity

The **intensity** of a beam of radiation is defined as the energy per second per unit area incident normally on a surface in the path of the beam.

Consider a monochromatic point source of light of power W. Because the source is monochromatic, it only emits photons of a single frequency. If the number of photons emitted per second is n, the light energy carried away per second is therefore nhf, where f is the light frequency. Hence $W = nhf$.

Assuming no absorption of photons by the medium through which they are travelling, the photons spread out from one another as they move away from the source. Imagine a sphere of radius r centred on the source. At distance r from the point source, all the photons pass through the surface of this sphere. Hence the number of photons per second passing through unit surface area of this sphere is $n/(4\pi r^2)$ since the surface area of the sphere is $4\pi r^2$. Therefore the light intensity I at distance r from the point source is $\frac{nhf}{4\pi r^2}$. The intensity therefore varies with distance according to the inverse square law,

$$I = \frac{k}{r^2} \qquad \text{where } k = \frac{nhf}{4\pi} = \frac{W}{4\pi}$$

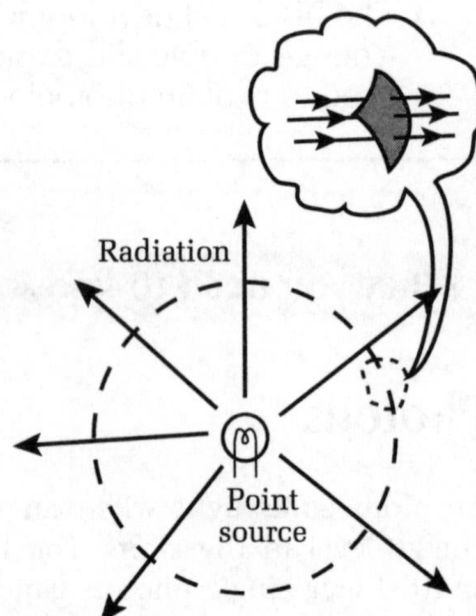

Fig 17.2 Intensity

Polarisation of light

An electromagnetic wave in a vacuum consists of sinusoidally varying electric and magnetic fields perpendicular to each other and to the direction of propagation. An electromagnetic wave is said to be **plane polarised** if its electric field vibrates in one plane only. The plane of vibration of an electromagnetic wave is defined by the plane of vibration of its electric field.

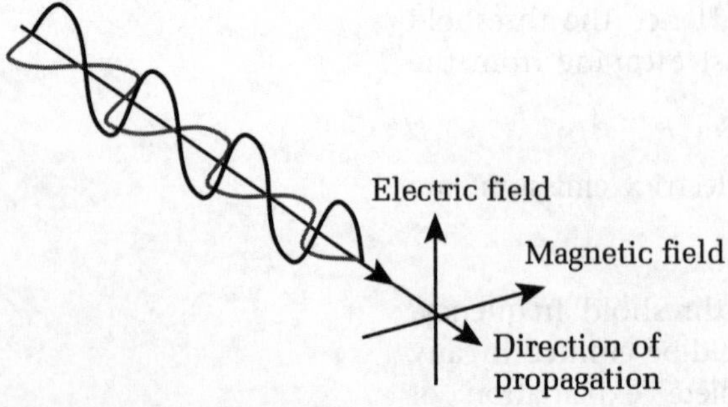

Fig 17.3 A plane polarised electromagnetic wave

- Light from a filament lamp is unpolarised because photons are emitted spontaneously at random and consequently its plane of polarisation changes at random.
- Light from a laser is polarised because photons already emitted produced by atoms in the laser cause other atoms to emit photons in a process referred to as 'stimulated' emission. The photons emerge from the laser with the same plane of polarisation.

Unpolarised light may be polarised by reflection, by scattering or by double refraction.

1. When a light ray is reflected by a non-conducting surface such as glass, the reflected ray is plane polarised and the refracted ray is partially polarised if the reflected ray is perpendicular to the refracted ray. The angle of incidence, i, at which this occurs is referred to as the 'Brewster angle' and is given by the equation $\tan i = n$, where n is the refractive index of the reflector. At this angle, only the component of vibrations perpendicular to the incident plane (i.e. the plane defined by the normal and the incident ray) is reflected.

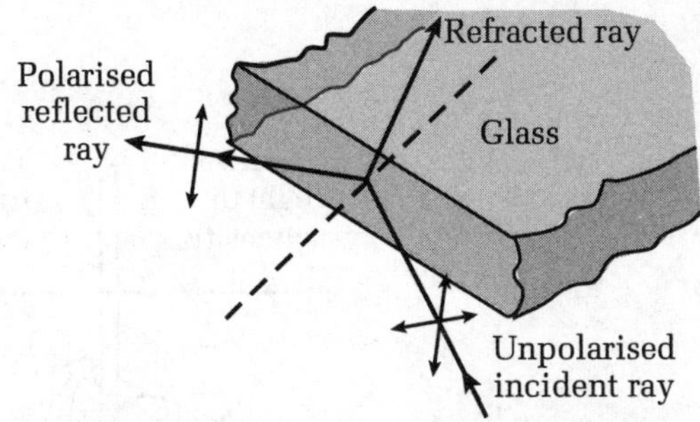

Fig 17.4 Polarisation by reflection

2. A light ray passed through a suspension of small particles is scattered by the particles. In any direction at 90° to the incident ray, the scattered ray is plane polarised with its vibrations perpendicular to both the incident ray and the scattered ray. The effect can be demonstrated with a few drops of milk in water. It is also the reason why blue sky viewed through polaroid sunglasses can appear dark.

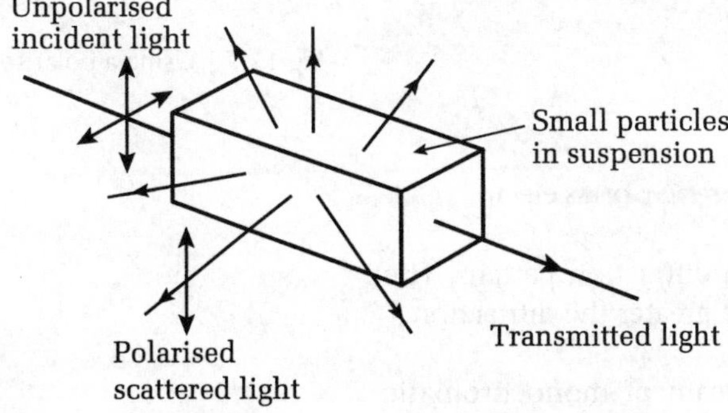

Fig 17.5 Polarisation by scattering

3. Certain crystals such as calcite produce a double image when placed on a printed page. If the crystal is rotated on the page, one image referred to as the 'extraordinary image' moves round the other. This effect, known as double refraction, occurs because the speed of light in the crystal varies according to direction, being greatest along the 'optic

axis' of the crystal. When unpolarised light enters the crystal, the component of vibrations parallel to the optic axis travels faster through the crystal than the component perpendicular to the optic axis. The parallel components create the extraordinary image and the perpendicular components create the normal image. Some double-refracting crystals, referred to as 'dichroic' possess two optic axes causing the ordinary image to disappear. A polaroid filter contains millions of tiny synthetic dichroic crystals aligned parallel to one another. Hence unpolarised light passed through a polaroid filter emerges polarised in a certain direction determined by the orientation of the crystal.

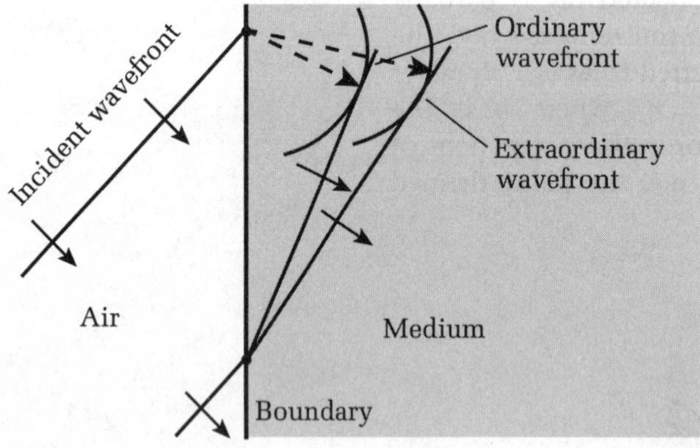

Fig 17.6 Double refraction

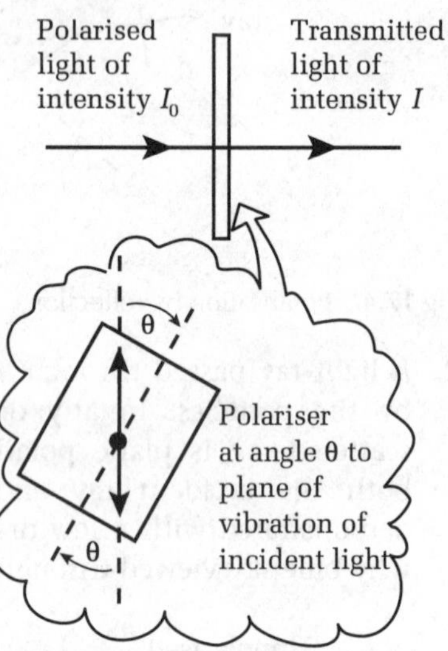

Fig 17.7 Using a polariser

NOTE: The energy of a vibrating object is proportional to (amplitude of vibration)^2. The intensity of a wave is therefore proportional to the square of its amplitude. For polarised light passing through a polaroid, the transmitted intensity I varies with the angle θ between the plane of vibrations and the direction of maximum transmission according to the formula $I = I_0 \cos^2 \theta$ where I_0 is the incident intensity. This is because vibrations of amplitude a have amplitude components $a \cos \theta$ and $a \sin \theta$ parallel and perpendicular to the direction of maximum transmission respectively. Hence the transmitted amplitude is $a \cos \theta$ and therefore the above formula follows since intensity is proportional to (amplitude)^2.

Diffraction by gaps

Light passing through a gap spreads out forming a diffraction pattern. The narrower the gap or the smaller the wavelength, the greater the diffraction.

1. **For a single slit** illuminated by a parallel beam of monochromatic light, the intensity distribution for the diffracted light is shown in Fig 17.8. To understand the formation of the intensity minima, consider the slit divided into elements of equal width δx. At any point P on the screen, the contributions of adjacent elements are out of phase by an angle $\delta\phi = 2\pi \dfrac{\delta x \sin \theta}{\lambda}$ since the path difference between adjacent elements and P is $\delta x \sin \theta$.

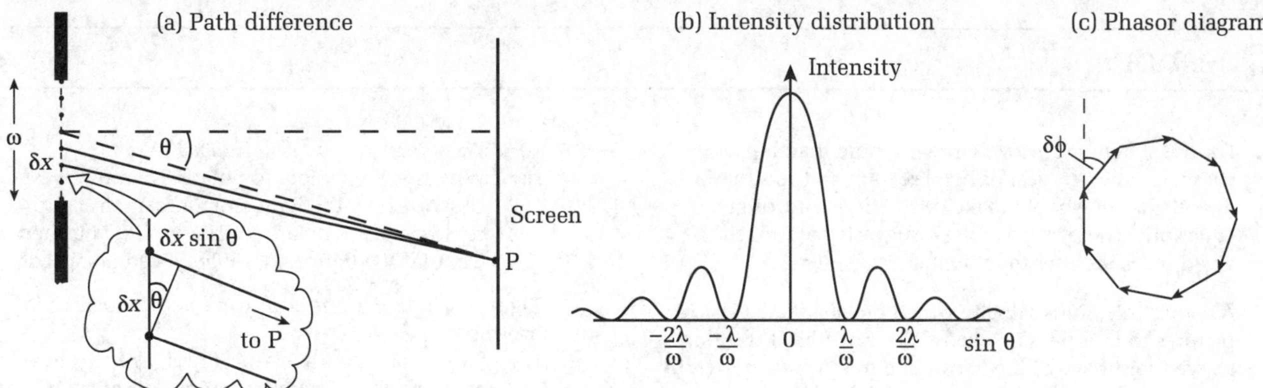

Fig 17.8 Single slit diffraction

The contribution of each element may therefore be represented by a phasor, as in Fig 17.8(b). The angle between phasors of adjacent elements is $\delta\phi$. The phasors are of the same length since the elements are of equal width. Hence the intensity minima correspond to $N\,\delta\phi = 2\pi m$ where m is a **positive** integer and N is the number of elements. Therefore $\dfrac{2\pi\omega\sin\theta}{\lambda} = 2\pi m$ since $N\,\delta x$ is the slit width which gives the condition for the diffraction minima,

$$\sin\theta = \frac{m\lambda}{\omega}$$

Note that the central maximum is twice as wide as the subsidiary maxima for small angles.

2. **For a circular gap**, the diffraction pattern consists of a series of concentric rings surrounding a central spot.

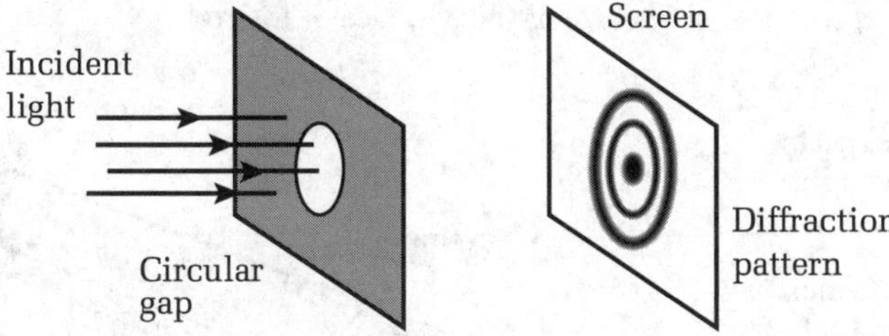

Fig 17.9 Diffraction by a circular gap

The intensity distribution is similar to Fig 17.8(b) except that the condition for the first diffraction minima is $\sin\theta = 1.22\lambda/\omega$. This condition was first derived in 1834 by Airy. Light from a point object such as a star gives a circular diffraction pattern on the retina as a result of passing through the eye pupil. Two close stars can just be resolved if the central maximum of one diffraction pattern falls on or outside the first minimum of the other pattern. Thus the above equation gives the condition for resolving two stars using a telescope with an objective of width ω. Hence the wider the diameter of the objective, the greater the resolving power of the instrument. Refraction effects in the upper atmosphere also spread out the light from a star; for this reason, ground based telescopes with objectives over about 0.10 m wide rarely achieve their theoretical resolving power.

Questions

1. For the statement below, write no more than a page showing how physical principles apply to the situation described. You should make calculations and/or give equations wherever possible. A suggested approach is given in italics after the statement.

A communications satellite which broadcasts television pictures to Europe is in a geostationary orbit 36 000 km above the surface of the Earth. The power transmitted by the satellite aerial is only about 100 W although calculations using the inverse square law suggest a much larger figure is required if the dish aerial on a house is to collect about 1 pW m^{-2} (10^{-12} W m^{-2}).

Data: diameter of transmitting dish = 0.7 m
wavelength of transmitted radiation = 0.025 m
surface area of a sphere, radius r = $4\pi r^2$

(You could start by using the inverse square law to calculate the larger power and go on to consider why much smaller powers are adequate.)

(O & C Nuffield June '93)

2. (a) The wavelength of the monochromatic light from a lamp is to be determined by means of a double-slit interference experiment.
   (i) Outline the experiment. State what measurements are taken and explain how these measurements are used to calculate the wavelength.
   (ii) Give approximate values for the separation of the two slits and the width of one of these slits.
   (iii) Explain briefly the parts played by diffraction and by interference in the production of the observed fringes.

   (b) (i) State what is meant by the *photoelectric effect*.
   (ii) Give **three** of the experimental observations associated with this effect.

   (c) (i) A lamp is placed above a metal surface which contains atoms of radius 2.0×10^{-10} m. Each electron in the metal requires a minimum energy of 3.2×10^{-19} J before it can be emitted from the metal surface, and it may be assumed that the electron can collect energy from a circular area which has a radius equal to that of the atom. The lamp provides energy at a rate of 0.40 W m^{-2} at the metal surface. Estimate, on the basis of wave theory, the time required for an electron to collect sufficient energy for it to be emitted from the metal.
   (ii) Comment on your answer to (c)(i).

(UCLES June '94)

3. (a) The electromagnetic spectrum may be classified into a number of different regions. Make a table to show clearly the name and an approximate wavelength of radiation in each main region.

   (b) (i) What is meant by *polarisation*?
   (ii) Why is it impossible to polarise sound waves?
   (iii) Describe how the light from a filament lamp could be plane-polarised. How could you then test that the light had, in fact, been polarised?

   (c) Light is said to exhibit both wave and particle aspects.
   (i) Show how the wave aspect of light helps to explain the interference pattern observed in the Young's slits experiment.
   (ii) Explain what is meant by *photoelectric emission*.

   Sketch a graph to show how the maximum kinetic energy of photoelectrons depends on the frequency of the incident radiation. How does the particle aspect of light account for the form of this graph?

   (d) The photon energy of a certain electromagnetic radiation is 1.66×10^{-15} J.
   (i) Calculate the wavelength of this radiation.
   (ii) To which region of the electromagnetic spectrum does this radiation belong?
   (iii) Outline the principle of a method to produce such radiation.

(NICCEA June '92)

4. A clear perspex cylindrical rod of length 1.00 mm and diameter 1.0 cm is used to direct light from a source S to a disc sample P, also of 1.0 cm diameter. Both the source S and the sample P are in contact with the ends of the rod. The source has a total power output of light of 15 W and may be assumed to be emitting light of wavelength 700 nm equally in all directions from a point at the centre of the end face of the rod.

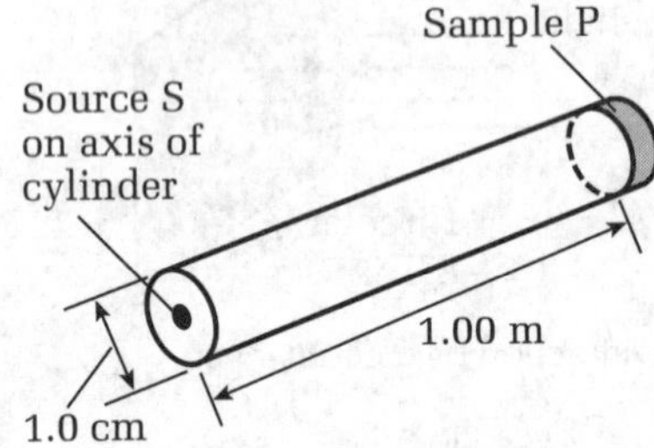

Fig 17.10

   (a) Explain, with the aid of a diagram, why the rod loses light close to the source only. You may ignore scattering in the perspex and any reflections from the flat end faces of the rod.

   (b) Calculate the total number of photons of light emitted per second by the source.

   (c) (i) Estimate the number of photons per second reaching the sample end of the rod. You may assume there is no absorption of light by the perspex and that the refractive index of perspex is 1.49.

(ii) Estimate the number of photons arriving per second at the sample P if the rod were replaced by a blackened tube of the same dimensions, assuming no reflections from the inner surface of the tube.

(NEAB June '91, Special Paper)

5. (a) The human eye, when fully adapted to the dark, can just see a candle flame 10 km away. If the candle flame is equivalent to a light source of power 4 mW and all the light has wavelength 600 nm, and if the pupil of the eye has area under these conditions of 10 mm^2, calculate
(i) the energy of a photon of wavelength 600 nm,
(ii) the smallest number of photons per second which the eye can detect.
($c = 3.0 \times 10^8\,\mathrm{m\,s^{-1}}$, $h = 6.6 \times 10^{-34}\,\mathrm{J\,s}$)

(b)

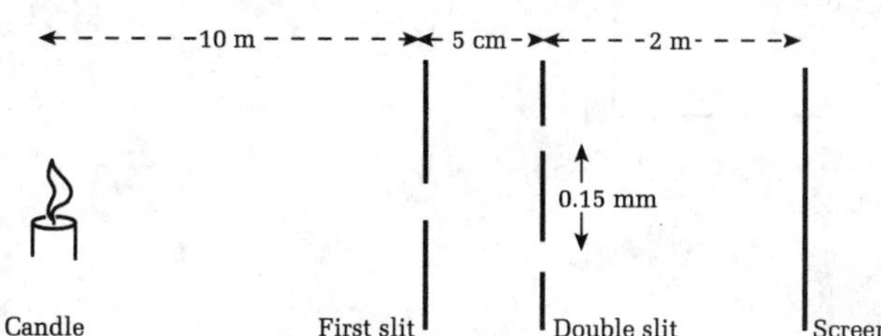

Fig 17.11

The diagram shows a Young's two slits arrangement. The candle is the same as the candle in (a) above. Each slit is 15 mm long and 30 μm wide.
(i) How many photons arrive at the first slit per second?
(ii) Estimate the number of photons arriving per second at each slit in the double slit structure. You may assume that all the photons falling on the first slit are spread uniformly into an angular width of $\frac{2\lambda}{a}$ radians where λ is the wavelength of the light and a is the width of the slit.
(iii) Using the familiar wave theory result, calculate the separation of the interference bands on the screen.
(iv) Calculate, making the same assumption as in (ii), the width of the part of the screen which is illuminated.
(v) How many interference bands are there in this width? How many photons per second reach each bright band?
(vi) Discuss whether or not these interference bands are visible.

(c) Quantum theory has to account for interference phenomena in terms of the behaviour of photons (This is one aspect of wave–particle duality.) Discuss briefly the conceptual problem which arises when individual photons are considered.

(ULEAC June '89, Special Paper)

6. Explain the term *diffraction*.
Discuss briefly how you would attempt to show experimentally that diffraction effects occur for sound waves.
Explain why, when parallel light is incident on a wide slit, a quite clearly defined patch of light of the same shape as the slit appears on a screen beyond the slit, whilst for a very narrow slit the pattern on the screen may extend beyond the geometrical shadow cast by the edges of the slit and show maxima and minima of intensity. Discuss the meaning of 'wide' and 'narrow' slits in this context.
Parallel light is incident on a narrow slit and the diffraction pattern observed in the focal plane of the converging lens. Illustrate by diagram the variation of intensity in the pattern as the angle of observation is varied. State the angular position of the first minimum in the pattern.

(a) Suggest reasons for the occurrence of subsidiary maxima in the pattern at angles greater than the first minimum.

(b) Explain why these subsidiary maxima are much weaker than the central maximum.

(c) Explain why, when intensity is plotted against $\sin\theta$, the separation of the central maximum and first minimum is equal to the separation of the first and second minima.

(O & C June '91, Special Paper)

7. (a) What experimental features of the photoelectric effect demonstrate that any one electron absorbs *one and only one* photon?

(b) In an experiment to study the photoelectric effect, the light input is derived from a standard diffraction grating spectrometer. The spectrometer employs an intense white light source which emits radiation of all wavelengths greater than 300 nm. (Wavelengths less than 300 nm are absorbed at the source, for safety reasons.) The white light beam is normally incident on the grating, which has 800 lines per mm.
When the light input is taken from a 32° deflection angle at the spectrometer, it is found that the stopping voltage to reduce the photoelectric current to zero is 2.5 V.
(i) Indicate with a rough sketch how you might carry out the experiment.
(ii) Explain why the light input for this deflection angle is not monochromatic.
(iii) Calculate the work function of the cathode in the photoelectric cell.
(iv) When the deflection angle is varied, the stopping voltage varies. However the same value, 2.5 V, is found at certain other angles besides 32°. Explain, and calculate these other angles.

(c) Many photographic films use silver bromide (AgBr) as their light-sensitive compound. The film is 'exposed' when light essentially dissociates the AgBr molecule. The energy of dissociation is $1.0 \times 10^5\,\mathrm{J\,mol^{-1}}$. Hence suggest why the film, although sensitive to visible light ($\lambda = 300$–700 nm), is insensitive to exposure to infra-red radiation.
($h = 6.6 \times 10^{-34}\,\mathrm{J\,s}$, $c = 3.0 \times 10^8\,\mathrm{m\,s^{-1}}$)

(O & C June '92, Special Paper)

18 PHOTONS AND ELECTRONS

What you need to know now

- ❑ The relationship between photon frequencies and energy level differences.
- ❑ The general features of line emission, line absorption and continuous spectra and how they are produced.
- ❑ The principle of operation of an X-ray tube and the main characteristics of the X-ray output from a tube.
- ❑ The de Broglie formula for matter waves.
- ❑ Evidence for the wave nature of the electron from electron diffraction.

What you need to know next

Energy levels and spectra

The electron energy levels of an atom are worked out from the photon frequencies emitted or absorbed by the atom when electron transitions occur. For a transition between two levels E_1 and E_2, the frequency f of the photon emitted or absorbed is given by equating the photon energy hf to the energy level difference. Energy levels quoted in electron volts must be converted to joules before using the formula above. Note that $1\,\text{eV} = 1.6 \times 10^{-19}\,\text{J}$. Some further points on spectra are summarised below.

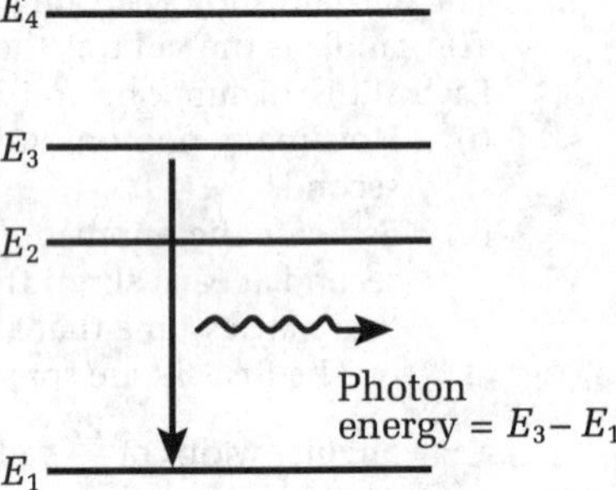

Fig 18.1 Photon emission

- ❑ **The energy levels of the hydrogen atom** can be calculated using wave mechanics and fit the formula $E = -E_0/n^2$ where E_0 is the ionisation energy and n is an integer. The Bohr model of the hydrogen atom can also be used to derive this formula but it cannot explain other features such as the number of electrons allowed in each shell whereas wave mechanics can. Other atoms possess more than one electron each and are too complicated to analyse precisely because the electrons interact with each other.
- ❑ **The width of a spectral line** in a line emission or a line absorption spectrum is broadened through two main causes.
  1. **Collision broadening** is due to a light-emitting atom colliding with other atoms whilst it is emitting a photon. Suppose an excited atom emits a photon in less than a nanosecond giving a wavepacket of the order of 0.30 m in length. During this time, the atom is likely to collide repeatedly with other atoms, each collision causing the phase of the emitted light to change abruptly. Thus the 'coherence length' of each wavepacket is much less than 0.30 m corresponding to coherent emission in a time of much less than a nanosecond. Use the Uncertainty Principle and the photon energy

equation to show that a coherence length of 10 mm for a photon of wavelength 500 nm would give an uncertainty of 0.005% in the photon energy and hence an approximate width for the spectral line of about 0.05 nm. For comparison, note that the prominent yellow D-line of the sodium spectrum which can easily be observed is a doublet of wavelengths 589.0 and 589.6 nm.

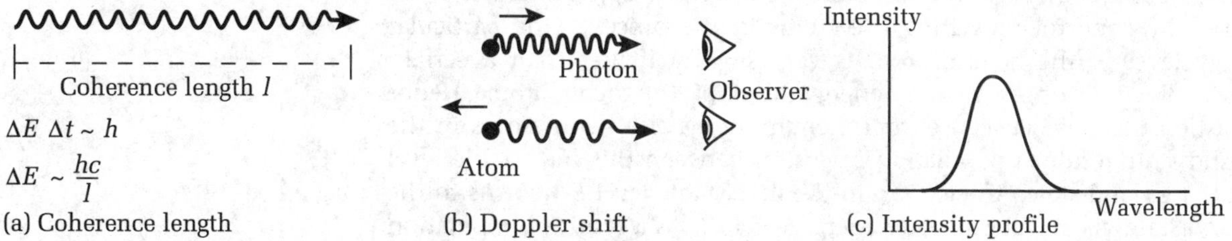

Fig 18.2 Spectral broadening

2. **Doppler broadening**, sometimes referred to as 'thermal broadening', is due to the random motion of the light-emitting atoms. A wavepacket emitted by an atom in the direction of its velocity is 'blue-shifted' to shorter wavelength and is 'red-shifted' to longer wavelength if emitted in the opposite direction to the atom's velocity. Since atoms emit light in random directions and are moving in random directions, there is a continuous spread of wavelengths about each spectral line. Raising the temperature causes the line to broaden because the speed distribution of the atom broadens and hence the spread of wavelengths for each spectral line broadens. For an ideal gas at temperature T, the r.m.s. speed of its atoms, $v_{\rm rms} = \sqrt{\frac{3RT}{M}}$ where M is the molar mass of the gas. The doppler shift of wavelength $\Delta\lambda = v_{\rm rms}\,\lambda/c$ where c is the speed of light and so the doppler broadening $(= 2\,\Delta\lambda)$ can be estimated.

The laser

A laser emits monochromatic light in a highly coherent parallel beam. This is achieved as a result of the process of stimulated emission in which photons of a certain frequency passing through excited atoms cause the atoms to de-excite and emit further photons of the same frequency. The photons would be absorbed if there were fewer atoms in the excited state than in the lower energy state. However, in a laser, the proportion of atoms in the excited state is made larger than in the lower energy state.

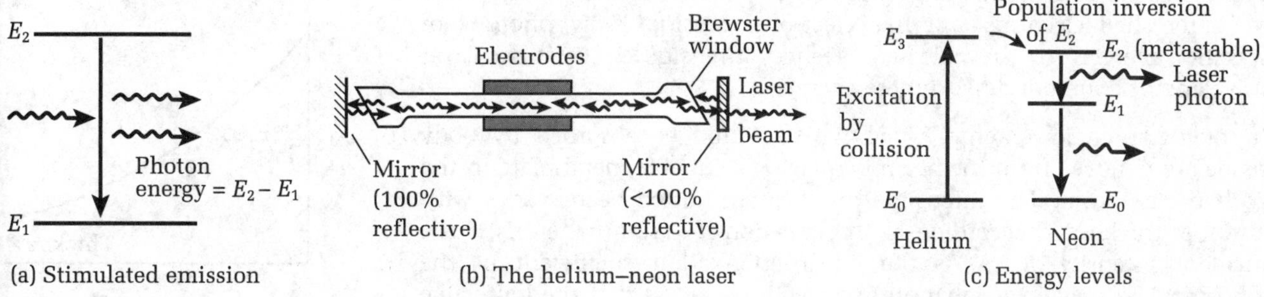

Fig 18.3 The laser

This 'population inversion' does not normally occur as the proportion of excited atoms is usually less than in the lower energy state, in accordance with the Boltzmann factor $\exp - (E_1 - E_2)/kT$.

The mechanism by which population inversion is achieved depends on the type of laser. The helium–neon gas laser consists of a sealed glass tube containing helium and neon gas in proportions of approximately 8 to 1 at a pressure of about 1 kPa. A radio frequency signal is applied to electrodes surrounding the tube, exciting the atoms in the process. One particular energy level of the helium atom is very slightly higher than a certain metastable (i.e. longer lasting) energy level of the neon atom. Hence inelastic collisions between excited helium atoms and neon atoms in the ground state result in population inversion between this metastable level and the ground state. An electron in the metastable level E_1 returns to the ground state via an intermediate energy level E_2. As a result of population inversion, this transition is stimulated by a passing photon of energy $E_1 - E_2$, corresponding to a wavelength of 632.8 nm. The photon released as a result of this transition therefore has the same wavelength as the passing photon, is emitted in phase with it and has the same polarisation.

A plane mirror is positioned outside each end of the tube to reflect photons back into the tube, thus stimulating further emission of similar photons. One mirror is slightly less than perfect as a reflector and transmits a small proportion of the incident photons which therefore emerge as the laser beam. To prevent internal reflection at each end of the tube producing out-of-phase photons, a 'brewster window' is used at each end. This is a window such that the transmitted light is plane polarised. Each brewster window transmits almost 100% of the incident light. Hence the laser beam is plane polarised.

X-rays

In an X-ray tube, electrons from a heated filament are accelerated to high energies onto a target anode. The impact causes the electrons to lose kinetic energy rapidly, emitting X-rays in the process. The kinetic energy of each electron is due to work done by the tube p.d. This is equal to eV, where V is the tube p.d. and e is the charge of the electron. Hence the kinetic energy of each electron immediately before impact is eV. Since this is the maximum energy of an X-ray photon, the maximum X-ray frequency $f_{\max} = eV/h$ giving a minimum wavelength $\lambda_{\min} = hc/eV$, where c is the speed of light.

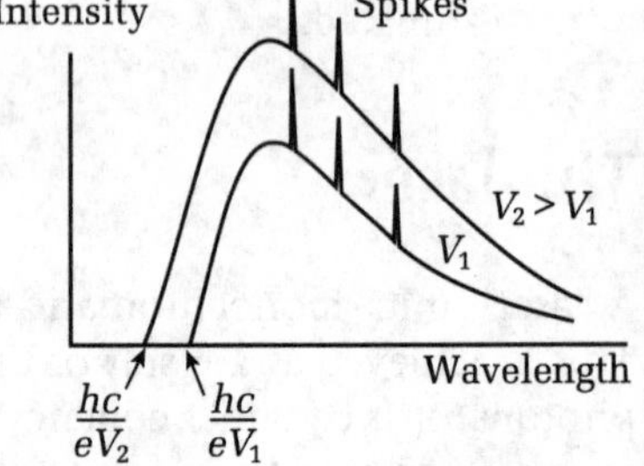

Fig 18.4 Intensity vs wavelength for an X-ray tube

There is a continuous range of wavelengths from $\lambda_{\min}$ upwards in the spectrum of X-rays from an X-ray tube, as shown in Fig 18.4. The graph also shows intensity 'spikes' which are characteristic of the target element. These spikes are caused by beam electrons ejecting orbital electrons from the innermost shells of the target atoms. The vacancies created are refilled by outer shell electrons and free electrons, causing X-ray photons of specific energies to be released. Hence intensity 'spikes' occur at wavelengths corresponding to these energies.

In radiography, low-energy X-rays which would be absorbed by body tissue are removed from the beam by placing a suitable metal plate in the path of the beam. The intensity I of the transmitted beam varies with absorber thickness x according to the equation $I = I_0 e^{-\mu x}$ where I_0 is the incident intensity and μ is the linear attenuation coefficient of the absorber. Use the above equation to prove for yourself that the half-value thickness $x_{1/2} = \ln 2/\mu$.

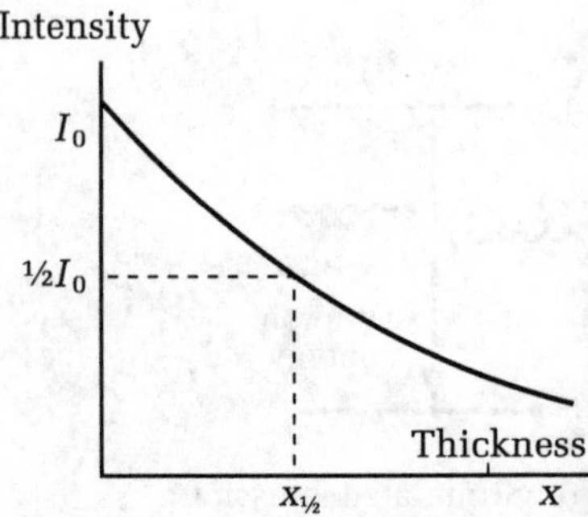

Fig 18.5 Attenuation of X-rays

The Compton effect provides direct evidence for the photon theory. The wavelengths of X-rays scattered by light solid elements change as a result of the scattering. This effect remained unexplained for over two decades until Compton in 1925 derived a formula for the change of wavelength using the photon theory. Compton verified the formula by precise measurements thus providing further evidence in addition to the explanation of photoelectricity for the photon theory.

NOTE: By considering $E = mc^2$ and $E = hf$, Compton assumed that the momentum of a photon $= h/\lambda$. By considering conservation of momentum and conservation of energy separately, he proved that the change of wavelength $= (1 - \cos\theta)\, h/m_0 c$, where m_0 is the rest mass of the electron and θ is the angle of scatter. For $\theta = 90°$, use the conservation laws as in Fig 18.6 to prove that the change of wavelength is 0.0024 nm.

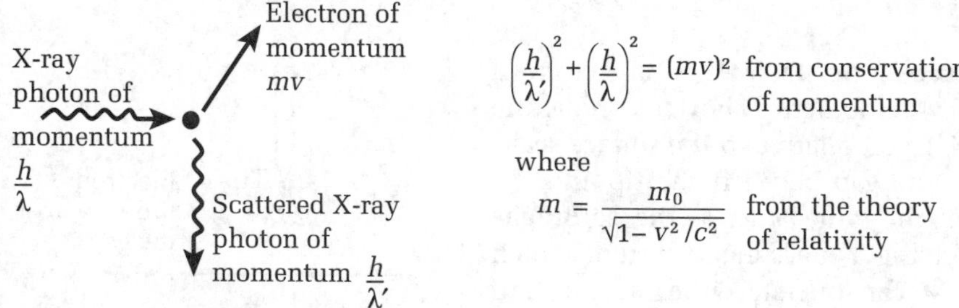

Fig 18.6 The Compton effect

Matter waves

The hypothesis that matter particles are capable of wave-like behaviour was put forward by de Broglie in 1924. He proposed that the wavelength λ of a matter particle is related to its momentum p according to the equation $\lambda = h/p$. This was confirmed experimentally in 1927 by electron diffraction experiments carried out by Davisson and Germer in 1927. Prove for yourself that the momentum of a beam of electrons accelerated through a p.d. V is $\sqrt{2meV}$ where m is the mass and e is the charge of the electron. Davisson and Germer proved that the de Broglie wavelength calculated from the equation $\lambda = h/\sqrt{2meV}$ is equal to the value measured using a thin crystal as a diffraction grating. Some further applications of matter waves are summarised below.

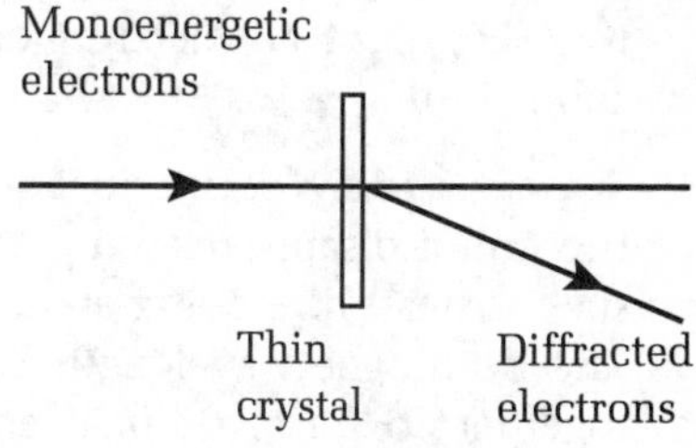

Fig 18.7 Electron diffraction

1. **Alpha particle tunnelling** occurs when an alpha particle escapes from an unstable nucleus. Alpha particles from a given nuclide are monoenergetic (except where the daughter nuclide is formed either in an excited state or in its ground state in which case there are two possible kinetic energy values). Measurements on different monoenergetic α-emitting nuclides show that the shorter the half-life of the nuclide, the greater the energy of the emitted α-particle. This occurs because the kinetic energy of an α-particle formed in the nucleus by two protons and two neutrons joining together is less than the work necessary to escape from the strongly attractive nuclear force holding the nucleons together. The kinetic energy is due to the binding energy released when two protons and two neutrons come together.

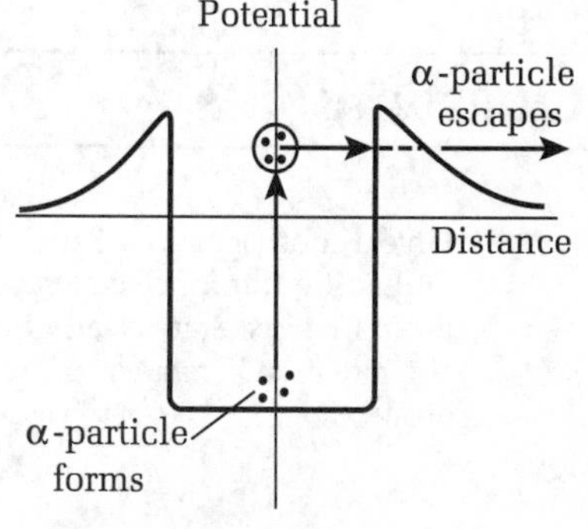

Fig 18.8 Tunnelling

The fact that α-particles do escape contradicts the classical laws of mechanics. However, the rules of quantum mechanics provide a complete explanation through the **uncertainty principle**. This states that it is not possible to specify the momentum and the position of a particle simultaneously with exact certainty and the uncertainty of each quantity is given by the relationship $\Delta p \Delta x \approx h$. In the nucleus, the uncertainty in position Δx is of the order of 10^{-15} m; hence the uncertainty in the momentum of an α-particle in the nucleus is of the order of $10^{-18}\,\mathrm{kg\,m\,s^{-1}}$. Prove for yourself that this gives uncertainty in the kinetic energy of an α-particle of the order of 100 MeV. Due to this uncertainty, there is a small probability that an α-particle can escape, equivalent to tunnelling through the potential barrier due to the nuclear force.

The greater the kinetic energy of the α-particle, the nearer the α-particle is to the top of the barrier. Since the barrier becomes thinner at increasing height, the α-particle can 'tunnel' through it more easily. Hence a nuclide with a short half life emits higher energy α-particles than a nuclide with a longer half life.

2. **The scanning tunnelling microscope (STM)** is an electron microscope in which a metal tip a few nanometres above a conducting surface at a potential of the order of 1 volt relative to the surface scans the surface. Electrons tunnel across the gap between the tip and the surface provided the gap width is of the same order as the de Broglie wavelength of the electrons, thus giving a measurable current which depends on the gap width. An STM can operate either at constant current or at constant height. In the former mode, the tip height is changed to keep the current constant whereas in the constant height mode, the tip height is fixed and the current varies due to surface features such as raised atoms. In either mode, the STM is linked to a computer which is programmed to display an image of the surface features scanned by the tip. Prove for yourself that the de Broglie wavelength of an electron of kinetic energy of the order of 1 eV is about 1 nm.

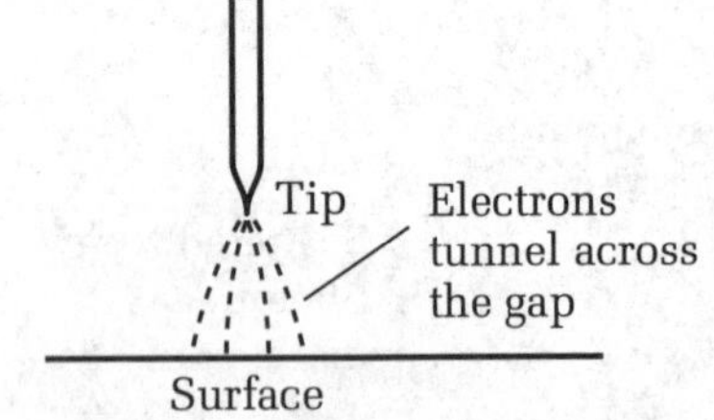

(a) The STM tip

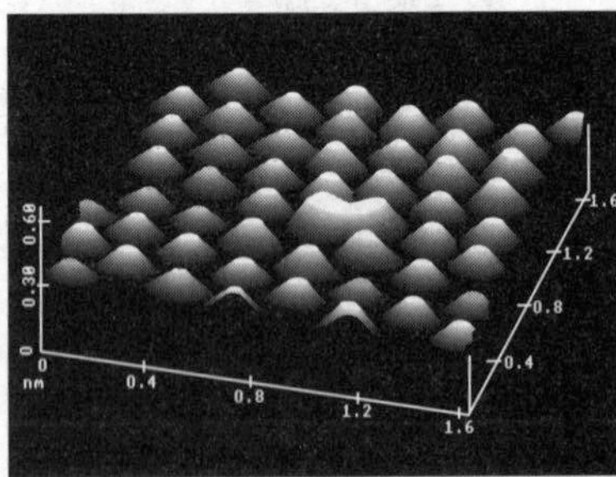

(b) an STM image

Fig 18.9 The scanning tunnelling microscope

3. **Superfluidity** occurs in liquid helium below 2.2 K. The viscosity of the liquid disappears completely and the atoms form a single energy state instead of moving about at random as in a normal liquid or gas. The de Broglie wavelength is sufficiently large for the atoms to link together to form a single energy state. Assuming the mean kinetic energy of a particle in a fluid at temperature T is $3kT/2$, prove for yourself that the de Broglie wavelength of a helium-4 atom at 2 K is of the order of 1 nm, the same order as the mean separation between the atoms at this temperature.

Questions

1. (a) Give a short account of the processes of emission and absorption of electromagnetic radiation by an atom in a gas. State clearly how the frequency of the radiation is related to the energy states of the atom.

   (b) The table gives the energies (in electron volts) of the first eight energy states of the hydrogen atom.

State	Energy *E*/eV
Lowest (ground) state	−13.64
First excited state	−3.41
Second excited state	−1.52
Third excited state	−0.85
Fourth excited state	−0.55
Fifth excited state	−0.38
Sixth excited state	−0.28
Seventh excited state	−0.21

(i) Use the data in the table to draw to scale on graph paper an energy level diagram for the hydrogen atom. Include the zero-energy level.

(ii) Visible light may be assumed to be electromagnetic radiation within a wavelength range from 750 nm to 400 nm. Calculate the photon energies (in eV) corresponding to these extreme wavelengths.
Deduce which transitions in the hydrogen atom could give rise to the emission of photons in this energy range (i.e. could produce visible radiation), and mark the transitions on your energy level diagram.

(iii) Calculate the wavelength of the electromagnetic radiation emitted when a hydrogen atom undergoes a transition from its first excited state to its lowest (ground) state. State the region of the electromagnetic spectrum in which this radiation occurs.

(c) (i) What is meant by *fluorescence*?

(ii) Explain, in terms of energy states, how some substances fluoresce when exposed to ultra-violet light.

(NICCEA June '91)

2. (a) (i) Explain what is meant by 'electron energy levels' in an atom.

(ii) How does this concept account for the characteristic emission line spectrum of an element?

(iii) Describe a simple laboratory demonstration of line spectrum emission.

(b) Fig 18.10 represents the lowest energy levels of the electron in the hydrogen atom, giving the principal quantum number n associated with each level and the corresponding values of the energy.

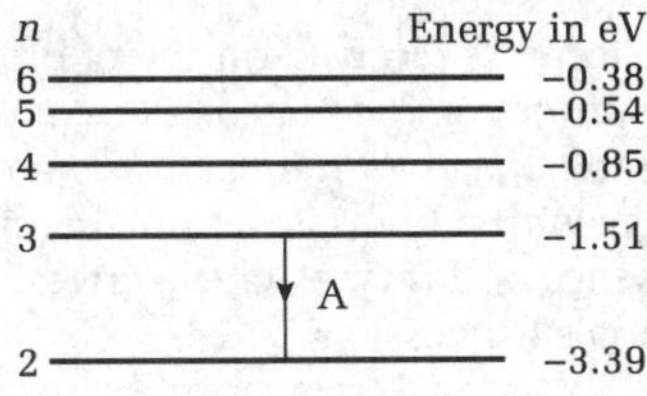

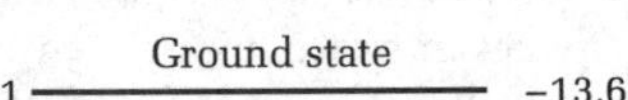

Fig 18.10

(i) Why are the energies quoted with negative values?

(ii) Calculate the wavelength of the line arising from the transition A, indicating in which region of the electromagnetic spectrum this occurs.

(iii) What happens when 13.6 eV of energy is absorbed by a hydrogen atom in its ground state?

(c) (i) Explain, in terms of electron energy levels, how X-ray line spectra are emitted, pointing out differences between production of X-ray line spectra and optical line spectra.

(ii) Electrons are accelerated from rest through a potential difference of 10 kV in an X-ray tube. Calculate the minimum wavelength of the X-rays emitted. Why do the remainder of the X-rays emitted have longer wavelengths than this?
[$e = 1.6 \times 10^{-19}$ C, $h = 6.6 \times 10^{-34}$ J s, $c = 3.0 \times 10^{8}$ m s^{-1}]

(WJEC June '91)

3. X-rays and gamma-rays are streams of photons with very similar properties. Both radiations are used extensively in medical physics. X-rays, like light, have both 'line' and continuous spectra. Gamma-rays have 'line' spectra only, resulting from energy transitions in atomic nuclei.

(a) Explain the origin of
(i) 'line' spectra
(ii) continuous spectra
in the *visible region* of the electromagnetic spectrum.

(b) A useful gamma-ray emitter is technetium-99 ($^{99}_{43}$Tc) which decays by gamma emission only. The gamma photons each have the an energy of 140 keV.
The electronic charge $e = -1.6 \times 10^{-19}$ C.
The Planck constant $h = 6.6 \times 10^{-34}$ J s.
The speed of light in free space $c = 3.0 \times 10^{8}$ m s^{-1}.

(i) State and explain whether or not the particle composition of the nucleus of the technetium varies during this emission.

(ii) Calculate the wavelength of the gamma emission from technetium-99.

(c) The radiation from a hospital X-ray tube consists of photons of many different energies: the higher energy radiation penetrates further into the human body. To limit radiation hazard to those undergoing treatment, metal filters are inserted into the X-ray beam. These filters reduce the quantity and change the wavelength distribution of the radiation.
Fig 18.11 shows the characteristics of the radiation before and after insertion of an aluminium filter.

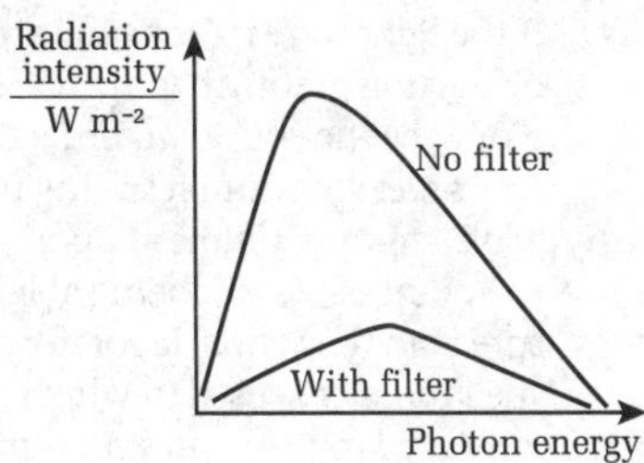

Fig 18.11

(i) Compare the wavelength distributions of the radiation before and after the insertion of the filter.

(ii) Reproduce the diagram and add a line showing the effects of using a thinner aluminium filter.

(iii) Explain whether the exterior regions of the human body nearer to the X-ray generator, or the interior regions, will receive the greater protection when a filter is used.

(d) Gamma-rays are also used in hospital treatments. The absorption characteristic of a material for a parallel beam of gamma-rays is given by the relation

$$I = I_0 e^{-\mu x}$$

where I_0 and I are the beam intensities before and after passing through a thickness x of the material. μ is a constant for a given wavelength and material, and has the value of 80 m^{-1} for photons of energy 20 keV in soft human tissue. The value for photons of energy 150 keV is 15 m^{-1}.

(i) Calculate the proportion of the incident intensity remaining after the passage of 20 keV radiation through 50 mm of soft tissue.

(ii) What thickness of tissue would be required to absorb the same proportion of 150 keV radiation?

(AEB Summer '94, Special Paper)

4. Monochromatic light from a hot gas arises when an electron in an atom moves from one energy level to another. If many atoms are present then the wavelengths of the individual photons are all nominally the same but in practice there is always a small spread. Some idea of the *range* of wavelengths involved can be gained by applying simple physical principles.
This question is about applying those principles to the light from a sodium lamp.
One cause of line broadening is the Doppler effect. If a source of light of frequency f_0 is moving away from an observer at a speed v then the observed frequency, f, is given by $f = f_0(1 - v/c)$, where c is the speed of light and v is small compared with c.

(a) The sodium in a sodium lamp is in the form of a gas which is heated by an electric discharge. A typical temperature for the gas might be 1200 °C.

(i) Find the mean square speed of the sodium atoms given that the molar mass of sodium is 0.023 kg mol^{-1}.

(ii) Use this value to estimate the spread in frequency and the fractional spread in frequency of light of wavelength 590 nm.

(iii) Now convert the results of part (ii) to a spread in wavelength and a fractional spread in wavelength.

(iv) If the light were to be examined using a diffraction grating having 600 lines per mm what would be the spread in diffraction angle in the first order spectrum resulting from this spread in wavelength? Comment upon your answer from the point of view of being able to measure the spread in the school laboratory, assuming that a spectrometer is used in which angles can be measured to the nearest minute of arc.

(b) Another mechanism is more subtle and depends upon the fact that a *truly* monochromatic beam of light has to have an infinite length. In practice, light is emitted in wave trains of finite length, the period of the emission being about 10^{-8} seconds. The fractional spread in frequency is then roughly equal to the reciprocal of the number of complete cycles in the wave train. Estimate the spread in wavelength from this mechanism.

(c) What implications would the finite length of the light 'beam' from an emitting atom have on the possibilities of producing an interference pattern by splitting the light from the source into two parts with a half silvered mirror, sending the two beams along different length paths and then recombining them on a screen?

(d) One method of measuring the temperature of a hot gas such as the sodium in a sodium lamp is to match the light from it with the light from an ordinary filament bulb. It is a difficult experiment to perform accurately and the details are not relevant here but one important piece of information which is needed is the temperature of the filament.
How would you try to estimate the temperature of a hot filament? What experiments would you perform and what information would you need to find out?

(O & C Nuffield June '93, Special Paper)

5. (a) (i) Describe with the aid of a sketch how you would set up a demonstration of light-wave interference using a double-slit method. Give approximate dimensions where appropriate and state the fringe separation you would aim to obtain.

(ii) State the principal factors that would affect the clarity of the fringes.

(b) Fig 18.12 illustrates an arrangement for demonstrating wave–particle duality.

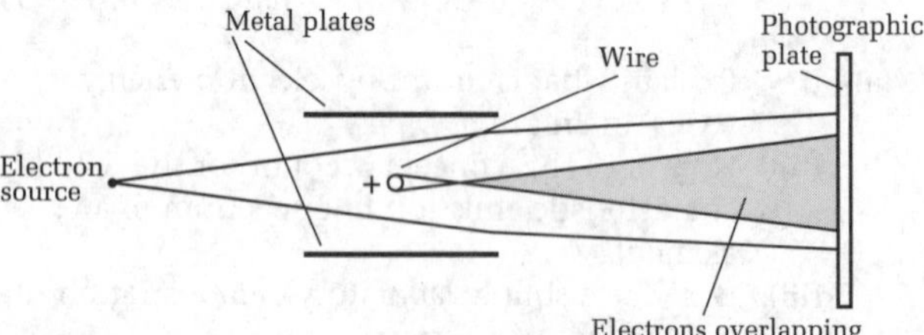

Fig 18.12

Electrons, produced by a hot-wire source, pass through close parallel metal plates. A fine positively-charged wire deflects the electrons. The overlapping electrons are received on the photographic plate. The photographic plate is subsequently processed and the image on it enlarged. Examination of the image with a high-power microscope reveals the presence of diffuse parallel fringes, resembling Young's fringes.

(i) Explain what is meant by *wave–particle duality*.

(ii) Explain how this demonstration provides evidence for wave–particle duality.

(iii) The wire divides the gap between the metal plates into two halves of mean separation 1.0 mm. Calculate the separation of the centres of interference fringes formed on the photographic plate placed 80 mm from the wire by electrons of wavelength 20 nm.

(c) (i) Calculate the speed of electrons having a wavelength of 20 nm. (Take the mass of an electron m_e as 9.1×10^{-31} kg and the Planck constant h as 6.6×10^{-34} J s.)

(ii) What class of electromagnetic waves would have a wavelength of 20 nm?

(d) Describe another piece of experimental evidence for wave–particle duality. Give details of the apparatus used, the experimental procedure, and how the results of the experiment confirm the theory.

(UODLE June '94, Special Paper)

19 CHARGED PARTICLES IN FIELDS

What you need to know now

- ❏ Work done $= qV$ for a charge q moved through a p.d. V.
- ❏ Force $F = qE$ for a charge q in an electric field of strength E.
- ❏ A charged particle moving across the lines of a uniform electric field follows a parabolic path.
- ❏ Force $F = Bqv$ for a charge q moving at speed v perpendicular to a uniform magnetic field of strength B.
- ❏ A charged particle moving perpendicular to the lines of a magnetic field follows a circular path.

What you need to know next

The anode gun equation

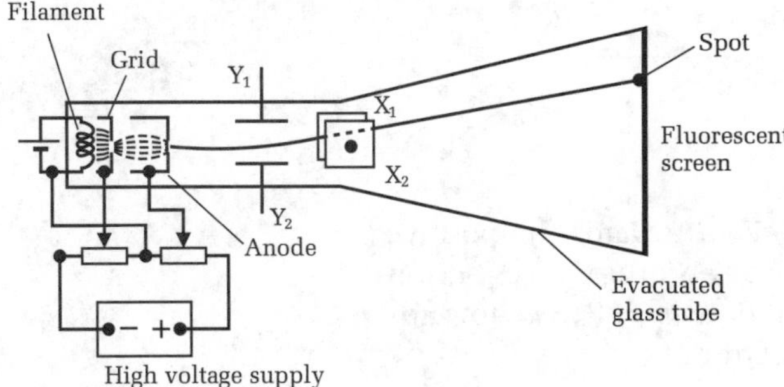

Fig 19.1 The oscilloscope tube

The work done on a charged particle in a vacuum accelerated through a p.d. V is converted into kinetic energy.

- ❏ Provided the final speed of the particle v is much less than the speed of light, c, its kinetic energy at speed v is $\frac{1}{2}mv^2$. Assuming negligible initial kinetic energy, v may be calculated from the equation

$$\tfrac{1}{2}mv^2 = qV$$

- ❏ If the final speed is not negligible compared with the speed of light, the above equation does not apply. The relativistic formula $E = mc^2$ relating energy E and mass m must be used. The total initial energy of the particle due to its rest mass m_0 is m_0c^2. Hence the final total energy $mc^2 = m_0c^2 + qV$.

NOTE: Since mass m depends on speed v in accordance with the equation $m = m_0(1 - v^2/c^2)^{-1/2}$, use the binomial expansion $(1 + x)^n \simeq 1 + nx$ for $x \ll 1$ to prove that $m \simeq m_0(1 + v^2/2c^2)$. Hence show that the equation $mc^2 = m_0c^2 + qV$ simplifies to $\frac{1}{2}mv^2 = qV$ for $v \ll c$.

The above analysis shows that the non-relativistic formula may be used provided $v \ll c$. This is equivalent to the condition that the work done qV is much less than the rest mass energy m_0c^2. For an electron, $m_0c^2 = 0.55\,\text{MeV}$ and hence the accelerating p.d. V must be much less than 0.55 MV for $v \ll c$ to apply to electrons. For a proton $m_0c^2 = 938\,\text{MeV}$; so accelerating p.d.s in excess of about 100 MV require the use of the relativistic formula for protons.

The theory of the cathode ray oscilloscope

The operation of an oscilloscope requires the deflection of the spot to be proportional to the p.d. across the deflecting plates. This applies to both the vertical and the horizontal deflection of the spot. To prove the deflection of the spot, y, is proportional to the p.d., V_p, consider the beam of electrons moving at speed v entering the plates along the mid-line, as in Fig 19.2. Let d represent the separation between the plates.

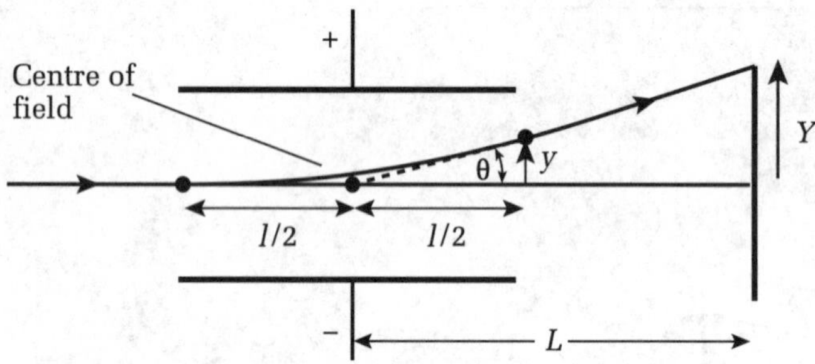

Fig 19.2 *Y*-sensitivity

In the field, each electron experiences a force eV_p/d towards the positive plate, where e is the charge of the electron. Since no other forces act on the electrons, each electron undergoes acceleration $a = eV_p/md$ towards the positive plate, where m is the mass of the electron.

At time t after entering the field, an electron will have moved a distance $x = vt$ parallel to the plates. Also, because its initial velocity is parallel to the plates, the deflection y at time t after entering the field is given by $y = \frac{1}{2}\left(\frac{eV_p}{md}\right)\frac{x^2}{v^2}$ and its velocity has components parallel and perpendicular to the plates of $v_x = v$ and $v_y = \left(\frac{eV_p}{md}\right)\frac{x}{v}$ respectively.

- If the plates are of length l, the deflection y on exit from the field is therefore $y = \frac{1}{2}\left(\frac{eV_p}{md}\right)\frac{l^2}{v^2}$.
- The direction of the beam on exit is given by $\tan\theta = \frac{v_y}{v_x} = \frac{eV_p}{md}\frac{l}{v^2}$. Since this is equal to $\frac{y}{(l/2)}$ the exit direction of the beam is as if it had come straight from the centre of the field.
- The beam continues without change of direction after leaving the field. Its overall deflection $Y = L\tan\theta$ where L is the distance from the centre of the field to the screen. Using the above expression for $\tan\theta$ therefore gives $Y = kV_p$ where $k = \frac{eLl}{mdv^2}$.

Charged particles in magnetic fields

Consider a particle of charge q and mass m which enters a uniform magnetic field at speed v.

1. Perpendicular to the lines of the magnetic field

The particle experiences a force Bqv perpendicular to its velocity direction and to the field direction. Hence the particle is forced on a circular path at constant speed v. No work is done on the particle by the field since the force is perpendicular to the velocity.

The centripetal acceleration $v^2/r = Bqv/m$ where r is the radius of curvature. Hence its angular speed $\omega = v/r = Bq/m$.

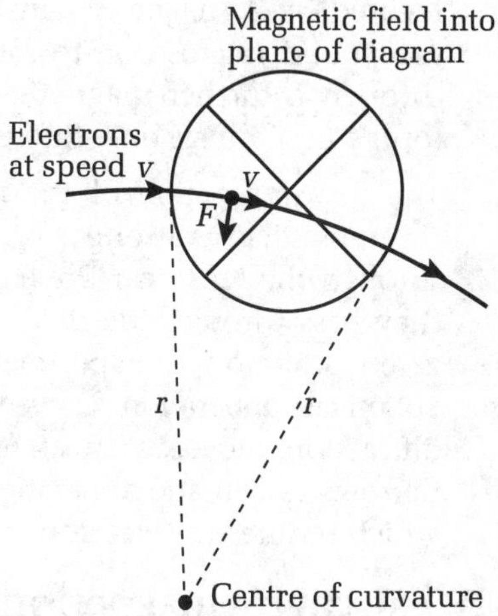

Fig 19.3 Circular motion

2. In a direction at angle θ to the field lines

The initial velocity has components $v\cos\theta$ and $v\sin\theta$ parallel and perpendicular to the field. The particle experiences force $F = Bqv\sin\theta$ perpendicular to its velocity direction and to the field direction. Its path is therefore a helix and it spirals about the field lines.

- Its velocity component parallel to the field is unchanged since the force is perpendicular to the field lines.
- The force due to the field makes it move on a circular path at the same time as it moves along the field line direction. Its angular speed is the same ($= Bq/m$) as if its initial velocity had been perpendicular to the field.

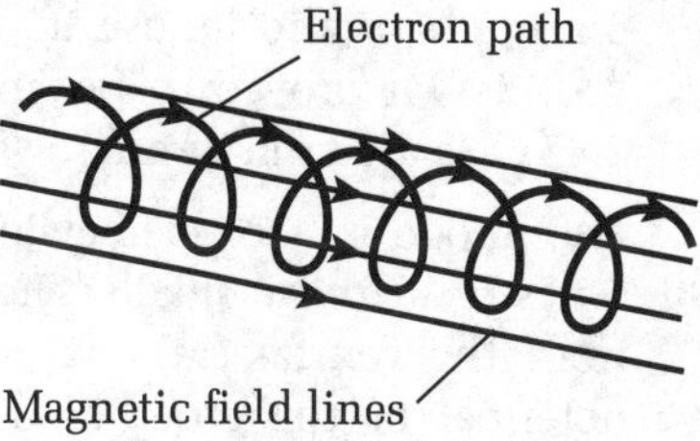

Fig 19.4 Electron spirals

Applications

Magnetic fields created by current-carrying coils have a wide range of applications. For example, they are used in television receivers to control the electron beams and in medical scanners. Two further applications are given below.

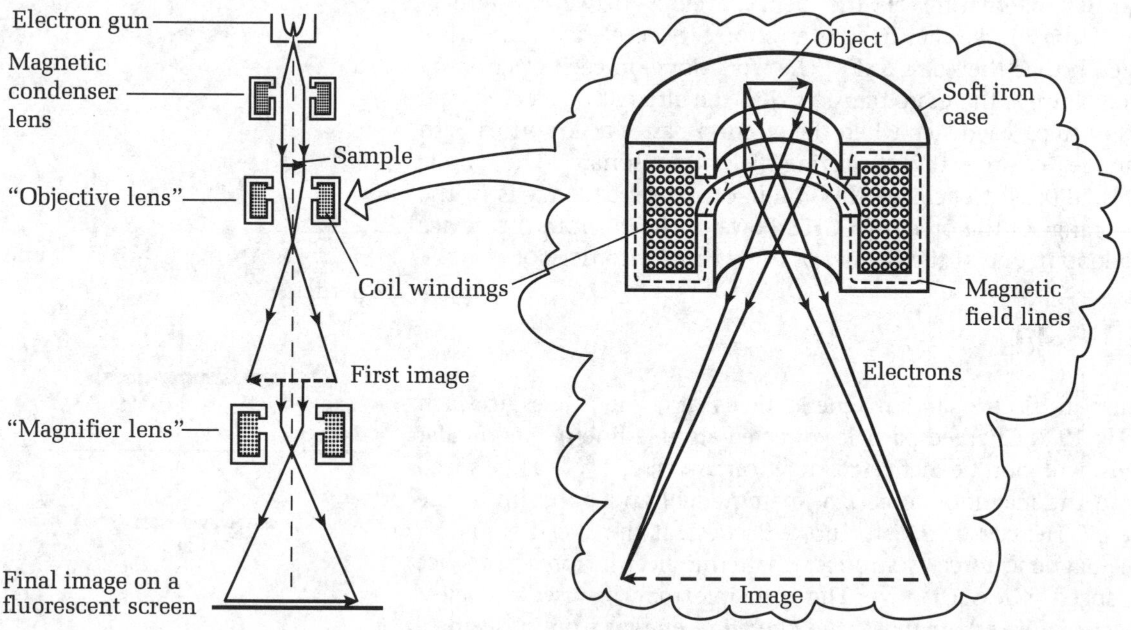

Fig 19.5 The electron microscope

❑ The magnetic lens

The transmission electron microscope (TEM) makes use of the wave nature of the electron to form highly magnified images. A thin specimen is placed in the path of a beam of electrons which are scattered by the structures in the specimen. The scattered electrons are focused by a magnetic 'lens' which acts like the objective lens of a compound microscope to form a real image. The electrons then pass through a further magnetic lens which magnifies the real image to form a final image on a fluorescent screen.

The focusing action of the magnetic lens is shown in Fig 19.5. The magnetic field is stronger nearer the edge and hence electrons passing through the lens near the edge are forced to spiral towards the axis as they pass through the field. The result is that the electrons from any given point on the specimen are focused to the same image point. Spherical abberation is reduced by narrowing the aperture, but diffraction increases to an unacceptable level if the aperture is too narrow. Chromatic abberation is reduced by a suitable anode design which ensures the electrons have a very small range of wavelengths.

❑ The cavity magnetron

This device is used to produce high-intensity microwave radiation of wavelengths of the order of 10 cm for use in radar systems. It was invented in 1940 by J T Randall and H A Boot at the University of Birmingham and its use in allied aircraft and warships in the Second World War proved to be invaluable. Low power devices operating at 2.45 GHz are used in microwave ovens.

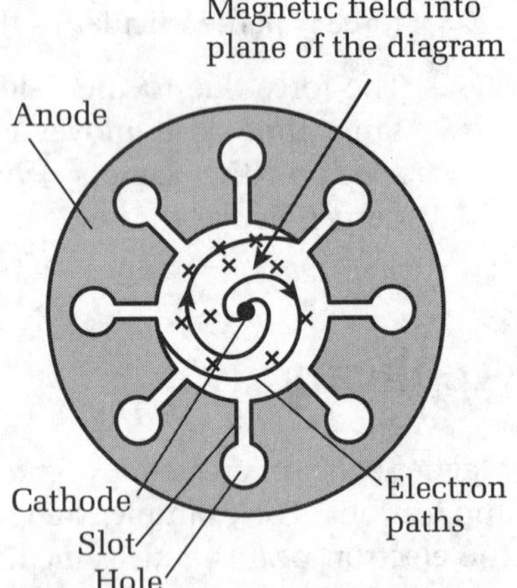

Fig 19.6 Cavity magnetron (cross section)

The anode is a copper cylinder with a central cavity connected to a series of identical smaller 'hole and slot' cavities. Electrons are emitted from the central cathode and attracted to the anode which is at a potential of the order of 50 kV. A strong uniform magnetic field is applied parallel to the axis. As a result, electrons from the cathode are forced by the magnetic field to follow a path which curves round. Each cavity is a high-frequency resonant circuit with the slot as an inductance in parallel with the hole as a capacitor. If the electrons sweep past the slots at the same frequency as the resonant frequency of each cavity, a high-frequency alternating electric field develops between alternate segments of the block, causing the electrons to decelerate and move outwards each time they pass a slot. The work done on each electron by the anode voltage is therefore transferred to the alternating electric field in a series of steps, each step when the electron passes a slot on its path to the anode, causing the oscillating field to resonate. The anode potential is adjusted to achieve this condition. The frequency is in the microwave range of the order of 3 GHz. Power is drawn from the device through a loop in one of the cavities or through an external slot.

Balanced fields

Consider uniform electric and magnetic fields at right angles to each other, as in Fig 19.7. Charged particles directed along a line perpendicular to both fields will not be deflected at a certain speed v_0. This speed corresponds to the magnetic force Bqv_0 being equal and opposite to the electric force qE. Hence $v_0 = E/B$ for no deflection. If the speed is greater than v_0, the magnetic force is stronger than the electric force and vice versa if the speed is less than v_0. The principle may be used to select charged particles of a certain speed and therefore energy from a beam of particles of widely differing energies.

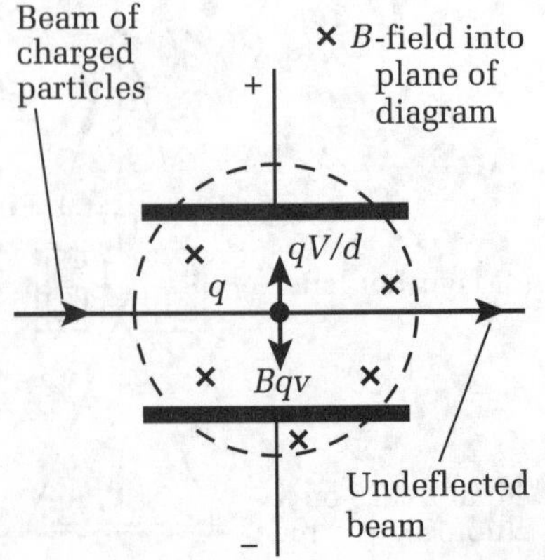

Fig 19.7 Velocity selector

Questions

1. (a) Describe by means of a diagram and a simple equation the force due to
(i) an electric field,
(ii) a magnetic field,
acting on an electron moving at right angles to each field.
Hence explain how an electric field and a magnetic field may be used in the selection of the velocity of negatively charged particles.

(b) Ions having charge $+Q$ and mass M are accelerated from rest through a potential difference V. They then move into a region of space where there is a uniform magnetic field of flux density B, acting at right angles to the direction of travel of the ions, as shown in Fig 19.8.

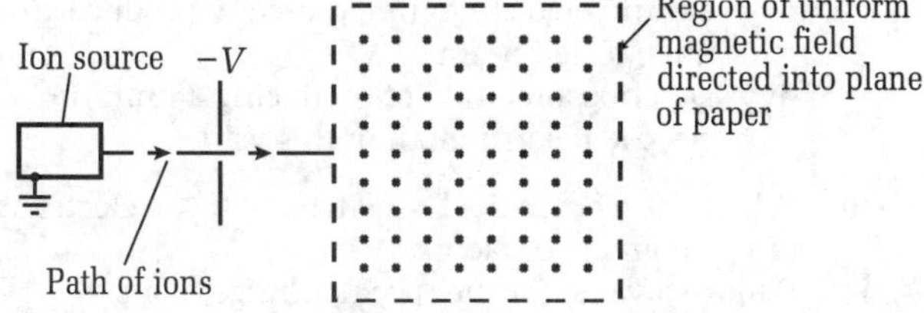

Fig 19.8

(i) Show that v, the speed with which the ions enter the magnetic field, is given by

$$v = \sqrt{\frac{2QV}{M}}$$

(ii) Hence derive an expression, in terms of M, Q, B and V, for the radius of the path of the ion in the magnetic field.
(iii) Briefly describe and explain any change in the path in the magnetic field of an ion of twice the specific charge (i.e. for which the ratio Q/M is doubled).

(UCLES June '92)

2. (a) Describe, with the aid of a labelled diagram, the basic structure of a cathode-ray tube in a cathode-ray oscilloscope (c.r.o.).

(b) In one type of c.r.o., the electrostatic deflection system consists of two parallel metal plates, each of length 2.0 cm, with a separation of 0.50 cm, as shown in Fig 19.9.

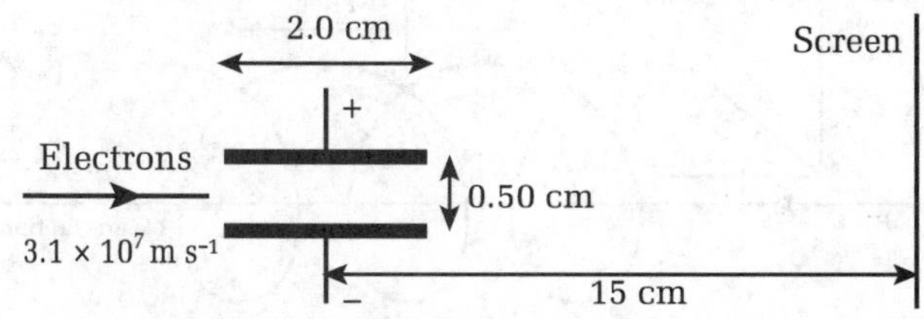

Fig 19.9

The centre of the plates is situated 15 cm from a screen. A potential difference of 80 V between the plates provides a uniform electric field in the region between the plates. Electrons of speed 3.1×10^7 m s^{-1} enter this region at right angles to the field. Calculate
(i) the time taken for an electron to pass between the plates,
(ii) the electric field strength between the plates,
(iii) the force on an electron due to the electric field,
(iv) the acceleration of the electron along the direction of the electric field,
(v) the speed of the electron at right angles to its original direction of motion as it leaves the region between the plates.

(c) Hence, by considering your answer to (b)(v) and the original speed of the electron, estimate the deflection of the electron beam on the screen.

(d) (i) Fig 19.10 represents the front of the screen of the c.r.o.

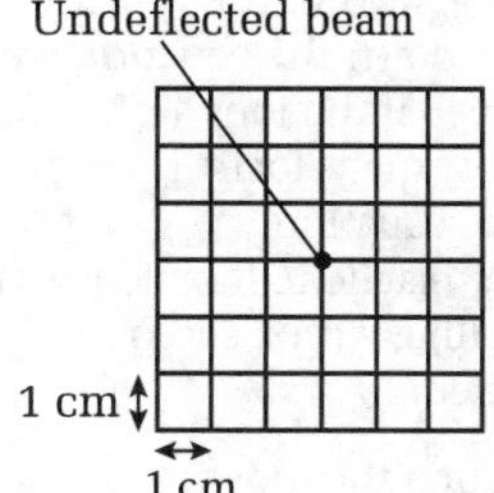

Fig 19.10

Copy Fig 19.10 onto your paper and mark on your diagram the position of the deflected beam of electrons.
(ii) Draw similar sketch diagrams to show the trace on the screen if the p.d. across the plates is
(1) varying sinusoidally with r.m.s. value 80 V,
(2) a half-wave rectified sinusoidal voltage of r.m.s. value 80 V.

(UCLES June '94)

3. The diagram shows a mass spectrometer used for measuring the masses of isotopes. It consists of an ion generator and accelerator, a velocity selector and an ion separator, all in a vacuum.

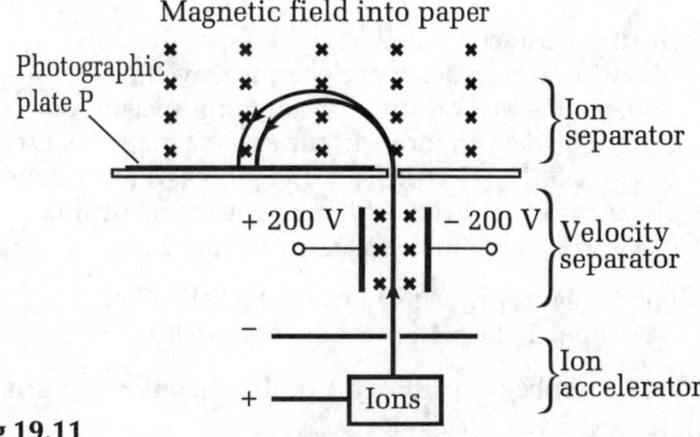

Fig 19.11

In one experiment, tin ions, each of which carries a charge $+1.6 \times 10^{-19}$ C, are produced in the ion generator and are then accelerated by a p.d. of 20 000 V. Tin has a number of isotopes, two of which are tin-118 (^{118}Sn) and tin-120 (^{120}Sn).

(a) (i) State one similarity and one difference between the isotopes of tin.
(ii) Assuming that an ion of tin-120 is at rest before being accelerated, show that the final speed after acceleration is 177 km s^{-1}.
Mass of a nucleon $= 1.7 \times 10^{-27}$ kg.
(iii) What will be the final speed of an ion of tin-118?

(b) In practice all ions produced by the ion generator have a range of speeds. A velocity selector is used to isolate ions with a single speed. In the velocity selector the force produced by the electric field is balanced by that due to the magnetic field which is perpendicular to the plane of the paper.
(i) The plates producing the electric field have a separation of 2.0 cm. The potentials of the plates are marked on the diagram. What is the magnitude of the force on an ion due to this electric field in the velocity selector?
(ii) Write down the equation which must be satisfied if the ions are to emerge from the exit hole of the velocity selector. Define the terms in the equation.
(iii) What magnetic flux density is required if ions travelling with a speed of 177 km s^{-1} are to be selected?

(c) After selection the ions are separated using a magnetic field on its own, as shown in the diagram.
(i) Explain why the ions move in circular paths in this region.
(ii) Show that the radius of the path is directly proportional to the mass of the ion.
(iii) The ions are detected using the photographic plate P. Determine the distance between the points of impact on the photographic plate of the two isotopes of tin when a magnetic flux density of 0.75 T is used in the ion separator.

(d) Explain whether the distance between the points of impact of the ions would be the same, greater or smaller for two isotopes of uranium, one with a nucleon number of 236 and the other 238, assuming that they have the same velocity at the tin ions.

(AEB June '92)

4. In an experiment to determine the specific charge (e/m) for an electron, a beam of electrons, travelling horizontally in a vacuum with uniform speed v, enters a region R where uniform electric and magnetic fields can be applied. The electric field strength has a magnitude E and acts in the direction shown. The magnetic flux density, B, acts into the plane of the paper.

(a) Explain why, when a magnetic field alone is applied, the path is the arc of a circle.

(b) Describe the path of the beam when it is exposed to the electric field alone.

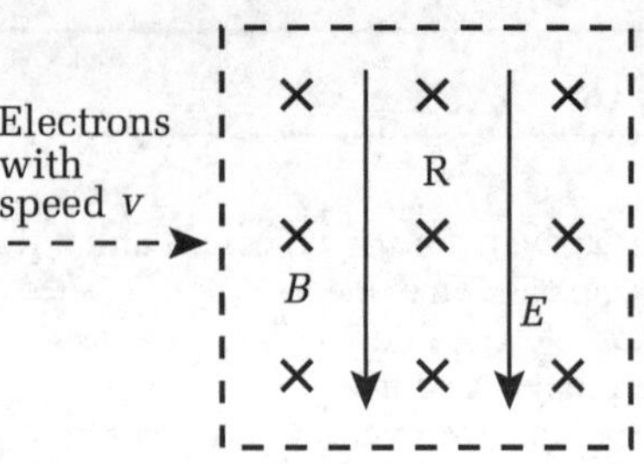

Fig 19.12

(c) The strength of the fields, when applied in combination, can be adjusted so that the beam remains undeflected during its passage through R.
(i) Explain why this is possible.
(ii) Derive a relation between E, B and v for no deflection of the beam.
(iii) Electrons with a speed 3.3×10^7 m s^{-1} are produced using an electron gun. The magnetic flux density used is 3.0 mT. Determine the electric field strength required to produce an undeflected beam.
(iv) Describe a method of producing a uniform electric field strength of this value.

(d) When the electric field is switched off the electrons move in an arc of radius 6.0 cm.
Deduce a value for the specific charge of an electron.

(e) The electron gun could be replaced by a source emitting 5 MeV alpha particles.
(i) Determine the speed of 5 MeV alpha particles.
(ii) Calculate a value for the specific charge of an alpha particle.
Mass of a proton = mass of a neutron $= 1.7 \times 10^{-27}$ kg.
Charge on an electron $= -1.6 \times 10^{-19}$ C.

(f) Discuss briefly the feasibility of using the above apparatus and procedure for a determination of *the specific charge of an alpha particle*, using particles of energy 5 MeV.

(AEB November '92)

5. Charged particles moving at high speeds in the Earth's magnetic field well outside the atmosphere may be trapped into helical paths which converge towards the Earth's magnetic poles. The diagram shows part of the trajectory of such a particle which enters a region of approximately uniform magnetic field such that its initial direction of motion makes an angle θ with the direction of the field.

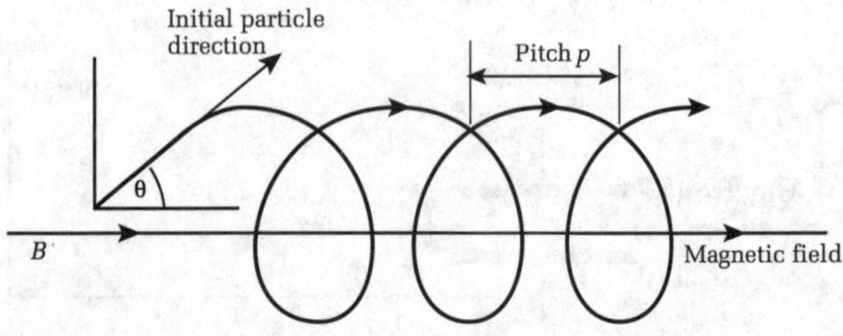

Fig 19.13

(a) Explain concisely and non-mathematically why the trajectory followed is a circular helix.

(b) A proton of mass 1.67×10^{-27} kg and charge 1.60×10^{-19} C enters a region in which the magnetic flux density is approximately uniform and of magnitude 2.0×10^{-7} T. The speed of the proton is $1.50 \times 10^{6}\ \mathrm{m\,s^{-1}}$ and its initial direction of motion makes an angle of 30° with the direction of the field. Calculate
(i) the radius of the helix,
(ii) the period of revolution of the proton,
(iii) the pitch of the helix p, shown in the diagram.

(c) During periods of intense solar activity large numbers of high-speed protons enter the Earth's upper atmosphere in the region above the poles and produce luminous effects known as auroras. Explain briefly the processes which might give rise to the emission of visible light during these events, and suggest how a study of these emissions might lead to an understanding of the composition of the upper atmosphere.

(NEAB June '91, Special Paper)

6. In a small television tube electrons are accelerated from rest through a potential difference of 4550 V before entering a region of uniform magnetic flux density with a speed v, as shown. When the flux density is zero the electron beam strikes the centre of the screen at a point K; when the flux density is increased to its maximum value a deflection of 33 mm is observed, so that the beam strikes the screen at point P.

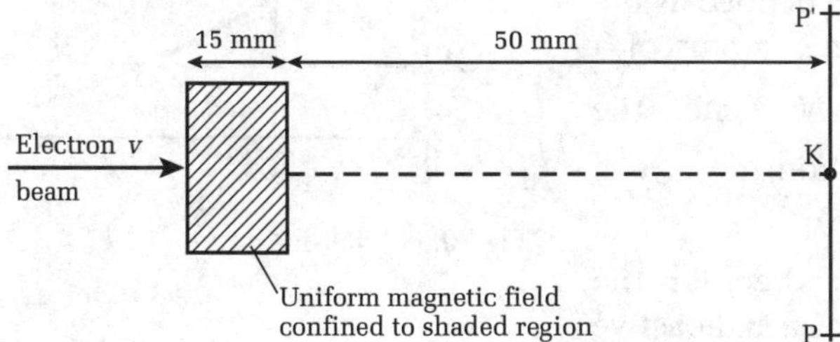

Fig 19.14

(a) (i) Determine the speed v of the electrons on entering the magnetic field.
(ii) State clearly the direction of the magnetic field needed to produce the deflection.
(iii) Draw a sketch, not necessarily to scale, to show the path of the electrons from the point where they enter the magnetic field to the point P.
(iv) With reference to your sketch, show **by calculation** that a maximum flux density of 7.6×10^{-3} T is sufficient to achieve a deflection of 33 mm at the screen.

(b) For deflections up to 33 mm the deflection of the beam may be assumed to be directly proportional to the magnitude of the flux density. In use, the beam is traversed across the screen at a constant speed from P′ to P; on reaching P the beam is instantly returned to P′ to begin its next traverse, and this process is repeated without pause at a frequency of 15.625 kHz.
Sketch a graph showing how the flux density must vary as a function of time over several cycles, labelling your axes and marking in significant flux density and time values.

(c) On striking the screen, the cross-section of the beam is a circle of diameter 0.5 mm. To achieve the correct value of light output from the screen phosphor, the power density of the incident beam must be $3.5 \times 10^{7}\ \mathrm{W\,m^{-2}}$.
Assuming that the beam is incident at a fixed position on the screen, answer the following:
(i) Determine the kinetic energy of an electron just before it strikes the screen.
(ii) Determine the number of electrons which must hit the screen every second to achieve the correct light output from the phosphor.
(iii) Hence or otherwise determine the beam current necessary for correct operation.
(iv) Explain why damage to the screen phosphor may occur if the beam is not traversed periodically across the screen.

(NEAB June '94, Special Paper)

20 FURTHER RADIOACTIVITY

What you need to know now

- ❑ The main properties and nature of α, β and γ radiation and the equations for each type of decay,
- ❑ The meaning of atomic number, mass number and the term 'isotope'.
- ❑ The theory of radioactive decay, including use of $\frac{dN}{dt} = -\lambda N$, $N = N_0 e^{-\lambda t}$ and $T_{1/2} = \ln 2/\lambda$.

What you need to know next

Activity and power

- ❑ The **number of atoms N** in a sample of an isotope of mass $m = mN_A/M$ where N_A is the Avogadro constant and M is the molar mass of the sample. For example, the number of atoms in 1 g of the isotope $^{238}_{92}U$ is equal to $N_A/238$.
- ❑ The **activity** of a certain mass of a radioactive isotope is defined as the rate of disintegration of the nuclei of the isotope. For N atoms of a radioactive isotope, activity A = magnitude of $\frac{dN}{dt} = \lambda N$; hence the activity decreases exponentially according to the equation $A = A_0 e^{-\lambda t}$ where the initial activity $A_0 = \lambda N_0$.

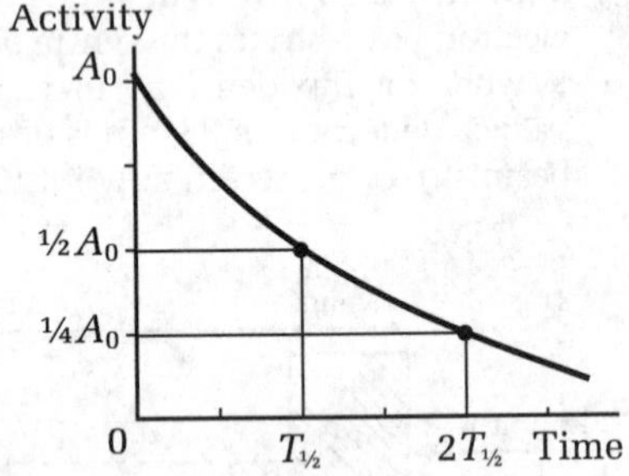

Fig 20.1 Half-life curve

- ❑ The power released as a result of radioactive decay $= AE$ where E is the energy released per disintegration. Hence for mass m of a radioactive isotope, the power released $= \lambda NE = \lambda m N_A E/M$. Thus the power released per unit mass $= \lambda N_A E/M$.
  Two examples of the use of this equation are as follows.
  1. **A long-life power unit**, for example in an artificial satellite.
     The radioactive isotope is usually an α-emitter which heats the surrounding material, causing a temperature difference, which is used to generate electricity. Prove for yourself that the power from 1 kg of plutonium $^{238}_{94}Pu$ which emits 5.5 MeV α-particles with a half life of 91.5 years is over 0.5 kW.
  2. **Storage of radioactive waste.**
     Spent fuel rods contain radioactive isotopes with a wide range of half lives. The activity per unit mass of a short half-life isotope is greater than that of a long-lived isotope because its decay constant λ is greater. Hence spent fuel rods are placed in cooling ponds for several years after removal from the reactor until the activity of the short half-life isotopes has decreased considerably. The spent fuel rods are then processed to separate plutonium and unused uranium from the fission products which then must be stored in safe conditions for many years until the activity of the longer-lived

isotopes has become insignificant. Such isotopes produce much less power per unit mass than shorter-lived isotopes but they remain active for much longer. They are stored underground in geologically safe areas after being 'vitrified' in glass.

Radioactive isotopes in medicine

Effective half life

The activity of a radioactive tracer in the body decreases for physiological reasons such as excretion as well as due to radioactive decay. The **biological half life** T_b of an isotope in the body is defined as the time taken for half the initial mass of isotope to be removed.

- For N atoms of a radioactive isotope in the body, the activity due to radioactive decay is $-\lambda_p N$ where λ_p is the radioactive decay constant.
- The activity due to physiological processes is $-\lambda_b N$ where $\lambda_b = \ln 2/T_b$. Hence the total activity $\frac{dN}{dt} = -\lambda_p N - \lambda_b N = -\lambda N$, where the effective decay constant $\lambda = \lambda_b + \lambda_p$.

  The **effective half life** T_{eff} is therefore given by the equation $1/T_{eff} = 1/T_b + 1/T_{1/2}$.

Producing useful radioactive isotopes

Radioactive isotopes used in medicine are usually produced artificially, directly or indirectly, either by neutron bombardment of a stable isotope in a nuclear reactor or by ion bombardment in a cyclotron. Neutron bombardment results in unstable neutron rich isotopes which usually decay by β^--emission. The cyclotron method is used to produce radioactive isotopes of oxygen, carbon and nitrogen.

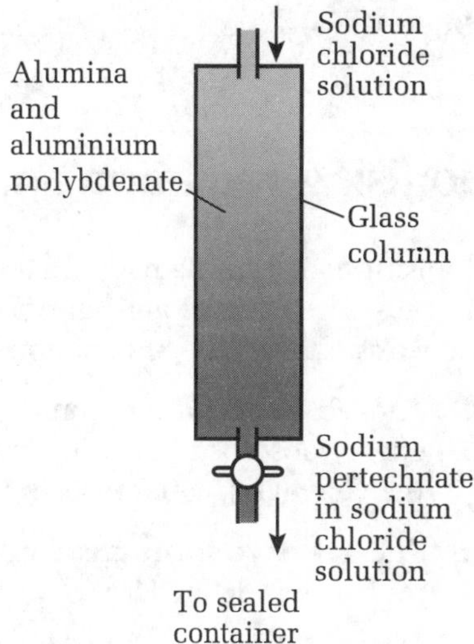

Fig 20.2 Ion exchange column

The desired radioactive isotope may be the daughter product of a radioactive isotope created artificially. For example, technetium $^{99}Tc^m$ is a γ-emitting metastable isotope with a half life of six hours and is used to measure thyroid uptake and for scanning purposes. It is produced as result of the radioactive decay of molybdenum ^{99}Mo which is a β^--emitter with a half life of 67 hours produced in a nuclear reactor. The isotope $^{99}Tc^m$ decays to the ground state of ^{99}Tc which has a half life of 2.1×10^5 years. The parent isotope, ^{99}Mo, is in the form of aluminium molybdenate and is absorbed by alumina in a glass column. After about six hours, pertechnate ions are removed from the column by passing a solution of sodium chloride through it. The chloride ions are exchanged for the pertechnate ions but not the molybdenate ions. The solution therefore contains $^{99}Tc^m$ nuclei with no ^{99}Mo nuclei present.

In the above example, a radioactive isotope X decays to a daughter isotope Y which is also radioactive.

- The rate of disintegration $\frac{dN_X}{dt}$ of the parent isotope X is given by the equation $\frac{dN_X}{dt} = -\lambda_X N_X$. Hence $N_X = N_0 e^{-\lambda_X t}$.
- The rate of change of the number of atoms $\frac{dN_Y}{dt}$ of the daughter isotope Y is equal to the sum of the rate of change of production due to the disintegration of the parent nuclei $+\lambda_X N_X$ and the rate of disintegration of the daughter nuclei $-\lambda_Y N_Y$. In other words $\frac{dN_Y}{dt} = -\lambda_Y N_Y + \lambda_X N_X$.

The solution of this equation is $N_Y = \frac{\lambda_X N_0}{(\lambda_Y - \lambda_X)}(e^{-\lambda_X t} - e^{-\lambda_Y t})$ as outlined in the mathematical note below.

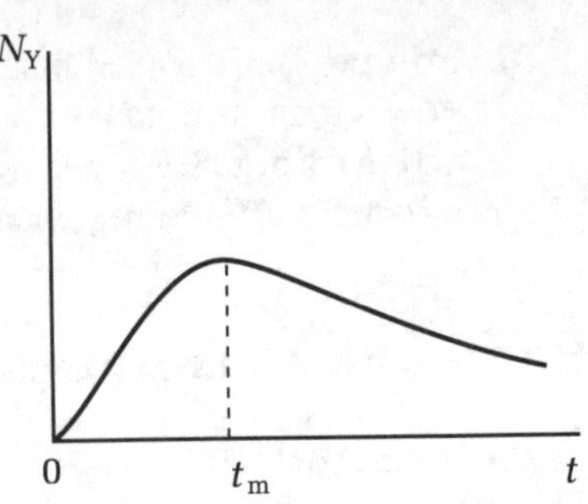

Fig 20.3 Variation of the activity of an unstable daughter product with time

Fig 20.3 shows how N_Y varies with time. Note the following points.

1. Maximum mass of the daughter isotope Y is when $\frac{dN_Y}{dt} = 0$. Prove for yourself by differentiation that this occurs at time $t_m = \frac{\ln(\lambda_Y/\lambda_X)}{(\lambda_Y - \lambda_X)}$ when $\lambda_X N_X = \lambda_Y N_Y$.

2. If the parent X has a much longer half life than the daughter Y, then $\lambda_X \ll \lambda_Y$ and $N_Y = \frac{\lambda_X N_0}{(\lambda_Y - \lambda_X)} e^{-\lambda_X t} = \frac{\lambda_X N_X}{(\lambda_Y - \lambda_X)}$.

In the example above, the half life of molybdenum is 67 hours and the half life of its daughter product, $^{99}Tc^m$, is six hours. Prove for yourself that the maximum mass of the daughter is reached after about 23 hours and the mass reaches 90% of this maximum after about 5.5 hours.

NOTE: To solve, assume $N_Y = Ae^{-\lambda_X t} + Be^{-\lambda_Y t}$ where A and B are constants to be determined. Since $N_Y = 0$ at $t = 0$, then $A = -B$. Hence $N_Y = A[e^{-\lambda_X t} - e^{-\lambda_Y t}]$. Since $\lambda_X N_X = \lambda_Y N_Y$ for maximum N_Y, and $N_X = N_0 e^{-\lambda_X t}$, prove for yourself that $A = \frac{\lambda_X N_0}{(\lambda_Y - \lambda_X)}$.

Ionising radiation and safety

Ionising radiation damages living cells as a result of creating free radicals in cells. The effect of a given type of radiation on a particular type of tissue depends on the type of radiation and the type of tissue.

- The **absorbed dose** from a certain type of radiation is the radiation energy absorbed per unit mass of tissue. The unit of absorbed dose is the Gray (Gy), equal to $1\,\mathrm{J\,kg^{-1}}$.
- The **relative biological effectiveness (r.b.e.)** of a certain type of radiation is defined as

  $\frac{\text{the absorbed dose of 250 kV X-radiation}}{\text{the absorbed dose of the given radiation}}$ for the same biological effect

  The table in Fig 20.4 gives r.b.e. values for different types of ionising radiation.

Type of radiation	Relative biological effectiveness
X- and γ-rays	1
High-energy β-particles	1
Thermal neutrons	2
α-particles	20

Fig 20.4 Ionising radiation

- The **dose equivalent** of a given absorbed dose of ionising radiation is the absorbed dose × the relative biological effectiveness of that type of radiation. The unit of dose equivalent is the Sievert (Sv), equal to

$1\,J\,kg^{-1}$. The total dose equivalent in a given period is the sum of the dose equivalents for each type of radiation. For example, 5 mGy of X-radiation and 1 mGy of α-radiation would give a total dose equivalent of 25 mSv since the r.b.e. for X-radiation is 1 and the r.b.e. for α-radiation is 20.

Maximum permissible safe limits for exposure to ionising radiations are legal requirements on organisations to ensure the safety of personnel and members of the public. The effect of ionising radiations caused by the atomic bombs dropped on Hiroshima and Nagasaki on the survivors has been monitored since 1945 and the results used to establish maximum permissible limits. A dose equivalent of 1 mSv per year corresponds to 3 in 100 000 deaths per year. For the general public, the maximum permitted dose equivalent was 1 mSv per year. This was reduced to 0.5 mSv per year in 1989.

In the school laboratory

Some typical data for a radioactive source used in a school laboratory experiment are given below. The data are then used to estimate the dose equivalent received by a person carrying out the experiment.

Activity: 0.15 MBq
Type of radiation: 0.6 MeV γ-photons
Minimum distance from source: 1.5 m
Exposure time: 30 minutes

The energy transferred from the source in 30 minutes due to gamma emission = activity × time × photon energy = $0.15 \times 10^6 \times 30 \times 60 \times 0.6$ MeV $= 1.6 \times 10^8 \times 1.6 \times 10^{-13}\,J = 2.6 \times 10^{-5}\,J$.

Hence the energy received per m^2 at 1.5 m is $2.6 \times 10^{-5}/4\pi(1.5)^2 \approx 1 \times 10^{-6}\,J\,m^{-2}$.

Assuming an exposed area of $1\,m^2$ and a mass of 60 kg for a typical person, the absorbed dose is therefore of the order of $1 \times 10^{-6}\,J/60\,kg \approx 2 \times 10^{-8}$ Gy. The dose equivalent is therefore of the order of $0.02\,\mu Sv$. Prove for yourself that the dose equivalent would be 36 times greater if the source distance was 0.5 m and it was used for 2 hours. Compare these results with the maximum permissible safe limit of 0.5 mSv per year.

Questions

1. (i) When iron is irradiated with neutrons, a small proportion of a stable isotope, ${}^{58}_{26}Fe$, becomes ${}^{59}_{26}Fe$. ${}^{59}_{26}Fe$ decays into ${}^{59}_{27}Co$ and has a half-life of 45 days. ${}^{59}_{27}Co$ is stable. Write down equations which describe
(1) the neutron absorption reaction by ${}^{58}_{26}Fe$, and
(2) the decay of ${}^{59}_{26}Fe$ into ${}^{59}_{27}Co$.

(ii) A technique for measuring engine wear is to use radioactive engine parts and to measure the increase in the activity of the engine oil after a period of time. In one engine a thin steel disc was inserted in a bearing below a heavy axle and surrounded by 40 g of oil as shown in Fig 20.5.

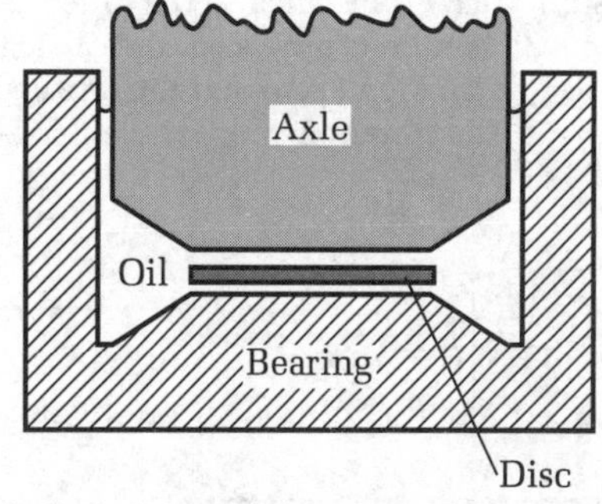

Fig 20.5

The thin steel disc had a mass of 22 g and an activity of 8.9×10^5 Bq after irradiation by neutrons. What would the activity of the disc have been after 20 days had there been no engine wear? In fact the engine was working continuously for these 20 days and the activity of the oil in the bearing had increased by 144 Bq. Calculate the mass of iron removed from the bearing by friction. Describe how, using a similar disc freshly irradiated with neutrons, you would determine the half-life of $^{59}_{26}$Fe in the laboratory. (Assume that you could visit the laboratory regularly for a period of several weeks.)

(ULEAC June '91)

2. A cardiac pacemaker is a device which is used to ensure that a faulty heart beats at a suitable rate. In one pacemaker the required electrical energy is provided by converting the energy of radioactive plutonium-238 ($^{238}_{94}$Pu). The atoms of plutonium decay by emitting 5.5 MeV *alpha* particles. The daughter nucleus is an isotope of uranium (U). The plutonium has a decay constant of 2.4×10^{-10} s^{-1}.

(a) (i) How many neutrons are in the nucleus of the radioactive plutonium?
(ii) Write down the equation representing the decay indicating clearly the atomic (proton) number and the mass (nucleon) number of each nucleus.

(b) (i) Define the term *half-life*.
(ii) Calculate the half-life of plutonium-238.
(iii) State why *alpha* particles are more suitable than either *beta* particles or *gamma* radiation for use in the power source.

(c) A new pacemaker contains 180 mg of plutonium.
(i) Determine the number of radioactive atoms in a new pacemaker.
(ii) Show that approximately 1×10^{11} disintegrations occur each second when the power supply is new.
(iii) Determine the initial power, in W, of the source when it is new.
Avogadro constant, $N_A = 6.0 \times 10^{23}$ mol^{-1}.
Charge on an electron, $e = -1.6 \times 10^{-19}$ C.

The pacemaker has to provide 70 electrical pulses per minute. The pulse rate is controlled by the charging of a capacitor. The output voltage V_s from the supply charges a 15 μF capacitor through a resistor. After a time equal to the time constant of the circuit a pulse is produced, the capacitor discharges rapidly to zero and the process is repeated. The system is shown schematically in Fig 20.6.

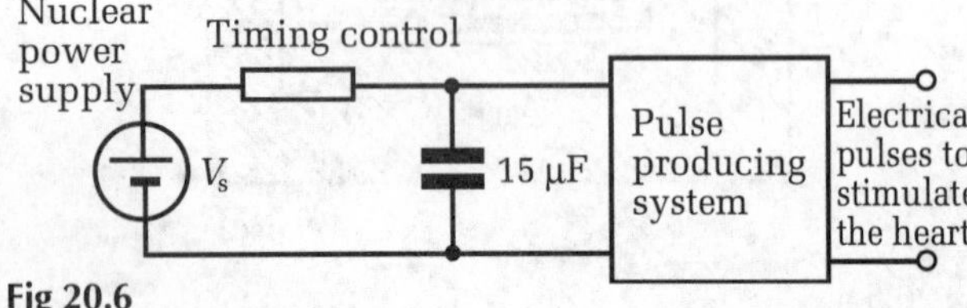

Fig 20.6

(d) (i) Sketch a graph showing the voltage variation across the capacitor, indicating clearly your voltage and time scales.
(ii) Determine the value of the resistor which should be used.

(AEB Summer '94)

3. (a) Compare the following properties of α, β^- and γ radiation:
(i) their speed,
(ii) the amount of ionisation each produces in air,
(iii) their penetrating power.

(b) Draw a diagram to show the shape and direction of the path of β^- radiation travelling in the plane of the paper when a magnetic field is directed into, and at right angles to, the plane of the paper. Explain your diagram, and state and explain how the paths of α radiation and γ radiation would differ from that shown.

(c) With reasons, compare the biological hazards in each of the following cases:
(i) α radiation and γ radiation incident on the skin,
(ii) a small quantity of an α emitter and a small quantity of a γ emitter which have been swallowed.

(d) ^{238}U is a radioactive isotope with a half life of 4.5×10^9 years. It gives a series of decay products which ends in a stable lead isotope, ^{206}Pb.
A sample of rock is found to contain 0.20 g of ^{206}Pb, and 1.00 g of ^{238}U.
(i) Calculate the number of atoms of ^{206}Pb and the number of atoms of ^{238}U in the sample.
(ii) Assume that all the lead present was produced by the decay of ^{238}U. Hence show that the number of atoms of ^{238}U present in this sample when the rock was formed was 3.11×10^{21}.
(iii) Calculate the age of the rock.
Molar mass of ^{238}U = 0.238 kg.
Molar mass of ^{206}Pb = 0.206 kg.
The Avogadro constant = 6.02×10^{23} mol^{-1}.

(NEAB June '95)

4. A small maintenance-free energy source is needed to provide 5.0 W of power to a remote isolated weather station. The radioactive isotope ^{90}Sr, which is a β-emitter with a half-life of 28 years, is chosen. The β-particles are stopped by the surrounding absorbing material, heating it. The main energy of the β-particles is 0.40 MeV. The efficiency of absorption and conversion of the internal energy of the absorber to electricity by thermocouples is 20%.

(a) Show that the initial activity from the source required to produce 5.0 W of electrical power is 3.9×10^{14} Bq.

(b) Hence find the mass of strontium in the source to produce 5.0 W.

(c) Sketch the power against time curve for the strontium source for the first 28 years of its life. Use the curve to make a rough estimate of the total energy of the radiation from the source over this time. Explain your method.

(d) The minimum power on which the weather station will function is 2.0 W. Find the maximum time for which the station can operate before the power source must be replaced.

(e) Another isotope, suggested for use as the energy source, is plutonium-239, an α-emitter of half-life 2.4×10^4 years and energy 5.1 MeV. Suggest one possible advantage or disadvantage that this isotope may have compared to strontium. Justify your answer.

(Take 1 year to be 3.1×10^7 seconds)

(O & C June '93)

5. (a) Explain what is meant by the *half-life* and the *decay constant* of a radioactive isotope and show how these quantities are related.

(b) It is proposed to dispose of a radioactive isotope by dispersing it uniformly throughout some molten glass before casting the glass in the form of a long cylinder.

(i) If the radioactive isotope generates heat at a rate of P watts per unit volume of glass and the thermal conductivity of the glass is k, show that the temperature difference between the core and the outside surface of the cylinder, of radius r, is given by

$$\Delta\theta = \frac{Pr^2}{4k}$$

You may consider the heat loss from the ends of the cylinder to be negligible.
(Hint: consider the rate of flow of heat across the surface of an elemental cylinder.)

(ii) The isotope has a half-life of 1.00×10^5 years and each nucleus decays by the emission of a single alpha particle of energy 5.0 MeV, to form a stable daughter nucleus. The glass cylinders have a diameter of 10 cm and are of length 2.0 m. The thermal conductivity of the glass is $0.15\ \mathrm{W\,m^{-1}\,K^{-1}}$.
Determine the maximum number of nuclei of the radioactive isotope that can be dispersed within a single cylinder if the temperature difference between the core and the surface is not to exceed 50 °C.
Estimate the corresponding value for the ratio

$$\left(\frac{\text{mass of isotope in the cylinder}}{\text{mass of glass in the cylinder}}\right)$$

(c) State **one** advantage and **one** disadvantage of using this method for disposing of radioactive waste by comparison with a named alternative.

(NEAB June '91, Special Paper)

21 ENERGY AND THE NUCLEUS

What you need to know now

- ❑ How to calculate the binding energy of a nucleus.
- ❑ Energy changes due to fission and fusion processes.
- ❑ Use of equations representing nuclear changes to relate energy and mass.
- ❑ The principle of operation of particle accelerators and the thermal nuclear reactor.

What you need to know next

Energy from the nucleus

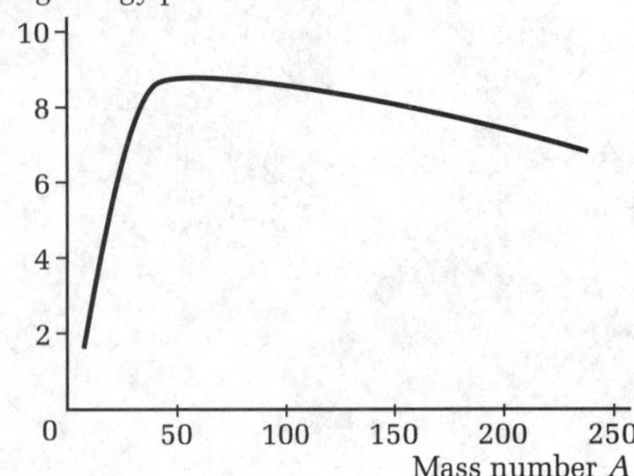

Fig 21.1 Binding energy

The energy released when an unstable nucleus emits an α-particle is much less than the energy released when a large unstable nucleus fissions.

1. **In α-particle emission**, two protons and two neutrons trapped in the nucleus form a cluster, releasing about 28 MeV of binding energy. Much of this is used by the cluster to overcome the strong nuclear force of attraction. Little change occurs in the binding energy of each remaining nucleon in the nucleus. Hence the energy released is of the order of 1 MeV.

2. **In the process of fission**, a large unstable nucleus oscillates so much that it splits into two smaller nuclei, releasing two or three neutrons in the process. As the nucleus begins to split, the kinetic energy associated with its oscillating motion decreases as its surface area increases and more nucleons become near the surface. If there is insufficient kinetic energy, the nucleons will pull together and the nucleus will remain as a single body; if not, the nucleus will form into two parts which repel

each other due to their electrostatic charge. Neutron-induced fission occurs when a slow neutron collides with an oscillating nucleus at its most unstable position.

The energy released is due to electrostatic repulsion overcoming nuclear attraction. Because electrostatic energy has been released, the nucleons in the two daughter nuclei are more tightly bound due to the strong nuclear force than in the parent nucleus. The binding energy of each nucleon increases by about 0.5 MeV; hence, fission of an unstable nucleus containing approximately 200 nucleons releases about 100 MeV in total. Note that induced fission of uranium 235 is much more probable with slow neutrons than with fast neutrons. Fission neutrons are slowed down by collisions with moderator atoms so as to produce further fission.

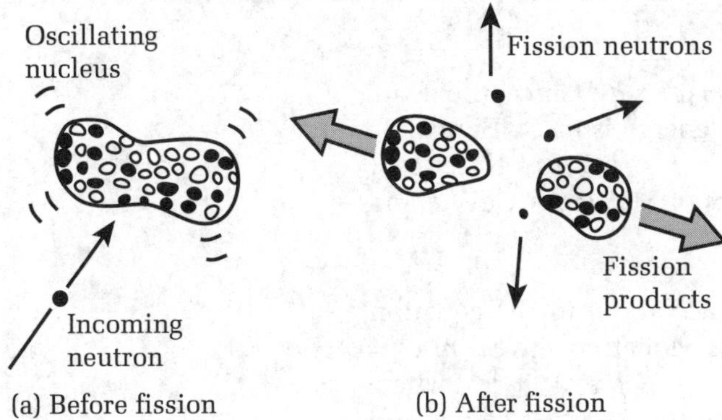

Fig 21.2 The process of induced nuclear fission

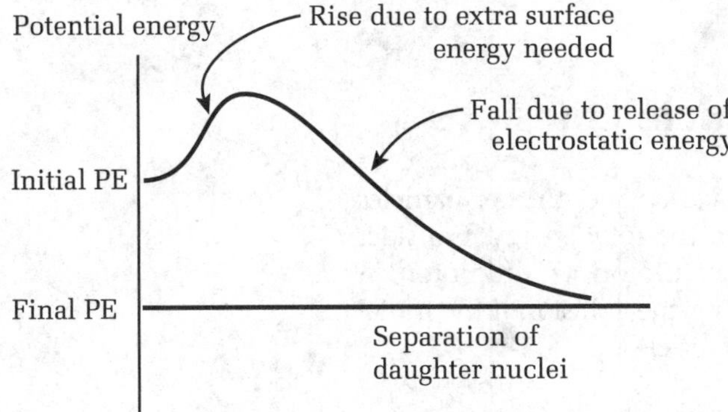

Fig 21.3 Variation of PE with separation

Using $E = mc^2$

❑ To calculate energy changes in reactions

The total mass of a system changes whenever energy is released or supplied to the system. For example, if energy E is stored in a capacitor, its total mass increases by E/c^2. Such mass changes are usually negligible in comparison with the total mass except in reactions where nuclear forces are involved.

1. In α- or β-decay or a fission process, a single particle disintegrates into two or more particles. Energy is released equal to $\Delta m/c^2$ where Δm is the difference between the mass of the initial particle and the total mass of the products.

$${}^{A}_{Z}X \rightarrow {}^{A-4}_{Z-2}Y + {}^{4}_{2}\alpha + Q$$

$${}^{A}_{Z}X \rightarrow {}^{A}_{Z+1}Y + {}^{0}_{-1}\beta + \bar{\upsilon} + Q$$

Fig 21.4 Equations for radioactive disintegration

2. In a reaction due to two particles colliding, energy is released if $\Delta m > 0$. If $\Delta m < 0$, energy must be supplied to cause the reaction. Where $\Delta m > 0$, energy may still need to be supplied if there is an energy threshold which the initial particles must overcome. For example, nuclear transmutation can be caused by bombarding a nucleus with high-energy α-particles but not with low-energy α-particles. A low-energy α-particle would be unable to overcome the repulsive electrostatic force of the nucleus. In nuclear fusion, light nuclei collide at very high speed and fuse together to release binding energy; the initial kinetic energy is necessary to overcome the electrostatic repulsion of the nuclei.

$${}^{4}_{2}\alpha + {}^{9}_{4}\text{Be} \rightarrow {}^{1}_{0}\text{n} + {}^{12}_{6}\text{C}$$

Fig 21.5 Nuclear transmutation

❑ To calculate the energy and momentum of a high-energy particle

Consider a particle of rest mass m_0 and charge q accelerated from rest through a potential difference V.

1. The final energy of the particle $E = m_0c^2 + qV$ since the work done on the particle is qV and its initial energy is m_0c^2. Hence the final mass of the particle, $m = E/c^2 = m_0 + qV/c^2$. Note that particle mass is usually expressed in units of MeV/c^2 or GeV/c^2 and $1\,\text{u} = 931\,\text{MeV}/c^2$.

2. The particle's mass varies with speed v according to the equation $m = m_0(1 - v^2/c^2)^{-1/2}$. Rearranging this equation gives $m^2c^4 = m^2v^2c^2 + m_0{}^2c^4$ which may be written $E^2 = p^2c^2 + m_0{}^2c^4$, where $p = mv$ = the particle's momentum. Given the particle's energy and rest mass, its momentum can therefore be calculated from this equation. Note that the momentum of a particle is often expressed in units of MeV/c or GeV/c.

Energy and momentum in particle collisions

When two particles or an antiparticle and particle collide, further particles and antiparticles may be produced depending on the total energy. Consider the example of a proton colliding with another proton or antiproton. A further proton and an antiproton can emerge from the collision if the initial total energy is sufficient to create the extra two particles.

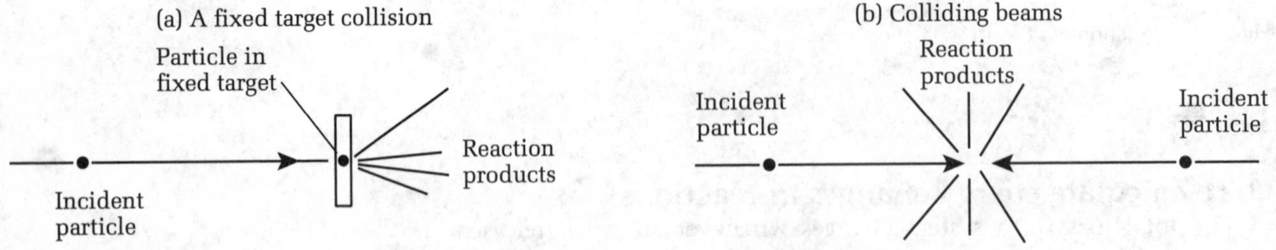

Fig 21.6

1. If a proton of energy E collides with an antiproton of energy E moving in opposite directions, the total momentum is zero. Hence all the total energy $2E$ may be used to create new particles. The rest mass of a proton is approximately $1\,\text{GeV}/c^2$; hence the extra two particles may be created if the energy of each initial particle is 2 GeV. The total energy of 4 GeV is sufficient to create two protons and two antiprotons.

2. If the antiproton collides with a stationary proton, the initial kinetic energy T of the antiproton must be greater than 6 GeV if a further proton–antiproton pair is to be created.

- ❑ The energy of the incident antiproton in GeV is $T + 1$, where T is the work done on it in GeV. Hence its momentum p in GeV/c is given by $p^2c^2 = E^2 - m_0{}^2c^4 = (T + 1)^2 - 1$. This is the total momentum and the target proton has no initial momentum.
- ❑ The total energy of the two initial particles in GeV $= T + 2$ and the total momentum is p. To create a further proton–antiproton pair, the final rest mass must be at least 4 GeV/c^2. Applying $E^2 = p^2c^2 + m_0{}^2c^4$ to the final products therefore gives $(T + 2)^2 = (T + 1)^2 - 1 + 4^2$. Hence $T = 6$ GeV.

This example illustrates that the creation of particle–antiparticle pairs in a high-energy collision is achieved at a lower energy threshold in a colliding beam system than in a fixed target system. The CERN SPS was initially designed to make 300 GeV protons collide with stationary protons. However, this type of collision releases no more than about 24 GeV to create new particles. By converting it to a colliding beam arrangement in which 300 GeV protons collide with 300 GeV antiprotons, much more energy became available to create new particles.

Worked example

A particle of rest mass 1.0 GeV/c^2 and charge $+2e$ is accelerated from rest through a p.d. of 200 MV. Calculate its resulting energy, its mass in atomic mass units and its momentum. 4 marks

Solution

The work done on the particle $= qV = 400$ MeV $= 0.4$ GeV; ✓ hence its total energy $E = 1.4$ GeV. ✓

Its mass $m = E/c^2 = 1.4\,\text{GeV}/c^2 = 1400\,\text{MeV}/c^2 = 1400/931 = 1.5\,\text{u}$. ✓

Using $E^2 = p^2c^2 + m_0{}^2c^4$ to determine its momentum p therefore gives $pc = (E^2 - m_0{}^2c^4)^{1/2} = (1.4^2 - 1.0^2)^{1/2} = 0.98$ GeV. Hence $p = 0.98$ GeV/c. ✓

Questions

1. Three adjacent elements in a long radioactive series are actinium, francium and radium.

$$\rightarrow \text{actinium (Ac)} \xrightarrow{\alpha} \text{francium (Fr)} \xrightarrow{\beta^-} \text{radium (Ra)} \rightarrow$$

(a) An atom of $^{223}_{87}$Fr is formed when an atom of actinium decays with the emission of an α-particle. The masses of the atoms in atomic mass units (u) are: actinium *atom* 227.0278 u, francium *atom* 223.0198 u, helium *atom* 4.0026 u.

(i) Write a nuclear reaction equation describing this change.

(ii) Compare the mass of the parent actinium atom with the sum of the masses of the decay products. Show how the values you obtain are consistent with the emission of the α-particle with considerable kinetic energy.

(b) (i) The mass of a proton is 1.0073 u, of an electron is 0.0005 u and that of a neutron is

1.0087 u. Calculate the difference in mass between a $^{223}_{87}$Fr *nucleus* and the sum of the masses of its nucleons.
(ii) How do you account for this difference?

(c) The $^{223}_{87}$Fr atom decays with the emission of a β^--particle into an atom of radium. Write a nuclear reaction equation for this change.

(d) The half-life of the actinium isotope is 19 days and that of the francium isotope is 21 mins.
(i) Explain what is meant by the term *half-life*.
(ii) A sample of pure actinium is monitored for one day. Without any calculation, comment briefly on how the concentration of francium varies during this time.

($1\,u \equiv 931$ MeV)

(O & C June '94)

2. (a) Explain the meaning of the symbol $^{238}_{92}$U. What is meant by an isotope?

(b) Certain types of nucleus may spontaneously lose a small amount of mass by the process known as radioactivity.
(i) Describe the nature of the radiations which may be emitted during this process.
(ii) Define *radioactive decay* and *briefly* explain how this leads to the equation $\frac{dN}{dt} = -\lambda N$. Why is there a negative sign?
(iii) Sketch the variation of N with time and explain what is meant by half life.

(c) (i) Draw a sketch of the variation of binding energy per nucleon with mass number. Use the sketch to explain why nuclear fusion occurs in some circumstances and nuclear fission in others.
(ii) Explain why very high temperatures are required for nuclear fusion.
(iii) A future fusion reactor might use the reaction

$$^2_1\text{H} + ^2_1\text{H} \rightarrow ^4_2\text{He} + \text{energy}$$

to produce useful energy. From the following data calculate the number of reactions required to produce 1 J of energy.
(iv) Calculate the mass of $^2_1$H required to provide 1 J of energy.
(Mass of $^2_1$H = 2.0136 amu; mass of $^4_2$He = 4.0015 amu; 1 amu = 1.661×10^{-27} kg; velocity of light $c = 3.00 \times 10^8$ m s^{-1}.)

(WJEC June '92)

3. A proton is accelerated through a potential difference of 3.00 GV from rest. Its rest mass m_0 is 0.94 GeV/c^2. Calculate

(a) its total energy,

(b) its mass in terms of its rest mass, m_0, at this energy,

(c) its speed in terms of the speed of light, c.

4. A moving antiproton of kinetic energy 2.42 GeV collides with a stationary proton. The particles annihilate and create a new particle. The rest mass of a proton is 0.94 GeV/c^2.

(a) Show that the total energy available is 4.30 GeV and the total momentum is 3.22 GeV/c.

(b) Hence show that the rest mass of the particle created is 2.85 GeV/c^2.

5. (a) (i) Distinguish carefully between a *nuclear fission process* and a *nuclear fusion process*.
(ii) How is a nuclear fission process initiated?
(iii) Describe why a nuclear fusion process is difficult to (1) produce, (2) control, under laboratory conditions.

(b) The Sun generates energy by nuclear fusion. Use the following data to estimate the rate at which the mass of the Sun is decreasing. Express your answer in tonnes s^{-1}.
(Maximum rate of arrival of solar energy on unit area of the Earth's surface (assuming no atmospheric absorption) = 1.4 kW m^{-2}. Sun–Earth distance = 150×10^6 km. Speed of light = 3.0×10^8 m s^{-1}. 1 tonne = 1000 kg.)

(c) The fuel for a fission reactor is usually a mixture of uranium isotopes U-238 and U-235. Currently all deposits of uranium ore are found to contain these isotopes with the atoms of U-235 forming 0.72% of the combined uranium isotope content. However, geologists have calculated that when the Earth was formed the percentage of U-235 atoms present would have been 17% (that is 17 U-235 atoms to every 83 U-238 atoms).
The decay constants of these isotopes can be represented by the symbols λ (for U-238) and λ' (for U-235).
(i) The half-life of U-238 is 4.5×10^9 years and that of U-235 is 7.0×10^8 years. Calculate the numerical values of λ and λ' corresponding to the unit year^{-1}.
(ii) Show that the ratio of U-235 to U-238 atoms in uranium ores at time t after the formation of the Earth was given by

$$\left(\frac{17}{83}\right) e^{(\lambda - \lambda')t}$$

(d) (i) A chain reaction is possible in deposits of uranium ore provided U-235 atoms form at least 1.0% (= 1:99) of the uranium mixture. Use your results from (c) to calculate the length of the period, after the formation of the Earth, during which such a chain reaction might have occurred.
(ii) French scientists have analysed samples of ore from a uranium mine in a west-African country and have deduced that a large-scale chain reaction occurred there many millions of years ago. They were aware that U-235 is more fissile than U-238.
What properties of the samples might have led the scientists to this conclusion?

(UODLE June '94, Special Paper)

6. (a) Explain what is meant by the *binding energy* of a nucleus, and sketch a graph of the binding energy per nucleon as a function of nucleon number. Use your graph to explain briefly why you would expect a nuclear fusion reaction to yield more energy per unit mass of fuel than a nuclear fission reaction.

(b) For nucleon numbers greater than about 80, the atomic mass of a stable or long-lived isotope is given approximately by

$$M = \alpha A + \beta A^2$$

where M is the atomic mass in terms of the unified atomic mass constant (u), A is the nucleon number, and α and β are constants with values of 0.99819 and 8.41×10^{-6} respectively. In a simplified model of the *fission* of ^{235}U, a uranium nucleus splits into fragments with nucleon numbers of 95 and 138, and an appropriate number of neutrons. Calculate the energy released by this process. [The mass of a neutron is 1.009 u.]

(c) Hence estimate the mass of uranium consumed per year in a 1 GW power station. (Assume perfect efficiency.)

(d) In practice, sustainable *fusion* reactions are very difficult to produce because of the high energies that must be given to the nuclei in order to overcome their electrostatic repulsion. The nuclei can be assumed to be single protons which will fuse if they approach one another closer than 10^{-14} m. By equating the electrostatic potential energy in this situation to the translational kinetic energy of a hydrogen atom in a gas at temperature T, estimate the minimum temperature required to initiate a nuclear fusion reaction.

(The potential V at a distance r from a point charge q is given by $V = \dfrac{Q}{4\pi\varepsilon_0 r}$.)

(UCLES June '94, Special Paper)

ANSWERS TO NUMERICAL QUESTIONS

Chapter 1

1. (b) 1.98 kN,
   (c) (i) 1.50 kN, 40° above the horizontal,
   (ii) 1.15 kN,
   (iii) 20 kW
2. (a) (i) 100 N,
   (ii) 50 J,
   (b) 58 N,
   (c) 58 N
3. 790 N
4. (b) (ii) 420 N,
   (iii) 420 N,
   (iv) 8.4 J
5. (a) 215 N, 264 N

Chapter 2

1. (b) (i) 2.0 kN,
   (ii) 24 kW,
   (iii) 1200 kJ
2. (b) 155 $m\,s^{-1}$
3. (b) (i) 0.60 $m\,s^{-2}$,
   (ii) 7508 m,
   (iii) 12 kN,
   (iv) 10 $m\,s^{-1}$
4. (b) (i) 12 kN,
   (ii) 30 000 kg
5. (a) (ii) 1.1 W,
   (iii) 0.9 W,
   (b) 0.5 m above the lift floor,
   (ii) 0.63 m,
   (iii) 1.0 $m\,s^{-1}$ upwards,
   (iv) 0.68 m
6. (d) (i) 9.8 $m\,s^{-2}$,
   (ii) 7.0 $m\,s^{-1}$,
   (e) 2.9 μm

Chapter 3

1. (c) (i) 4.90 MeV,
   (ii) 0.086 MeV,
   (iii) 4.89 MeV,
   (d) (ii) 0.12 nm
2. (c) (i) 1.6 $kg\,m\,s^{-1}$,
   (ii) 5.5×10^5 $m\,s^{-1}$ in the reverse direction
3. (a) (iii) 0.27 $m\,s^{-1}$, 1.07 $m\,s^{-1}$,
   (iv) 0.107 $kg\,m\,s^{-1}$
4. (a) 4.0×10^{-14} m,
   (b) 0,
   (c) 4.0×10^{-15} m
5. (a) 1.53×10^7 $m\,s^{-1}$,
   (b) 0.24 MeV,
   (c) 6.1×10^6 $m\,s^{-1}$, -9.2×10^6 $m\,s^{-1}$,
   (d) alpha, 4.8×10^6 $m\,s^{-1}$; proton, 1.2×10^7 $m\,s^{-1}$

Chapter 4

1. (a) 17.3 $m\,s^{-1}$,
   (b) 30 m
2. (c) (i) (1) 20.6 $m\,s^{-2}$, (2) 646 N,
   (ii) (1) 8232 J, (2) 20.5 $m\,s^{-1}$
3. (b) (ii) 30.0 m,
   (c) (i) 5880 N,
   (ii) 6061 N
4. (b) 18.5 N,
   (c) 12.5 m
5. (b) 0.035 Hz,
   (c) 4.9 $m\,s^{-2}$,
   (e) 51.5 kJ

Chapter 5

1. (ii) 83,
   (iii) 1.7
2. (b) 6.0×10^{26} kg,
   (c) 5.2×10^4 s,
   (d) 24.0 $m\,s^{-1}$
3. (c) (iii) 7.1×10^{18} $kg\,m^{-3}$
4. (b) 2.0×10^{30} kg,
   (c) 1.88,
   (d) 7.7×10^{12} J
5. (b) (ii) 0.05%,
   (iii) -6.0×10^9 J,
   (v) 6×10^6 s
6. (a) (i) 2.3×10^8 J,
   (ii) -4.2×10^9 J,
   (b) (i) 5.4×10^3 s,
   (ii) 2.1×10^9 J,
   (c) -2.1×10^9 J,
   (d) (i) -3.1×10^6 J,
   (ii) $+1.5 \times 10^6$ J,
   (iii) -1.5×10^6 J,
   (f) 1.6×10^5 s

Chapter 6

1. 1.5×10^8 Pa
2. (i) 9 N,
   (ii) 135 mJ,
   (iii) 6.7 $m\,s^{-1}$
3. (a) 1.9×10^{11} Pa,
   (b) 0.43 mm
4. (a) 1020 °C,
   (b) 1.8×10^8 Pa
5. (b) (i) 49.0 N,
   (ii) 1.73 mm, 42.4 J,
   (iii) 0.85 mm,
   (iv) 116 mm from A
6. (i) 1.34×10^{11} Pa,
   (ii) 1.37×10^{10} Pa

Chapter 7

1. (i) 18.4 kg,
   (ii) 3.40×10^4 $J\,K^{-1}$,
   (iii) 3.50 kW
2. (a) (i) 36 kJ,
   (ii) 16 g,
   (b) 33 °C
3. (a) (i) 1.52×10^{-2} $kg\,s^{-1}$,
   (ii) 1.21×10^{-2} $m^3\,s^{-1}$,
   (b) 2.20×10^{-2} $kg\,s^{-1}$
4. (c) (i) 1.53 MJ,
   (ii) 0.224 kg
5. (a) (i) 93%,
   (b) (i) 356 J,
   (c) (i) 1.7×10^{13} m^2,
   (ii) 10^{21} J,
   (d) 2.8×10^{12} $m^3\,yr^{-1}$, 5.5 $mm\,yr^{-1}$

Chapter 8

1. (a) 774 $m\,s^{-1}$,
   (b) 804 $m\,s^{-1}$
2. (a) 3.2×10^{-4} kg,
   (b) 4.8×10^{22},
   (c) 1.37×10^3 $m\,s^{-1}$
3. (a) (i) 0.05,
   (ii) 2.0×10^{-4} kg,
   (b) (i) 187 kPa
4. (b) 0.08 moles,
   (c) (i) 400 kPa,
   (ii) 600 kPa,
   (iii) 300 kPa,
   (iv) 200 kPa
5. (c) 1.24 $kg\,m^{-3}$
6. (b) 478 $m\,s^{-1}$,
   (d) 1.70×10^{-10} Pa,
   (e) 10^4 s

Chapter 9

1. (i) 600 W,
   (ii) 83 W
2. (e) 9000 W,
   (f) 88 W,
3. (b) $1.5\rho/x$,
   (d) (i) 140 W,
   (ii) 29 °C
4. (c) 6.0×10^{-2} $W\,m^{-1}\,K^{-1}$

Chapter 10

1. −24 mJ
2. (b) (i) 0.075 m
4. (d) (i) $1.91Q^2/4\pi\varepsilon_0 a^2$
5. (b) (ii) −5.0 MJ,
   (c) -2.3×10^{-18} J,
   (d) -8.0×10^{-17} J
6. (b) 4.3×10^{-14} J,
   (c) (i) and (ii) 3.4×10^{-16} J,
   (iii) 2.1 kV,
   (d) (i) 100 V,
   (ii) 1.6×10^{-17} J,
   (iii) 7.1 $kV\,m^{-1}$

Chapter 11

1. (b) (i) 200 μC,
   (ii) 4.0 mJ,
   (iii) 2.0 mJ,
   (c) 20 ms,
   (ii) 92 s
2. (b) (i) 1.5 μF,
   (ii) 108 μJ,
   (iii) 9 V

3. (ii) (1) 33 nC, (2) 30 kV
4. (c) (i) 0.2 μF,
(ii) 150 V
5. (d) (i) 25 mJ,
(ii) 225 mJ
6. (c) $C_1/(C_1+C_2)$

Chapter 12

1. (a) (i) 1.5 V,
(ii) 4.0 Ω,
(iii) 1.0 Ω,
(iv) 0.9 J,
(b) 1.125 W
2. (a) (i) 0,
(ii) 0.06, 0.06, 0, 0.06, 0.06 A; 0.12 A,
(b) 960 μC
3. (a) 13 Ω in series and 667 Ω in parallel,
4. (c) (i) A 0.1 A; B 0.4 A,
(ii) −2 V, +16 V
5. (b) (i) 5.0 Ω,
(ii) 4.875 Ω,
(c) 4.85 Ω
6. (b) (1) 3.33 Ω, 8 V, (2) 1.67 Ω, 2 V, (3) 0 V

Chapter 13

1. (c) (i) $F_{AD} = 5 \times 10^{-8}$ N towards the wire, $F_{BC} = 5 \times 10^{-8}$ N away from the wire, $F_{AB} = F_{CD} = 0$,
(ii) couple $= 1 \times 10^{-10}$ N m
2. (b) 9 A, 144 μN (repulsive),
(c) 0.36 mWb per turn
3. (b) (i) C, −2.5 V,
(c) (i) 75 mA,
(ii) 112.5 mW, 6 mJ
4. (c) with XY straddling Q,
(d) does not stop
5. (d) 42
6. (d) 32 Ω,
(g) 562 MJ,
(h) (i) 500 N,
(ii) 50 kN
7. (b) (ii) 70 W,
(c) (iii) 2.8 mm s^{-1}
8. (b) (ii) 0.49 N,
(iii) 0.40 N,
(c) 20 mJ s^{-1},
(iii) 27.4 $\mu\Omega$,
(iv) 27 A

Chapter 14

1. (i) 32 mA,
(ii) 37°,
(iii) 2.8 μF, 40 mA
2. (d) (i) 350 mA,
(ii) 2.0 V,
(iii) 3.8 Ω
3. (b) (ii) 240 V,
(c) (iii) 0.16 mH,
(iv) 4–8 kΩ
4. (c) (ii) 288 μm,
(iii) 28 pF,
(iv) 9.1 μH
5. (b) (i) 44 W,
(ii) 15%

Chapter 15

1. (a) (ii) 500 N m^{-1}
(b) (ii) 30
2. (b) 9.8 N m^{-1},
(c) 1.58 Hz,
(d) (i) 10 cm
3. 510 N m^{-1},
(i) infra-red
4. (b) (iii) 1.3 cm,
(c) (iii) 10 Hz
6. (a) 1.4 Hz,
(b) 0.5

Chapter 16

1. (i) 5 mm,
(ii) 50 Hz,
(iii) 6.6 m,
(iv) 330 Hz
2. (a) (i) $\lambda/4$
(ii) $\lambda/4$
3. (b) (v) 128 N
4. 340 m s^{-1},
(iii) 34.6 cm
5. (c) (ii) 4.2 kHz

Chapter 17

2. (c) (i) 6 s
3. (d) (i) 0.12 nm,
(ii) X-rays
4. (b) 5.3×10^{19} C,
(c) (i) 7.3×10^{18},
(ii) 1.3×10^{15}
5. (a) (i) 3.3×10^{-19} J,
(ii) 95,
(b) (i) 4.3×10^{6},
(ii) 6.4×10^{4},
(iii) 8 mm,
(iv) 80 mm,
(v) 10, 1.3×10^{4}
7. (b) (iii) 2.0×10^{-19} J,
(iv) 15.4°, 52.6°

Chapter 18

1. (b) (ii) 2.64×10^{-19} J, 4.95×10^{-19} J,
(iii) 121 nm, UV
2. (b) (ii) 658 nm, visible,
(c) (ii) 0.124 nm
3. (b) (ii) 8.8×10^{-12} m,
(d) (i) 1.8%,
(ii) 267 mm
4. (a) (i) 1.6×10^{6} m s^{-1},
(ii) 2.1×10^{9} Hz, 4.2×10^{-6},
(iii) 2.5×10^{-12} m, 4.2×10^{-6},
(iv) 1.6×10^{-6} rad,
(b) 1.2×10^{-13} m
5. (b) (iii) 1.6 μm,
(c) (i) 3.6×10^{4} m s^{-1},
(ii) X-rays

Chapter 19

2. (b) (i) 0.65 ns,
(ii) 16 kV m^{-1},
(iii) 2.5×10^{-15} N,
(iv) 2.8×10^{15} m s^{-2},
(v) 1.85×10^{6} m s^{-1},
(vi) 9 mm
3. (a) (iii) 178.5 m s^{-1}
(b) 3.2×10^{-15} N,
(iii) 0.11 T,
(c) (iii) 9.8 mm
4. (c) (iv) 100 kV m^{-1},
(d) 1.8×10^{11} C kg^{-1},
(e) (i) 1.5×10^{7} m s^{-1},
(ii) 4.7×10^{7} C kg^{-1}
5. (b) (i) 39 km,
(ii) 0.33 s,
(iii) 426 km
6. (c) (i) 7.3×10^{-16} J,
(ii) 2.3×10^{16},
(iii) 3.8 mA

Chapter 20

1. (ii) 0.65 MBq, 4.8 mg
2. (a) (i) 144,
(b) (ii) 2.9×10^{9} s,
(c) (i) 4.5×10^{20},
(iii) 0.096 W,
(d) (ii) 57 kΩ
3. (d) (i) 5.8×10^{20}, 2.5×10^{21},
(ii) 1.4×10^{9} years
4. (b) 75 g,
(d) 37.0 years
5. (b) (ii) 6.7×10^{28}, 600

Chapter 21

1. (b) (i) 1.84 u
2. (c) (iii) 2.6×10^{11},
(iv) 1.7×10^{-15} kg
3. (a) 3.94 GeV,
(b) 4.2 m_0
(c) 0.97c
5. (b) 4.4×10^{6} tonne yr^{-1},
(c) (i) 1.54×10^{-10} yr^{-1}, 9.9×10^{-10} yr^{-1},
(d) (i) 3.6×10^{10} yr
6. (b) 3.1×10^{-11} J,
(c) 394 kg,
(d) 10^{9} K

INDEX